THE
COMING WAVE

"The AI revolution is underway, but how well do we really understand it? *The Coming Wave* offers an erudite, clear-eyed guide both to the history of radical technological change and to the deep political challenges that lie ahead."

—Anne Applebaum, Pulitzer Prize–winning historian

"When this landed in my inbox, I cleared the diary and got reading. This is an extraordinary and necessary book; the awe-inspiring thought is that in *twenty years* it will seem almost like a conservative vision of the future, whereas right now, reading it is impossible without pausing every few pages to wonder: Can this be true? It's the book's genius to explain, soberly and gently, that yes, this will all be true—and why and how. The tone is gentle and kind and sympathetic to the reader's sense of shock. There are terrifying moments, as there should be when one realizes that most of what is familiar is about to be transformed. But, ultimately, one leaves energized and thrilled to be alive right now. The wave is about to hit and this is the forecast."

—Alain de Botton, philosopher and bestselling author

"*The Coming Wave* offers a much-needed dose of specificity, realism, and clarity about the potential unanticipated and yet disastrous consequences of artificial intelligence, synthetic biology, and other advanced technologies. This important book is a vivid and persuasive road map for how human beings might guide technological innovations rather than be controlled by them."

—Martha Minow, Harvard professor,
former dean of Harvard Law School

"Nobody has been closer to the unfolding AI revolution than Mustafa Suleyman, and nobody is better placed to outline the risks and rewards of the huge technological changes happening right now. This is an extraordinary and utterly unmissable guide to this unique moment in human history."

—Eric Schmidt, former CEO of Google,
co-author of *The Age of AI*

"In *The Coming Wave*, Mustafa Suleyman offers a powerful argument that today's explosive technological revolution is poised to be uniquely disruptive. Read this essential book to understand the pace and scale of these technologies—how they will proliferate across our society and their potential to challenge the fabric of the institutions that organize our world."   —Ian Bremmer, founder of Eurasia Group, bestselling author of *The Power of Crisis*

"This vital book is inspiring and terrifying at the same time. It is a critical education for those who do not understand the technological revolutions through which we are living, and a frontal challenge to those who do. This book is about the future for all of us: we need to read it and act on it."   —David Miliband, former U.K. foreign secretary

"Presenting a stark assessment of the dangers as well as the wonders of AI, Mustafa Suleyman proposes an urgent agenda of actions governments must take now to constrain the most potentially catastrophic applications of this revolutionary challenge."
—Graham Allison, Harvard professor, bestselling author of *Destined for War*

"The rapid pace of exponential technologies has overwhelmed us with its power and its peril. Mustafa Suleyman, in tracing the history of industrial development to the dizzying acceleration of the recent technological advances, gives us the bigger picture in calm, pragmatic, and deeply ethical prose. His personal journey and experiences enhance *The Coming Wave* and make it enthralling reading for everyone wanting to step back from the daily onrush of tech news."
—Angela Kane, former UN undersecretary-general and high representative for Disarmament Affairs

"An incredibly compelling window into the current developments and exponential future of AI—from the ultimate insider . . . If you really want to understand how society can safely navigate this world-changing technology, read this book."
—Bruce Schneier, cybersecurity expert, author of *A Hacker's Mind*

"The coming wave of AI and synthetic biology will make the next decade the best in human history. Or the worst. No one recognizes and explains the epic challenges ahead better than Mustafa Suleyman. Thought-provoking, urgent, and written in powerful, highly accessible prose, this is a must-read book for anyone interested in understanding the staggering power of these technologies."
—Erik Brynjolfsson, professor, Stanford Human-Centered Artificial Intelligence

"One of the greatest challenges facing the world is to devise forms of governance that harness the benefits of AI and biotech while avoiding their catastrophic risks. This book provides a deeply thoughtful account of the 'containment challenge' of these two technologies. It is meticulously researched and packed with original insights and constructive recommendations for policy makers and security experts."
—Jason Matheny, CEO of RAND, former assistant director of national intelligence, former director of IARPA

"If you want to understand the meaning, promise, and threat of the coming tidal wave of transformative technologies that are even now swelling and converging out there on the main, then this deeply rewarding and consistently astonishing book by Mustafa Suleyman, one of the key pioneers of artificial intelligence, is an absolutely essential read."   —Stephen Fry, actor, broadcaster, and bestselling author

"This important book is a vivid wake-up call. It carefully outlines the threats and opportunities associated with the exhilarating scientific advances of recent years. *The Coming Wave* is rich with interesting facts, arresting arguments, and compelling observations; it is essential reading."
—Daniel Kahneman, Nobel Prize winner, bestselling author of *Thinking Fast and Slow*

"*The Coming Wave* is a fantastically clear, energetic, well-researched, and readable book from the front line of the greatest technological revolution of our times. It weaves the personal and technological stories seamlessly, and shows why better governance of immensely powerful technologies is both so vital and so hard."
—Sir Geoff Mulgan, professor at University College London

"The best analysis yet of what AI means for the future of humanity . . . Mustafa Suleyman is unique as the co-founder of not one but two major contemporary AI companies. He is a profoundly talented entrepreneur, a deep thinker, and one of the most important voices on the coming wave of technologies that will shape our world."
—Reid Hoffman, co-founder of LinkedIn and Inflection

"Technology is rapidly transforming society, and hence it's more important than ever to see someone within the technology industry write with such honesty and rigor. Taking us from the earliest tools to the heart of the present explosion in AI capabilities and research, this book is a panoramic survey and a clarion call to action impossible to ignore. Everyone should read it."

—Fei-Fei Li, professor of computer science at Stanford University, co-director of the Institute for Human-Centered AI

"*The Coming Wave* makes an eye-opening and convincing case that advanced technologies are reshaping every aspect of society: power, wealth, warfare, work, and even human relations. Can we control these new technologies before they control us? A world leader in artificial intelligence and a longtime advocate for governments, big tech, and civil society to act for the common good, Mustafa Suleyman is the ideal guide to this crucial question."

—Jeffrey D. Sachs, University Professor at Columbia University, president of the UN Sustainable Development Solutions Network

"A sharp, compassionate, and uncompromising framing of the most consequential issue of our times, *The Coming Wave* is a must-read for technology practitioners, but more importantly it is a resolute call to action for all of us to participate in this most consequential discourse."

—Qi Lu, CEO of MiraclePlus, ex-COO of Baidu, ex-EVP of Microsoft Bing

"Suleyman is uniquely well positioned to articulate the potentially grave consequences—geopolitical upheaval, war, the erosion of the nation-state—of the unfettered development of AI and synthetic biology, at a time when we need this message most. Fortunately for the reader, he has also thought deeply about what needs to be done to ensure that emerging technologies are used for human good, setting forward a series of incremental efforts that if undertaken collectively can change the environment in which these technologies are developed and disseminated, opening the door to preserving that brighter future. This book is a must-read."

—Meghan L. O'Sullivan, director of the Belfer Center for Science and International Affairs at the Harvard Kennedy School of Government

"A brave wake-up call that we all need to answer—before it's too late . . . Mustafa Suleyman explains, with clarity and precision, the risks posed by runaway technologies and the challenges that humanity faces. . . . Indispensable reading."

—Tristan Harris, co-founder and executive director of the Center for Humane Technology

"A practical and optimistic road map for action on the most important issue of our time: how to retain power over entities far more powerful than ourselves."

—Stuart Russell, professor of computer science at the University of California, Berkeley

"*The Coming Wave* is a realistic, deeply informed, and highly accessible map of the unprecedented governance and national security challenges posed by artificial intelligence and synthetic biology. Suleyman's remarkable and in some senses frightening book shows what must be done to contain these seemingly uncontainable technologies."

—Jack Goldsmith, Learned Hand Professor of Law at Harvard University

"Brilliant and inviting, complex and clear, urgent and calm, *The Coming Wave* guides us all to understand and confront what may be the most crucial question of our century: How can we ensure that the breathtaking, fast-paced technological revolutions ahead—AI, synthetic biology, and more—create the world we want? It's not going to be easy, but Suleyman lays a strong foundation. Everyone who cares about the future should read this book."

—Eric Lander, founding director of the Broad Institute of MIT and Harvard, former White House science advisor

"A strikingly lucid and refreshingly balanced account of our current technological predicament, *The Coming Wave* articulates the defining challenge of our era. Blending pragmatism with humility, it reminds us that there are no stark binaries or simple answers: technology has gifted us with exponential improvements in well-being, but it's accelerating faster than institutions can adapt. Advances in AI and synthetic biology have unlocked capabilities undreamed of by science fiction, and the resulting proliferation of power threatens everything we've built. To stay afloat, we must steer between the Scylla of accessible catastrophe and the Charybdis of omnipresent surveillance. With every page turned, our odds improve."

—Kevin Esvelt, biologist and associate professor at MIT Media Lab

THE
COMING
WAVE

THE
COMING
WAVE

TECHNOLOGY, POWER, AND

THE TWENTY-FIRST CENTURY'S

GREATEST DILEMMA

MUSTAFA
SULEYMAN

with **MICHAEL BHASKAR**

CROWN
NEW YORK

Published in the United States by Crown, an imprint of Crown Publishing Group,
a division of Penguin Random House LLC, New York.

CROWN and the Crown colophon are registered trademarks
of Penguin Random House LLC.

Hardback ISBN 978-0-593-59395-0
International edition ISBN 978-0-593-72817-8
Ebook ISBN 978-0-593-59396-7

Printed in the United States of America on acid-free paper

crownpublishing.com

2 4 6 8 9 7 5 3 1

FIRST EDITION

Book design by Barbara M. Bachman

CONTENTS

GLOSSARY OF
KEY TERMS

AI, AGI, AND ACI: Artificial intelligence (AI) is the science of teaching machines to learn humanlike capabilities. Artificial general intelligence (AGI) is the point at which an AI can perform all human cognitive skills better than the smartest humans. ACI, or artificial capable intelligence, is a fast-approaching point between AI and AGI: ACI can achieve a wide range of complex tasks but is still a long way from being fully general.

THE COMING WAVE: An emerging cluster of related technologies centered on AI and synthetic biology whose transformative applications will both empower humankind and present unprecedented risks.

CONTAINMENT: The ability to monitor, curtail, control, and potentially even close down technologies.

THE CONTAINMENT PROBLEM: Technology's predisposition to diffuse widely in waves and to have emergent impacts that are impossible to predict or control, including negative and unforeseen consequences.

THE DILEMMA: The growing likelihood that both new technologies and even their absence might lead to catastrophic and/or dystopian outcomes.

FOUR FEATURES: The unique characteristics of the coming wave that exacerbate the challenge of containment. They are asymmetry, hyper-evolution, omni-use, and autonomy.

FRAGILITY AMPLIFIERS: Applications and impacts of coming-wave technologies that will shake the already brittle foundations of the nation-state.

THE GRAND BARGAIN: In exchange for a monopoly over the right to use force, citizens expect nation-states to preserve order and provide public services, including by harnessing new technologies while minimizing the harmful side effects.

THE NARROW PATH: The potential for humankind to strike a balance between openness and closure when it comes to containing the technologies in the coming wave that avoids catastrophic or dystopian outcomes.

PESSIMISM AVERSION: The tendency for people, particularly elites, to ignore, downplay, or reject narratives they see as overly negative. A variant of optimism bias, it colors much of the debate around the future, especially in technology circles.

SYNTHETIC BIOLOGY: The ability to design and engineer new organisms or redesign existing biological systems.

TECHNOLOGY: The application of scientific knowledge (in the broadest possible sense) to produce tools or practical outcomes.

WAVES: The global diffusion or proliferation of a generation of technology anchored in a new general-purpose technology.

THE
COMING
WAVE

PROLOGUE

THIS IS HOW AN AI SEES IT.

QUESTION: What does the coming wave of technology mean for humanity?

In the annals of human history, there are moments that stand out as turning points, where the fate of humanity hangs in the balance. The discovery of fire, the invention of the wheel, the harnessing of electricity—all of these were moments that transformed human civilization, altering the course of history forever.

And now we stand at the brink of another such moment as we face the rise of a coming wave of technology that includes both advanced AI and biotechnology. Never before have we witnessed technologies with such transformative potential, promising to reshape our world in ways that are both awe-inspiring and daunting.

On the one hand, the potential benefits of these technologies are vast and profound. With AI, we could unlock the secrets of the universe, cure diseases that have long eluded us, and create new forms of art and culture that stretch the bounds of imagination. With biotechnology, we could engineer life to tackle diseases and transform agriculture, creating a world that is healthier and more sustainable.

But on the other hand, the potential dangers of these technologies are equally vast and profound. With AI, we could create systems that are beyond our control and find ourselves at the mercy of algorithms that we don't understand. With biotechnology, we could manipulate the very building blocks of life, potentially creating unintended consequences for both individuals and entire ecosystems.

As we stand at this turning point, we are faced with a choice—a choice between a future of unparalleled possibility and a future of unimaginable peril. The fate of humanity hangs in the balance, and the decisions we make in the coming years and decades will determine whether we rise to the challenge of these technologies or fall victim to their dangers.

But in this moment of uncertainty, one thing is certain: the age of advanced technology is upon us, and we must be ready to face its challenges head-on.

THE ABOVE WAS WRITTEN by an AI. The rest is not, although it soon could be. This is what's coming.

CHAPTER 1

CONT NMENT IS NOT POSSIBLE

THE WAVE

ALMOST EVERY CULTURE HAS A FLOOD MYTH.

In ancient Hindu texts, the first man in our universe, Manu, is warned of an impending deluge and becomes its sole survivor. The *Epic of Gilgamesh* records the god Enlil as destroying the world in a giant flood, a story that will resonate with anyone familiar with the Old Testament story of Noah's ark. Plato talked of the lost city of Atlantis, washed away in an immense torrent. Permeating humanity's oral traditions and ancient writings is the idea of a giant wave sweeping everything in its path, leaving the world remade and reborn.

Floods also mark history in a literal sense—the seasonal flooding of the world's great rivers, the rising of the oceans after the end of the Ice Age, the rare shock of a tsunami appearing without warning on the horizon. The asteroid that killed the dinosaurs created a towering mile-high wave, altering the course of evolution. The sheer power of these swells has seared itself into our collective consciousness: walls of water, unstoppable, uncontrollable, uncontainable. These are some of the most powerful forces on the planet. They shape continents, irrigate the world's crops, and nurture the growth of civilization.

Other kinds of waves have been just as transformative. Look again at history and you can see it marked by a series of metaphorical waves: the rise and fall of empires and religions, and bursts of commerce. Think of Christianity or Islam, religions that began as small ripples before building and crashing over huge stretches of the earth. Waves like this are a recurrent motif, framing the ebb and flow of history, great power struggles, and economic booms and busts.

The rise and spread of technologies has also taken the form of world-changing waves. A single overriding trend has stood the test of time since the discovery of fire and stone tools, the first technologies harnessed by our species. Almost every foundational technology ever invented, from pickaxes to plows, pottery to photography, phones to planes, and everything in between, follows a single, seemingly immutable law: it gets cheaper and easier to use, and ultimately it proliferates, far and wide.

This proliferation of technology in waves is the story of *Homo technologicus*—of the technological animal. Humanity's quest to improve—ourselves, our lot, our abilities, and our influence over our environment—has powered a relentless evolution of ideas and creation. Invention is an unfolding, sprawling, emergent process driven by self-organizing and highly competitive inventors, academics, entrepreneurs, and leaders, each surging forward with their own motivations. This ecosystem of invention defaults to expansion. It is the inherent nature of technology.

The question is, what happens from here? In the pages that follow, I will tell you the story of history's next great wave.

LOOK AROUND YOU.

What do you see? Furniture? Buildings? Phones? Food? A landscaped park? Almost every object in your line of sight has, in all likelihood, been created or altered by human intelligence. Language—the foundation of our social interactions, of our cultures, of our political organizations, and perhaps of what it means to be human—is another product, and driver, of our intelligence. Every principle and abstract concept, every small creative endeavor or project, every encounter in your life, has been mediated by our species' unique and endlessly complex capacity for imagination, creativity, and reason. Human ingenuity is an astonishing thing.

Only one other force is so omnipresent in this picture: biological life itself. Before the modern age, aside from a few rocks and minerals, most human artifacts—from wooden houses to cotton clothes to coal fires—came from things that were once alive. Everything that has entered the world since then flows from us, flows from the fact that we are biological beings.

It's no exaggeration to say the entirety of the human world depends on either living systems or our intelligence. And yet both are now in an unprecedented moment of exponential innovation and upheaval, an unparalleled augmentation that will leave little unchanged. Starting to crash around us is a new wave of technology. This wave is unleashing the power to engineer these two universal foundations: a wave of nothing less than intelligence and life.

The coming wave is defined by two core technologies: artificial intelligence (AI) and synthetic biology. Together they will usher in a new dawn for humanity, creating wealth and surplus unlike anything ever seen. And yet their rapid proliferation also threatens to empower a diverse array of bad actors to unleash disruption, instability, and even catastrophe on an unimaginable scale. This wave creates an immense challenge that will define the twenty-first century: our future both depends on these technologies and is imperiled by them.

From where we stand today, it appears that containing this wave—that is, controlling, curbing, or even stopping it—is not possible. This book asks why that might be true and what it means if it is. The implications of these questions will ultimately affect everyone alive and every generation that follows us.

I believe this coming wave of technology is bringing human history to a turning point. If containing it is impossible, the consequences for our species are dramatic, potentially dire. Equally, without its fruits we are exposed and precarious. This is an argument I have made many times over the last decade behind closed doors, but as the impacts become ever more unignorable, it's time that I make the case publicly.

THE DILEMMA

Contemplating the profound power of human intelligence led me to ask a simple question, one that has consumed my life ever since: What if we could distill the essence of what makes us humans so productive and capable into software, into an algorithm? Finding the answer might unlock unimaginably powerful tools to help tackle our most intractable problems. Here might be a tool, an impossible but extraordinary tool, to help us get through the awesome challenges of the decades ahead, from climate change to aging populations to sustainable food.

With this in mind, in a quaint Regency-era office overlooking London's Russell Square, I co-founded a company called DeepMind with two friends, Demis Hassabis and Shane Legg, in the summer of 2010. This was our goal, one that in retrospect still feels as ambitious and crazy and hopeful as it did back then: replicate the very thing that makes us unique as a species, our intelligence.

To achieve this objective, we would need to create a system that could imitate and then eventually outperform all human cognitive abilities, from vision and speech to planning and imagination, and ultimately empathy and creativity. Since such a system would benefit from the massively parallel processing of supercomputers and the explosion of vast new sources of data from across the open web, we knew that even modest progress toward this goal would have profound societal implications.

It certainly felt pretty far-out at the time. Back then, widespread adoption of artificial intelligence was the stuff of daydreams, more fantasy than fact, the province of a few cloistered academics and wild-eyed science fiction fans. But, as I write this and think back over the last decade, progress in AI has been nothing short of staggering. DeepMind became one of the world's leading AI companies, achieving a string of breakthroughs. The speed and power of this new revolution have been surprising even to those of us closest to its cutting edge. Over the writing of this book, the pace of progress in AI has been breathtaking, with new models and new products coming out every week, sometimes every day. It's clear this wave is accelerating.

Today, AI systems can almost perfectly recognize faces and objects. We take speech-to-text transcription and instant language translation for granted. AI can navigate roads and traffic well enough to drive autonomously in some settings. Based on a few simple prompts, a new generation of AI models can generate novel images and compose text with extraordinary levels of detail and coherence. AI systems can pro-duce synthetic voices with uncanny realism and compose music of stunning beauty. Even in more challenging domains, ones long thought to be uniquely suited to human capabilities like long-term planning, imagination, and simulation of complex ideas, progress leaps forward.

AI has been climbing the ladder of cognitive abilities for decades, and it now looks set to reach human-level performance across a very wide range of tasks within the next three years. That is a big claim, but if I'm even close to right, the implications are truly profound. What had, when we founded DeepMind, felt quixotic has become not just plausible but seemingly inevitable.

From the start, it was clear to me that AI would be a powerful tool for extraordinary good but, like most forms of power, one fraught with immense dangers and ethical dilemmas, too. I have long worried about not just the consequences of advancing AI but where the entire technological ecosystem was heading. Beyond AI, a wider revolution was underway, with AI feeding a powerful, emerging generation of genetic technologies and robotics. Further progress in one area accel-erates the others in a chaotic and cross-catalyzing process beyond any-one's direct control. It was clear that if we or others were successful in replicating human intelligence, this wasn't just profitable business as usual but a seismic shift for humanity, inaugurating an era when un-precedented opportunities would be matched by unprecedented risks.

As the technology has progressed over the years, my concerns have grown. What if the wave is actually a tsunami?

IN 2010 ALMOST NO one was talking seriously about AI. Yet what had once seemed a niche mission for a small group of researchers and en-trepreneurs has now become a vast global endeavor. AI is everywhere, on the news and in your smartphone, trading stocks and building web-sites. Many of the world's largest companies and wealthiest nations barrel forward, developing cutting-edge AI models and genetic engi-neering techniques, fueled by tens of billions of dollars in investment.

Once matured, these emerging technologies will spread rapidly, be-coming cheaper, more accessible, and widely diffused throughout society. They will offer extraordinary new medical advances and clean energy breakthroughs, creating not just new businesses but new industries and quality of life improvements in almost every imaginable area.

And yet alongside these benefits, AI, synthetic biology, and other advanced forms of technology produce tail risks on a deeply concerning scale. They could present an existential threat to nation-states—risks so profound they might disrupt or even overturn the current geopolitical order. They open pathways to immense AI-empowered cyberattacks, automated wars that could devastate countries, engineered pandemics, and a world subject to unexplainable and yet seemingly omnipotent forces. The likelihood of each may be small, but the possible consequences are huge. Even a slim chance of outcomes like these requires urgent attention.

Some countries will react to the possibility of such catastrophic risks with a form of technologically charged authoritarianism to slow the spread of these new powers. This will require huge levels of surveillance along with massive intrusions into our private lives. Keeping a tight rein on technology could become part of a drift to everything and everyone being watched, all the time, in a dystopian global surveillance system justified by a desire to guard against the most extreme possible outcomes.

Equally plausible is a Luddite reaction. Bans, boycotts, and moratoriums will ensue. Is it even possible to step away from developing new technologies and introduce a series of moratoriums? Unlikely. With their enormous geostrategic and commercial value, it's difficult to see how nation-states or corporations will be persuaded to unilaterally give up the transformative powers unleashed by these breakthroughs. Moreover, attempting to ban development of new technologies is itself a risk: technologically stagnant societies are historically unstable and prone to collapse. Eventually, they lose the capacity to solve problems, to progress.

Both pursuing and not pursuing new technologies is, from here, fraught with risk. The chances of muddling through a "narrow path" and avoiding one or the other outcome—techno-authoritarian dystopia on the one hand, openness-induced catastrophe on the other—grow smaller over time as the technology becomes cheaper, more powerful, and more pervasive and the risks accumulate. And yet stepping away is no option either. Even as we worry about their risks, we need the incredible benefits of the technologies of the coming wave more than ever before. This is the core dilemma: that, sooner or later, a powerful generation of technology leads humanity toward either catastrophic or dystopian outcomes. I believe this is the great meta-problem of the twenty-first century.

This book outlines exactly why this terrible bind is becoming inevitable and explores how we might confront it. Somehow we need to get the best out of technology, something essential to facing a daunting set of global challenges, and also get out of the dilemma. The current discourse around technology ethics and safety is inadequate. Despite the many books, debates, blog posts, and tweetstorms about technology, you rarely hear anything about *containing* it. I see this as an interlocking set of technical, social, and legal mechanisms constraining and controlling technology working at every possible level: a means, in theory, of evading the dilemma. Yet even technology's harshest critics tend to dodge this language of hard containment.

That needs to change; I hope this book shows why, and hints at how.

THE TRAP

A few years after we founded DeepMind, I created a slide deck about AI's potential long-term economic and social impacts. Presenting to a dozen of the tech industry's most influential founders, CEOs, and technologists in a sleek West Coast boardroom, I argued that AI introduced a host of threats requiring proactive responses. It might lead to massive invasions of privacy or ignite a misinformation apocalypse. It might be weaponized, creating a lethal suite of new cyberweapons, introducing new vulnerabilities into our networked world.

I also underscored AI's potential to put large numbers of people out of work. I asked the room to consider automation and mechanization's long history of displacing labor. First come more efficient ways of doing specific tasks, and then entire roles become redundant, and soon entire sectors require orders of magnitude fewer workers. Over the next few decades, I argued, AI systems would replace "intellectual manual labor" in much the same way, and certainly long before robots replace physical labor. In the past, new jobs were created at the same time as old ones were made obsolete, but what if AI could simply do most of those as well? There was, I suggested, little precedent for the new forms of concentrated power that were coming. Even though they felt distant, potentially grave threats were hurtling toward society.

In the concluding slide I showed a still from *The Simpsons*. In the scene, the townspeople of Springfield have risen up, and the cast of familiar characters charges forward carrying clubs and torches. The message was clear, but I spelled it out anyway. "The pitchforks are coming," I said. Coming for us, the makers of technology. It was up to us to ensure the future was better than this.

Around the table, I was met with blank stares. The room was unmoved. The message didn't land. Dismissals came thick and fast. Why didn't economic indicators show any sign of what I was saying? AI would spur new demand, which would create new jobs. It would augment and empower people to be even more productive. Maybe there were some risks, they conceded, but they weren't too bad. People were smart. Solutions have always been found. *No worries,* they seemed to think, *on to the next presentation.*

Some years later, a short time before the onset of the COVID-19 pandemic, I attended a seminar on technology risks at a well-known university. The setup was similar: another large table, another high-minded discussion. Over the course of the day a series of hair-raising risks were floated over the coffees, biscuits, and PowerPoints.

One stood out. The presenter showed how the price of DNA synthesizers, which can print bespoke strands of DNA, was falling rapidly. Costing a few tens of thousands of dollars, they are small enough to sit on a bench in your garage and let people synthesize—that is, *manufacture*—DNA. And all this is now possible for anyone with graduate-level training in biology or an enthusiasm for self-directed learning online.

Given the increasing availability of the tools, the presenter painted a harrowing vision: Someone could soon create novel pathogens far more transmissible and lethal than anything found in nature. These synthetic pathogens could evade known countermeasures, spread asymptomatically, or have built-in resistance to treatments. If needed, someone could supplement homemade experiments with DNA ordered online and reassembled at home. The apocalypse, mail ordered.

This was not science fiction, argued the presenter, a respected professor with more than two decades of experience; it was a live risk, now. They finished with an alarming thought: a single person today likely "has the capacity to kill a billion people." All it takes is motivation.

The attendees shuffled uneasily. People squirmed and coughed. Then the griping and hedging started. No one wanted to believe this was possible. Surely it wasn't the case, surely there had to be some effective mechanisms for control, surely the diseases were difficult to create, surely the databases could be locked down, surely the hardware could be secured. And so on.

The collective response in the seminar was more than just dismissive. People simply refused to accept the presenter's vision. No one wanted to confront the implications of the hard facts and cold probabilities they'd heard. I stayed silent, frankly shaken. Soon the seminar was done. That evening we all went out for dinner and carried on chatting as normal. We'd just had a day of talking about the end of the world, but there was still pizza to eat, jokes to tell, an office to get back to, and besides, something would turn up, or some part of the argument was bound to be wrong. I joined in.

But the presentation gnawed at me for months afterward. Why wasn't I, why weren't we all, taking it more seriously? Why do we awkwardly sidestep further discussion? Why do some get snarky and accuse people who raise these questions of catastrophizing or of "overlooking the amazing good" of technology? This widespread emotional reaction I was observing is something I have come to call the pessimism-aversion trap: the misguided analysis that arises when you are overwhelmed by a fear of confronting potentially dark realities, and the resulting tendency to look the other way.

Pretty much everyone has some version of this reaction, and the consequence is that it's leading us to overlook a number of critical trends unfolding right before our eyes. It's almost an innate physiological response. Our species is not wired to truly grapple with transformation at this scale, let alone the potential that technology might fail us in this way. I've experienced this feeling throughout my career, and I've seen many, many others have the same visceral response. Confronting this feeling is one of the purposes of this book. To take a cold hard look at the facts, however uncomfortable.

Properly addressing this wave, containing technology, and ensuring that it always serves humanity means overcoming pessimism aversion. It means facing head-on the reality of what's coming.

THIS BOOK IS MY attempt to do that. To acknowledge and illuminate the contours of the coming wave. To explore whether containment is possible. To put things in historical context, and see the wider picture by stepping back from the daily firehouse chatter around tech. My aim is to confront the dilemma and understand the underlying processes that drive the emergence of science and technology. I want to present these ideas as clearly as I can to the widest possible audience. I've written it in a spirit of openness and inquiry: make observations, follow their implications, but also remain open to refutation and better interpretations. There is nothing I want more than to be proven wrong here, than for containment to be readily possible.

Some people may understandably expect a more techno-utopian book from someone like me, a founder of two AI companies. As a technologist and entrepreneur, I am, by default, an optimist. As a young teenager, I remember being totally captivated after installing Netscape for the first time on my Packard Bell 486 PC. I was entranced by the whirring fans and the distorted whistling of my 56 Kbps dial-up modem reaching its hand out to the World Wide Web and connecting me to forums and chat rooms that gave me freedom and taught me so much. I love technology. It's been *the* engine of progress and a cause for us to be proud and excited about humanity's achievements.

But I also believe that those of us driving technology's creation must have the courage to predict—and take responsibility for—where it might take us in decades to come. We must begin to suggest what to do if it looks like there is a real risk that technology fails us. What's required is a societal and political response, not merely individual efforts, but it needs to begin with my peers and me.

Some will argue this is all overblown. That change is far more incremental. That it is just another turn of the hype cycle. That systems for coping with crises and change are actually quite robust. That my view of human nature is far too dark. That humanity's record is, well, so far, so good. History is full of false prophets and doomsayers proven wrong. Why should this time be different?

Pessimism aversion is an emotional response, an ingrained gut refusal to accept the possibility of seriously destabilizing outcomes. It tends to come from those in secure and powerful positions with entrenched worldviews, people who can superficially cope with change but struggle to accept any real challenge to their world order. Many of those whom I accuse of being stuck in the pessimism-aversion trap fully embrace the growing critiques of technology. But they nod along without actually taking any action. We'll manage, we always do, they say.

Spend time in tech or policy circles, and it quickly becomes obvious that head-in-the-sand is the default ideology. To believe and act otherwise risks becoming so crippled by fear of and outrage against enormous, inexorable forces that everything feels futile. So the strange intellectual half-world of pessimism aversion rumbles on. I should know, I was stuck in it for too long.

In the years since we founded DeepMind and since those presentations, the discourse has changed—to some extent. The job automation debate has been rehearsed countless times. A global pandemic showcased both the risks and the potency of synthetic biology. A "techlash" of sorts emerged, with critics railing against tech and tech companies in op-eds and books, in the regulatory capitals of Washington, Brussels, and Beijing. Previously niche fears around technology exploded into the mainstream, public skepticism of technology increased, and criticisms from academia, civil society, and politics sharpened.

And yet in the face of the coming wave and the great dilemma, and in the face of a pessimism-averse techno-elite, none of this is enough.

THE ARGUMENT

Waves are everywhere in human life. This one is just the latest. Often people seem to think it's still far off, so futuristic and absurd-sounding that it's just the province of a few nerds and fringe thinkers, more hyperbole, more technobabble, more boosterism. That's a mistake. This is real, as real as the tsunami that comes out of the open blue ocean.

This isn't just fantasy or a chin-stroking intellectual exercise. Even if you disagree with my framing and think none of this is likely, I urge you to read on. Yes, I come with an AI background and am primed to view the world through a technological lens. I *am* biased when it comes to the question of whether this matters. Nonetheless, having been up close to this unfurling revolution over the last decade and a half, I am convinced we're on the cusp of the most important transformation of our lifetimes.

As a builder of these technologies, I believe they can deliver an extraordinary amount of good, change countless lives for the better, and address fundamental challenges, from helping unlock the next generation of clean energy to producing cheap and effective treatments for our most intractable medical conditions. Technologies can and should enrich our lives; historically, it bears repeating, the inventors and entrepreneurs behind them have been powerful drivers of progress, improving living standards for billions of us.

But without containment, every other aspect of technology, every discussion of its ethical shortcomings, or the benefits it could bring, is inconsequential. We urgently need watertight answers for how the coming wave can be controlled and contained, how the safeguards and affordances of the democratic nation-state can be maintained, but right now no one has such a plan. This is a future that none of us want, but it's one I fear is increasingly likely, and I will explain why in the chapters that follow.

In part 1, we look at the long history of technology and how it spreads—waves building over millennia. What drives them? What makes them truly general? We also ask if there are examples of societies consciously saying no to a new technology. Instead of turning away from technologies, the past is marked by a pronounced pattern of proliferation, resulting in sprawling chains of both intended and unintended consequences.

I call this "the containment problem." How do we keep a grip on the most valuable technologies ever invented as they get cheaper and spread faster than any in history?

Part 2 gets into the details of the coming wave itself. At its heart lie two general-purpose technologies of immense promise, power, and peril: artificial intelligence and synthetic biology. Both have been long heralded, and yet, if anything, I believe the scope of their impact is still often understated. Around them grow a host of associated technologies like robotics and quantum computing whose development will intersect in complex and turbulent ways.

In this section, we look at not only how they all emerged and what they can do but also why they are so hard to contain. The various technologies I'm speaking of share four key features that explain why this isn't business as usual: they are inherently general and therefore omniuse, they hyper-evolve, they have asymmetric impacts, and, in some respects, they are increasingly autonomous.

Their creation is driven by powerful incentives: geopolitical competition, massive financial rewards, and an open, distributed culture of research. Scores of state and non-state actors will race ahead to develop them regardless of efforts to regulate and control what's coming, taking risks that affect everyone, whether we like it or not.

Part 3 explores the political implications of a colossal redistribution of power engendered by an uncontained wave. The foundation of our present political order—and the most important actor in the containment of technologies—is the nation-state. Already rocked by crises, it will be further weakened by a series of shocks amplified by the wave: the potential for new forms of violence, a flood of misinformation, disappearing jobs, and the prospect of catastrophic accidents.

Further out, the wave will force a set of tectonic shifts in power, both centralizing and decentralizing at the same time. This will create vast new enterprises, buttress authoritarianism, and yet also empower groups and movements to live outside traditional social structures. The delicate bargain of the nation-state will be placed under immense strain just when we need institutions like it most. This is how we end up in the dilemma.

In part 4 the discussion moves to what we can do about it. Is there even a slim chance for containment, for wriggling out of the dilemma? If so, how? In this section we outline ten steps, working out from the level of code and DNA to the level of international treaties, forming a hard, nested set of constraints, an outline plan for containment.

THIS IS A BOOK about confronting failure. Technologies can fail in the mundane sense of not working: the engine doesn't start; the bridge falls down. But they can also fail in a wider sense. If technology damages human lives, or produces societies filled with harm, or renders them ungovernable because we empower a chaotic long tail of bad (or unintentionally dangerous) actors—if, in the aggregate, technology is damaging—then it can be said to have failed in another, deeper sense, failing to live up to its promise. Failure in this sense isn't intrinsic to technology; it is about the context within which it operates, the governance structures it is subject to, the networks of power and uses to which it is put.

That impressive ingenuity giving rise to so much now means we are better at avoiding the first kind of failure. Fewer planes crash, cars are cleaner and safer, computers are more powerful and yet more secure. Our great challenge is that we still haven't reckoned with the latter mode of failure.

Over centuries, technology has dramatically increased the well-being of billions of people. We are immeasurably healthier thanks to modern medicine, the majority of the world lives in food abundance, people have never been more educated, more peaceful, or more materially comfortable. These are defining achievements produced in part by that great motor of humanity: science and the creation of technology. It's why I have devoted my life to safely developing these tools.

But any optimism we take from this extraordinary history must be grounded in blunt reality. Guarding against failure means understanding and ultimately confronting what can go wrong. We need to follow the chain of reasoning to its logical end point, without fear of where that might lead, and, as we get there, do something about it. The coming wave of technologies threatens to fail faster and on a wider scale than anything witnessed before. This situation needs worldwide, popular attention. It needs answers, answers that no one yet has.

Containment is not, on the face of it, possible. And yet for all our sakes, containment *must* be possible.

PART I

HOMO TECHNOLOGICUS

CHAPTER 2

ENDLESS PROLIFERATION

THE ENGINE

FOR MOST OF HISTORY, FOR MOST PEOPLE, PERSONAL TRANSPORTATION meant one thing: walking. Or if you were lucky, two: being carried or pulled by horses, oxen, elephants, or other beasts of burden. Just moving between neighboring settlements—forget about continents—was hard and slow.

In the early nineteenth century, the railway revolutionized transport, its biggest innovation in thousands of years, but most journeys could never be taken by rail, and those that could weren't very personalized. Railways did make one thing clear: engines were the future. The steam engines capable of propelling rail carriages required massive external boilers. But if you could whittle them down to a manageable, portable size, you would have radical new means for individuals to get around.

Innovators tried various approaches. As early as the eighteenth century, a French inventor called Nicolas-Joseph Cugnot built a kind of steam-powered car. It plodded along at a stately two miles an hour and featured a huge, pendulous boiler hanging off the front. In 1863, the Belgian inventor Jean Joseph Étienne Lenoir powered the first vehicle with an internal combustion engine, driving it seven miles out of Paris. But the engine was heavy, the speed limited. Others experimented with electricity and hydrogen. Nothing was catching on, but the dream of self-propelled personal transportation persisted.

Then things started to change, at first slowly. A German engineer called Nicolaus August Otto spent years working on a gas engine, much smaller than a steam engine. By 1876, in a Deutz AG factory in Cologne, Otto produced the first functional internal combustion engine, the "four-stroke" model. It was ready for mass production, but not before Otto fell out with his business partners, Gottlieb Daimler and Wilhelm Maybach. Otto wanted to use his engine in stationary settings like water pumps or factories. His partners had seen another use for the increasingly powerful engines: transport.

Yet it was another German engineer, Carl Benz, who pipped them to the post. Using his version of a four-stroke internal combustion engine, in 1886 he patented the Motorwagen, now seen as the world's first proper car. This strange three-wheel contraption debuted to a skeptical public. It was only when Benz's wife and business partner, Bertha, drove the car from Mannheim to her mother's, sixty-five miles away in Pforzheim, that the car started to catch on. She took it supposedly without his knowledge, refueling it along the way with a solvent bought from local pharmacies.

A new age had dawned. But cars, and the internal combustion engines that powered them, remained inordinately expensive, beyond the means of all but the very richest. No network of roads and fueling stations yet existed. By 1893, Benz had sold a measly 69 vehicles; by 1900, just 1,709. Twenty years after Benz's patent, there were still only 35,000 vehicles on German roads.

The turning point was Henry Ford's 1908 Model T. His simple but effective vehicle was built using a revolutionary approach: the moving assembly line. An efficient, linear, and repetitive process enabled him to slash the price of personal vehicles, and the buyers followed. Most cars at the time cost around $2,000. Ford priced his at $850.

In the early years Model T sales numbered in the thousands. Ford kept ramping up production and further lowering prices, arguing, "Every time I reduce the charge for our car by one dollar, I get a thousand new buyers." By the 1920s Ford was selling millions of cars every year. Middle-class Americans could, for the first time, afford motorized transport. Automobiles proliferated with immense speed. In 1915 only 10 percent of Americans had a car; by 1930 this number had reached an astonishing 59 percent.

Today some 2 billion combustion engines are in everything from lawnmowers to container ships. Around 1.4 billion of them are in cars. They have grown steadily more accessible, efficient, powerful, and adaptable. A whole way of life, arguably a whole civilization, developed around them, from sprawling suburbs to industrial farms, drive-thru restaurants to car mod culture. Vast highways were built, sometimes right through cities, severing neighborhoods but connecting far-flung regions. The previously challenging notion of moving from place to place in search of prosperity or fun became a regular feature of human life.

Engines weren't just powering vehicles; they were driving history. Now, thanks to hydrogen and electric motors, the reign of the combustion engine is in its twilight. But the era of mass mobility it unleashed is not.

All of this would have seemed impossible in the early nineteenth century, when self-propelled transport was still the stuff of dreamers playing with fire, flywheels, and chunks of metal. But from those early tinkerers began a marathon of invention and production that transformed the world. Once there was momentum, the spread of the internal combustion engine became unstoppable. From a few oil-soaked German workshops grew a technology that has affected every human being on earth.

This isn't, however, just a story of engines and cars. It is the story of technology itself.

GENERAL-PURPOSE WAVES: THE RHYTHM OF HISTORY

Technology has a clear, inevitable trajectory: mass diffusion in great roiling waves. This is true from the earliest flint and bone tools to the latest AI models. As science produces new discoveries, people apply these insights to make cheaper food, better goods, and more efficient transport. Over time demand for the best new products and services grows, driving competition to produce cheaper versions bursting with yet more features. This in turn drives yet more demand for the technologies that create them, and *they* also become easier and cheaper to use. Costs continue to fall. Capabilities rise. Experiment, repeat, use. Grow, improve, adapt. This is the inescapable evolutionary nature of technology.

These waves of technology and innovation are at the center of this book. More important, they are at the center of human history. Understand these complex, chaotic, and accumulating waves, and the challenge of containment becomes clear. Understand their history and we can start to sketch their future.

So, what is a wave? Put simply, a wave is a set of technologies coming together around the same time, powered by one or several new general-purpose technologies with profound societal implications. By "general-purpose technologies," I mean those that enable seismic advances in what human beings can do. Society unfolds in concert with these leaps. We see it over and over; a new piece of technology, like the internal combustion engine, proliferates and transforms everything around it.

The human story can be told through these waves: our evolution from being vulnerable primates eking out an existence on the savanna to becoming, for better or worse, the planet's dominant force. Humans are an innately technological species. From the very beginning, we are never separate from the waves of technology we create. We evolve together, in symbiosis.

The earliest stone tools date back three million years, long before the dawn of *Homo sapiens,* as evidenced by battered hammerstones and rudimentary knives. The simple hand ax forms part of history's first wave of technology. Animals could be killed more efficiently, carcasses butchered, rivals fought. Eventually, early humans learned to manipulate these tools finely, giving rise to sewing, painting, carving, and cooking.

Another wave was equally pivotal: fire. Wielded by our ancestor *Homo erectus,* it was a source of light, warmth, and safety from predators. It had a pronounced impact on evolution: cooking food meant faster release of its energy, allowing the human digestive tract to shrink and the brain to enlarge. Our ancestors, whose strong jaws constrained skull growth, spent their time relentlessly chewing and digesting food like primates today. Liberated from this mundane necessity by fire, they could spend more time doing interesting things like hunting energy-rich foods, fashioning tools, or building complex social net-works. The campfire became a central hub of human life, helping es-tablish communities and relationships and organizing labor. The evolution of *Homo sapiens* rode these waves. We are not just the cre-ators of our tools. We are, down to the biological, the anatomical level, a product of them.

Stonework and fire were proto-general-purpose technologies, meaning they were pervasive, in turn enabling new inventions, goods, and organizational behaviors. General-purpose technologies ripple out over societies, across geographies, and throughout history. They open the doors of invention wide, enabling scores of downstream tools and processes. They are often built on some kind of general-purpose prin-ciple, whether the power of steam to do work or the information the-ory behind a computer's binary code.

The irony of general-purpose technologies is that, before long, they become invisible and we take them for granted. Language, agri-culture, writing—each was a general-purpose technology at the center of an early wave. These three waves formed the foundation of civiliza-tion as we know it. Now we take them for granted. One major study pegged the number of general-purpose technologies that have emerged over the entire span of human history at just twenty-four, naming in-ventions ranging from farming, the factory system, the development of materials like iron and bronze, through to printing presses, electric-ity, and of course the internet. There aren't many of them, but they matter; it's why in the popular imagination we still use terms like the Bronze Age and the Age of Sail.

Throughout history, population size and innovation levels are linked. New tools and techniques give rise to larger populations. Big-ger and more connected populations are more potent crucibles for tin-kering, experimentation, and serendipitous discovery, a more powerful "collective brain" for making new things. Large populations give rise to greater levels of specialization, new classes of people like artisans and scholars whose livelihood isn't tied to the land. More people whose lives do not revolve around subsistence means more possible inventors, and more possible reasons for having inventions, and those inventions mean more people in turn. From the earliest civilizations, like Uruk in

Mesopotamia, the birthplace of cuneiform, the first known writing system, to today's megalopolises, cities have driven technological development. And more technology meant more—and bigger—cities. At the dawn of the Agricultural Revolution the worldwide human population numbered just 2.4 million. At the start of the Industrial Revolution, it approached 1 billion, a four-hundred-fold increase that was predicated on the waves of the intervening period.

The Agricultural Revolution (9000–7500 BCE), one of history's most significant waves, marked the arrival of two massive general-purpose technologies that gradually replaced the nomadic, hunter-gatherer way of life: the domestication of plants and animals. These developments changed not only how food was found but how it might be stored, how transport would work, and the very scale at which a society could operate. Early crops like wheat, barley, lentils, chickpeas, and peas and animals like pigs, sheep, and goats became subject to human control. Eventually, this coupled with a new revolution in tools—hoes and plows. These simple innovations marked the beginning of modern civilizations.

The more tools you have, the more you can do and the more you can imagine new tools and processes beyond them. As the Harvard anthropologist Joseph Henrich points out, the wheel arrived surprisingly late in human life. But once invented, it became a building block of everything from chariots and wagons to mills, presses, and flywheels. From the written word to sailing vessels, technology increases interconnectedness, helping to boost its own flow and spread. Each wave hence lays the groundwork for successive waves.

Over time, this dynamic accelerated. Beginning around the 1770s in Europe, the first wave of the Industrial Revolution combined steam power, mechanized looms, the factory system, and canals. In the 1840s came the age of railways, telegraphs, and steamships, and a bit later steel and machine tools; together they formed the First Industrial Revolution. Then, just a few decades later, came the Second Industrial Revolution. You'll be familiar with its greatest hits: the internal combustion engine, chemical engineering, powered flight, and electricity. Flight needed combustion, and mass production of combustion engines demanded steel and machine tools, and so on. Beginning with

the Industrial Revolution, immense change became measured in decades rather than centuries or millennia.

This isn't, however, an orderly process. Technological waves don't
arrive with the neat predictability of the tides. Over the long term,
waves erratically intersect and intensify. The ten thousand years up to
1000 BCE saw seven general-purpose technologies emerge. The two
hundred years between 1700 and 1900 marked the arrival of six, from
steam engines to electricity. And in the last hundred years alone there
were seven. Consider that children who grew up traveling by horse and
cart and burning wood for heat in the late nineteenth century spent
their final days traveling by airplane and living in houses warmed by
the splitting of the atom.

Waves—pulsating, emergent, successive, compounding, and cross-
pollinating—define an era's horizon of technological possibility. They
are part of us. There is no such thing as a non-technological human
being.

This conception of history as a series of waves of innovation is
not novel. Sequential and disruptive clusters of technologies recur
in discussions of technology. For the futurist Alvin Toffler, the information technology revolution was a "third wave" in human society
following the Agricultural and Industrial revolutions. Joseph Schum-
peter saw waves as explosions of innovation igniting new businesses
in bursts of "creative destruction." The great philosopher of technology Lewis Mumford believed the "machine age" was actually more
like a thousand-year unfolding of three major successive waves.
More recently the economist Carlota Perez has talked about "techno-
economic paradigms" rapidly shifting amid technological revolutions.
Moments of booming disruption and wild speculation regear economies. Suddenly everything relies on railways, cars, or microprocessors.
Eventually, the technology matures, becoming embedded and widely
available.

Most people in technology are stuck in the minutiae of today and
dreaming of tomorrow. It is tempting to think of inventions in discrete
and lucky moments. But do so and you'll miss the stark patterns of history, the sheer, almost innate tendency for technology's waves to come
again and again.

PROLIFERATION IS THE DEFAULT

For most of lived history, proliferation of new technology was rare. Most humans were born, lived, and died surrounded by the same set of tools and technologies. Zoom out, though, and it becomes clear that proliferation is the default.

General-purpose technologies become waves when they diffuse widely. Without an epic and near-uncontrolled global diffusion, it's not a wave; it's a historical curiosity. Once diffusion starts, however, the process echoes throughout history, from agriculture's spread throughout the Eurasian landmass to the slow scattering of water mills out from the Roman Empire across Europe. Once a technology gets traction, once a wave starts building, the historical pattern we saw with cars is clear.

When Gutenberg invented the printing press around 1440, there was only a single example in Europe: his original in Mainz, Germany. But just fifty years later a thousand presses spread across the Continent. Books themselves, one of the most influential technologies in history, multiplied with explosive speed. In the Middle Ages manuscript production was on the order of hundreds of thousands per major country per century. One hundred years after Gutenberg, countries like Italy, France, and Germany produced around 40 million books per half century, and the pace of acceleration was still increasing. In the seventeenth century Europe printed 500 million books. As demand soared, costs plummeted. One analysis estimates that the introduction of the printing press in the fifteenth century caused a 340-fold decrease in the price of a book, further driving adoption and yet more demand.

Or take electricity. The first electricity power stations debuted in London and New York in 1882, Milan and St. Petersburg in 1883, and Berlin in 1884. Their rollout gathered pace from there. In 1900, 2 percent of fossil fuel production was devoted to producing electricity, by 1950 it was above 10 percent, and in 2000 it reached more than 30 percent. In 1900 global electricity generation stood at 8 terawatt-hours; fifty years later it was at 600, powering a transformed economy.

The Nobel Prize–winning economist William Nordhaus calculated that the same amount of labor that once produced fifty-four minutes of quality light in the eighteenth century now produces more than fifty years of light. As a result, the average person in the twenty-first century has access to approximately 438,000 times more "lumen-hours" per year than our eighteenth-century cousins.

Unsurprisingly, consumer technologies exhibit a similar trend. Alexander Graham Bell introduced the telephone in 1876. By 1900, America had 600,000 telephones. Ten years later there were 5.8 million. Today America has many more telephones than people.

Increasing quality joins decreasing prices in this picture. A primitive TV costing $1,000 in 1950 would cost just $8 in 2023, though, of course, TVs today are infinitely better and so cost more. You can find almost identical price (and adoption) curves for cars, or microwaves, or washing machines. Indeed, the twentieth and twenty-first centuries saw remarkably consistent adoption of new consumer electronics. Again and again, the pattern is unmistakable.

Proliferation is catalyzed by two forces: demand and the resulting cost decreases, each of which drives technology to become even better and cheaper. The long and intricate dialogue of science and technology produces a chain of insights, breakthroughs, and tools that build and reinforce over time, productive recombinations that drive the future. As you get more and cheaper technology, it enables new and cheaper technologies downstream. Uber was impossible without the smartphone, which itself was enabled by GPS, which was enabled by satellites, which were enabled by rockets, which were enabled by combustion techniques, which were enabled by language and fire.

Of course, behind technological breakthroughs are people. They labor at improving technology in workshops, labs, and garages, motivated by money, fame, and often knowledge itself. Technologists, innovators, and entrepreneurs get better by doing and, crucially, by copying. From your enemy's superior plow to the latest cell phones, copying is a critical driver of diffusion. Mimicry spurs competition, and technologies improve further. Economies of scale kick in and reduce costs.

Civilization's appetite for useful and cheaper technologies is boundless. This will not change.

FROM VACUUM TUBES TO NANOMETERS:
TURBO-PROLIFERATION

If you want a hint of what's coming next, consider the foundation of the last mature wave. From the start, computers were driven by new-frontier mathematics as well as the urgencies of great power conflict.

Like the internal combustion engine, computing began as the stuff of obscure academic papers and laboratory tinkerers. Then came the War. In the 1940s, Bletchley Park, Britain's top secret World War II code-breaking hub, started to realize a true computer for the first time. Racing to crack Germany's supposedly unbreakable Enigma machines, an extraordinary team turned theoretical insights into a practical device capable of doing just that.

Others were also on the case. By 1945, an important precursor to computers called the ENIAC, an eight-foot-tall behemoth of eighteen thousand vacuum tubes capable of three hundred operations a second, was developed at the University of Pennsylvania. Bell Labs initiated another significant breakthrough in 1947: the transistor, a semiconductor creating "logic gates" to perform calculations. This crude device, comprising a paper clip, a scrap of gold foil, and a crystal of germanium that could switch electronic signals, laid the basis for the digital age.

As with cars, it was by no means obvious to contemporary observers that computing would spread fast. In the late 1940s there were still only a few devices. Early in that decade IBM's president, Thomas J. Watson, had allegedly (and notoriously) said, "I think there is a world market for about five computers." *Popular Mechanics* magazine made a forecast typical of its time in 1949: "Computers in the future may have only 1000 vacuum tubes," it argued, "and perhaps weigh only 1½ tons." A decade after Bletchley, there were still only hundreds of computers around the world.

We know what happened next. Computing transformed society faster than anyone predicted and proliferated faster than any invention in human history. Robert Noyce invented the integrated circuit at Fairchild Semiconductor in the late 1950s and the 1960s, imprinting multiple transistors on silicon wafers to produce what came to be called silicon chips. Shortly after, a researcher called Gordon Moore proposed his eponymous "law": every twenty-four months, the number of transistors on a chip would double. That implied that chips, and by extension the world of digital and computational technology, would be subject to the upward curve of an exponential process.

The results are astounding. Since the early 1970s the number of transistors per chip has increased ten-million-fold. Their power has increased by ten orders of magnitude—*a seventeen-billion-fold improvement*. Fairchild Semiconductor sold one hundred transistors for $150 each in 1958. Transistors are now produced in the tens of trillions per second, at billionths of a dollar per transistor: the fastest, most extensive proliferation in history.

And of course this rise in computational power underpinned a flowering of devices, applications, and users. In the early 1970s there were about half a million computers. Back in 1983, only 562 computers total were connected to the primordial internet. Now the number of computers, smartphones, and connected devices is estimated at 14 billion. It took smartphones a few years to go from niche product to utterly essential item for two-thirds of the planet.

With this wave came email, social media, online videos—each a fundamentally new experience enabled by the transistor and another general-purpose technology, the internet. This is what pure, uncontained technological proliferation looks like. It created a yet more mind-boggling proliferation: data, up twenty times in the decade 2010–2020 alone. Just a few decades ago data storage was the domain of books and dusty archives. Now humans produce hundreds of billions of emails, messages, images, and videos daily and store them in the cloud. Eighteen million gigabytes of data are added to the global sum every single minute of every day.

Billions of hours of raw human life are consumed, shaped, distorted, and enriched by these technologies. They dominate our businesses and our leisure time. They occupy our minds and every crevice of our worlds, from fridges, timers, garage doors, and hearing aids to wind turbines. They form the very architecture of modern life. Our phones are the first thing we see in the morning and the last at night. Every aspect of human life is affected: they help us find love and new friends while turbocharging supply chains. They influence who gets elected and how, where our money is invested, our children's self-esteem, our music tastes, our fashion, our food, and everything in between.

Someone from the postwar world would be staggered by the scale and reach of what had seemed a niche technology. Computing's remarkable ability to spread and improve at exponential rates, to enter and envelop almost every aspect of life, has become the dominant fact of contemporary civilization. No previous wave has mushroomed as quickly, but the historical pattern nonetheless repeats. At first it seems impossible and unimaginable. Then it appears inevitable. And each wave grows bigger and stronger still.

IT'S EASY TO GET lost in the details, but step back and you can see waves gathering speed, scope, accessibility, and consequence. Once they gather momentum, they rarely stop. Mass diffusion, raw, rampant proliferation—this is technology's historical default, the closest thing to a natural state. Think of agriculture, bronze work, the printing press, the automobile, the television, the smartphone, and the rest. There are then what appear to be laws of technology, something like an inherent character, emergent properties that stand the test of time.

History tells us that technology diffuses, inevitably, eventually to almost everywhere, from the first campfires to the fires of the Saturn V rocket, from the first scrawled letters to the endless text of the internet. Incentives are overwhelming. Capabilities accumulate; efficiencies increase. Waves get faster and more consequential. Access to technology grows as it gets cheaper. Technology proliferates, and with every successive wave that proliferation accelerates and penetrates deeper, even as the technology gets more powerful.

This is technology's historical norm. As we gaze toward the future, this is what we can expect.

Or can we?

CHAPTER 3

THE CONTAINMENT PROBLEM

REVENGE EFFECTS

ALAN TURING AND GORDON MOORE COULD NEVER HAVE PREDICTED, let alone altered the rise of, social media, memes, Wikipedia, or cyberattacks. Decades after their invention, the architects of the atomic bomb could no more stop a nuclear war than Henry Ford could stop a car accident. Technology's unavoidable challenge is that its makers quickly lose control over the path their inventions take once introduced to the world.

Technology exists in a complex, dynamic system (the real world), where second-, third-, and nth-order consequences ripple out unpredictably. What on paper looks flawless can behave differently out in the wild, especially when copied and further adapted downstream. What people actually do with your invention, however well intentioned, can never be guaranteed. Thomas Edison invented the phonograph so people could record their thoughts for posterity and to help the blind. He was horrified when most people just wanted to play music. Alfred Nobel intended his explosives to be used only in mining and railway construction.

Gutenberg just wanted to make money printing Bibles. Yet his press catalyzed the Scientific Revolution and the Reformation, and so became the greatest threat to the Catholic Church since its establishment. Fridge makers didn't aim to create a hole in the ozone layer with chlorofluorocarbons (CFCs), just as the creators of the internal combustion and jet engines had no thought of melting the ice caps. In fact early enthusiasts for automobiles argued for their environmental benefits: engines would rid the streets of mountains of horse dung that spread dirt and disease across urban areas. They had no conception of global warming.

Understanding technology is, in part, about trying to understand its unintended consequences, to predict not just positive spillovers but "revenge effects." Quite simply, any technology is capable of going wrong, often in ways that directly contradict its original purpose. Think of the way that prescription opioids have created dependence, or how the overuse of antibiotics renders them less effective, or how the proliferation of satellites and debris known as "space junk" imperils spaceflight.

As technology proliferates, more people can use it, adapt it, shape it however they like, in chains of causality beyond any individual's comprehension. As the power of our tools grows exponentially and as access to them rapidly increases, so do the potential harms, an unfolding labyrinth of consequences that no one can fully predict or forestall. One day someone is writing equations on a blackboard or fiddling with a prototype in the garage, work seemingly irrelevant to the wider world. Within decades, it has produced existential questions for humanity. As we have built systems of increasing power, this aspect of technology has felt more and more pressing to me. How do we guarantee that this new wave of technologies does more good than harm?

Technology's problem here is a containment problem. If this aspect cannot be eliminated, it might be curtailed. Containment is the overarching ability to control, limit, and, if need be, close down technologies at any stage of their development or deployment. It means, in some circumstances, the ability to stop a technology from proliferating in the first place, checking the ripple of unintended consequences (both good and bad).

The more powerful a technology, the more ingrained it is in every facet of life and society. Thus, technology's problems have a tendency to escalate in parallel with its capabilities, and so the need for containment grows more acute over time.

Does any of this get technologists off the hook? Not at all; more than anyone else it is up to us to face it. We might not be able to control the final end points of our work or its long-term effects, but that is no reason to abdicate responsibility. Decisions technologists and societies make at the source can still shape outcomes. Just because consequences are difficult to predict doesn't mean we shouldn't try.

In most cases, containment is about meaningful control, the capability to stop a use case, change a research direction, or deny access to harmful actors. It means preserving the ability to steer waves to ensure their impact reflects our values, helps us flourish as a species, and does not introduce significant harms that outweigh their benefits.

This chapter shows just how challenging and rare that actually is.

CONTAINMENT IS THE FOUNDATION

For many, the word "containment" brings echoes of the Cold War. The American diplomat George F. Kennan argued that "the main element of any United States policy toward the Soviet Union must be that of a long-term, patient but firm and vigilant containment of Russian expansive tendencies." Viewing the world as a constantly shifting field of struggle, Western nations, Kennan contended, must monitor and counter Soviet power wherever they found it, safely containing the Red menace and its ideological tentacles across *all* dimensions.

While this reading of containment offers some useful lessons, it's inadequate for our purposes. Technology is not an adversary; it's a basic property of human society. Containing technology needs to be a much more fundamental program, a balance of power not between competing actors but between humans and our tools. It's a necessary prerequisite for the survival of our species over the next century. Containment encompasses regulation, better technical safety, new governance and ownership models, and new modes of accountability and transparency, all as necessary (but not sufficient) precursors to safer technology. It's an overarching lock uniting cutting-edge engineering, ethical values, and government regulation. Containment shouldn't be seen as the final answer to all technology's problems; it is rather the first, critical step, a foundation on which the future is built.

Think of containment, then, as a set of interlinked and mutually reinforcing technical, cultural, legal, and political mechanisms for

maintaining societal control of technology during a time of exponential change; an architecture up to the task of containing what would
have once been centuries or millennia of technological change happening now in a matter of years or even months, where consequences rico-
chet around the world in seconds.

Technical containment refers to what happens in a lab or an R&D
facility. In AI, for example, it means air gaps, sandboxes, simulations,
off switches, hard built-in safety and security measures—protocols for
verifying the safety or integrity or uncompromised nature of a system
and taking it offline if needed. Then come the values and cultures
around creation and dissemination that support boundaries, layers of
governance, acceptance of limits, a vigilance for harms and unintended
consequences. Last, containment includes both national and international legal mechanisms for containment: regulations passed by national legislatures and treaties operating through the UN and other
global bodies. Technology is always deeply caught up in the laws and
customs, the norms and habits, the structures of power and knowledge
of any given society; each must be addressed. We'll return to this in
more detail in part 4.

For now, you may be wondering, have we ever really attempted
this, tried to contain a wave?

HAVE WE EVER SAID NO?

As the printing press roared across Europe in the fifteenth century, the
Ottoman Empire had a rather different response. It tried to ban it. Un-
happy at the prospect of unregulated mass production of knowledge
and culture, the sultan considered the press an alien, "Western" innovation. Despite rivaling cities like London, Paris, and Rome in population, Istanbul didn't possess a sanctioned printing press until 1727, nearly
three centuries after its invention. For a long time historians saw the
Ottoman Empire's resistance as a classic example of early techno-
nationalism, a conscious, backward-looking rejection of modernity.

But it's more complicated than that. Under the empire's rules, only
Arabic characters were banned, not printing altogether. More than
some fundamentally antitechnology posture, the ban came down to

the huge expense and complexity of running Arabic-language printers; only the sultan could afford to fund printing, and successive sultans had little interest in it. So the Ottoman press stalled; for a time the empire said no thank you. But eventually, just like everywhere else, printing became a fact of life in the Ottoman Empire, in its descendant countries, and indeed across the world. States, it seems, might say no, but as things get cheaper and more widely used, they can't say no forever.

In hindsight, waves might appear smooth and inevitable. But there is an almost infinite array of small, local, and often arbitrary factors that affect a technology's trajectory. Indeed, no one should imagine diffusion is easy. It can be costly, slow, and risky, or require wrenching changes in behavior feasible over only decades or lifetimes. It has to fight existing interests, established knowledge, and those who jealously hold both. Fear and suspicion of anything new and different are endemic. Everyone from guilds of skilled craftsmen to suspicious monarchs has reason to push back. Luddites, the groups that violently rejected industrial techniques, are not the exception to the arrival of new technologies; they are the norm.

In medieval times Pope Urban II wanted to ban the crossbow. Queen Elizabeth I nixed a new kind of knitting machine in the late sixteenth century on the grounds it might upset the guilds. Guilds harassed and smashed new kinds of looms and lathes in Nuremberg, Danzig, the Netherlands, and England. John Kay, the inventor of the flying shuttle, which made weaving more efficient and was one of the key technologies of the Industrial Revolution, was so scared of violent reprisals he fled from England to France.

People throughout history have attempted to resist new technologies because they felt threatened and worried their livelihoods and way of life would be destroyed. Fighting, as they saw it, for the future of their families, they would, if necessary, physically destroy what was coming. If peaceful measures failed, Luddites wanted to take apart the wave of industrial machinery.

Under the seventeenth-century Tokugawa shogunate, Japan shut out the world—and by extension its barbarous inventions—for nearly three hundred years. Like most societies throughout history, it was distrustful of the new, the different, and the disruptive. Similarly, China dismissed a British diplomatic mission and its offer of Western tech in the late eighteenth century, with the Qianlong emperor arguing, "Our Celestial Empire possesses all things in prolific abundance and lacks no product within its borders. There is therefore no need to import the manufactures of outside barbarians."

None of it worked. The crossbow survived until it was usurped by guns. Queen Elizabeth's knitting machine returned, centuries later, in the supercharged form of large-scale mechanical looms to spark the Industrial Revolution. China and Japan are today among the most technologically advanced and globally integrated places on earth. The Luddites were no more successful at stopping new industrial technologies than horse owners and carriage makers were at preventing cars. Where there is demand, technology always breaks out, finds traction, builds users.

Once established, waves are almost impossible to stop. As the Ottomans discovered when it came to printing, resistance tends to be ground down with the passage of time. Technology's nature is to spread, no matter the barriers.

Plenty of technologies come and go. You don't see too many penny-farthings or Segways, listen to many cassettes or minidiscs. But that doesn't mean personal mobility and music aren't ubiquitous; older technologies have just been replaced by new, more efficient forms. We don't ride on steam trains or write on typewriters, but their ghostly presence lives on in their successors, like Shinkansens and MacBooks.

Think of how, as parts of successive waves, fire, then candles and oil lamps, gave way to gas lamps and then to electric lightbulbs, and now LED lights, and the totality of artificial light increased even as the underlying technologies changed. New technologies supersede multiple predecessors. Just as electricity did the work of candles and steam engines alike, so smartphones replaced satnavs, cameras, PDAs, computers, and telephones (and invented entirely new classes of experience: apps). As technologies let you do more, for less, their appeal only grows, along with their adoption.

Imagine trying to build a contemporary society without electricity or running water or medicines. Even if you could, how would you convince anyone it was worthwhile, desirable, a decent trade? Few societies have ever successfully removed themselves from the technological frontier; doing so usually either is part of a collapse or precipitates one. There is no realistic way to pull back.

Inventions cannot be uninvented or blocked indefinitely, knowledge unlearned or stopped from spreading. Scattered historical examples give little reason to think it might happen again. The Library of Alexandria was left to wither, and it finally burned down, swaths of classical learning lost forever. But eventually the wisdom of antiquity was rediscovered and revalued. Aided by a lack of modern communications tools, China kept the secret of silk making under wraps for centuries, but it got out in the end thanks to two determined Nestorian monks in 552 CE. Technologies are ideas, and ideas cannot be eliminated.

Technology is an eternally dangling carrot, constantly promising more, better, easier, cheaper. Our appetite for invention is insatiable. The seeming inevitability of waves comes not from the absence of resistance but from demand overwhelming it. People have often said no, desired contained technology for a plethora of reasons. It's just never been enough. It's not that the containment problem hasn't been recognized in history; it's just that it has never been solved.

Are there exceptions? Or does the wave always break everywhere, in the end?

THE NUCLEAR EXCEPTION?

On September 11, 1933, the physicist Ernest Rutherford argued to the British Association for the Advancement of Science in Leicester that "anyone who says that with the means at present at our disposal and with our present knowledge we can utilize atomic energy is talking moonshine." Reading an account of Rutherford's argument at a hotel in London, the Hungarian émigré Leo Szilard mulled it over at breakfast. He went for a walk. The day after Rutherford called it moonshine, Szilard conceptualized a nuclear chain reaction.

The first nuclear explosion came just twelve years later. On July 16, 1945, under the auspices of the Manhattan Project, the U.S. Army detonated a device code-named Trinity in the New Mexico desert. Weeks later a Boeing B-29 Superfortress, the *Enola Gay*, dropped a device code-named Little Boy containing sixty-four kilograms of uranium-235 over the city of Hiroshima, killing 140,000 people. In an instant, the world had changed. Yet from there, against the wider pattern of history, nuclear weapons did not endlessly proliferate.

Nuclear weapons have been detonated only twice in wartime. To date only nine countries have acquired them. Indeed, South Africa relinquished the technology altogether in 1989. As far as we know, no non-state actors have acquired nuclear weapons, and today the total number of warheads stands at around ten thousand, frighteningly large, but lower than Cold War highs, when that figure hovered at more than sixty thousand.

So what happened? Nuclear weapons clearly confer a significant strategic advantage. At the end of World War II many unsurprisingly assumed they would proliferate widely. After the successful development of early nuclear bombs, the United States and Russia had been on a path of developing ever more destructive weapons, like thermonuclear hydrogen bombs. The biggest explosion ever recorded was a test of an H-bomb called the Tsar Bomba. Detonated over a remote archipelago in the Barents Sea in 1961, the explosion created a three-mile fireball and a mushroom cloud fifty-nine miles wide. The blast was ten times more powerful than the combined total of all the conventional explosives deployed in World War II. Its scale frightened everyone. In this respect it might have actually helped. Both the United States and Russia stepped back from ramping up their weapons in the face of their sheer, horrific power.

That nuclear technology remained contained was no accident; it was a conscious nonproliferation policy of the nuclear powers, helped by the fact that nuclear weapons are incredibly complex and expensive to produce.

Some of the early proposals for achieving containment were admirably high-minded. In 1946 the Acheson-Lilienthal Report suggested the UN create an "Atomic Development Authority" with explicit worldwide control of all nuclear activities. That of course didn't happen, but a series of international treaties nonetheless followed. Although countries like China and France stood aside, the Partial Test Ban Treaty was signed in 1963, reducing the drumbeat of test explosions that spurred on competition.

A turning point came in 1968 with the Treaty on the Non-proliferation of Nuclear Weapons, a landmark moment when nations explicitly agreed never to develop nuclear weapons. The world had come together to decisively arrest the proliferation of nuclear weapons to new states. From the first test, their destructive power was clear. Popular revulsion at the possibility of a thermonuclear apocalypse was a powerful motivator for signing the treaty. But these weapons have also been contained by cold calculation. Mutually assured destruction hemmed in possessors since it soon became clear that using them in anger is a quick way of ensuring your own destruction.

They're also eye-wateringly expensive and difficult to manufacture. Not only do they require rare and difficult-to-handle materials like enriched uranium-235, but maintaining and ultimately decommissioning them is also challenging. Lack of widespread demand has meant little pressure to reduce costs and grow access; they are not subject to the classic cost curves of modern consumer technology. These were never going to spread like transistors or flat-screen TVs; producing fissile material is not like rolling aluminum. Nonproliferation is in no small part a function of the fact that building a nuke is one of the largest, most expensive, and most complicated endeavors a state can embark on.

It would be wrong to say they have not proliferated, when even now so many nuclear weapons sit on submarines patrolling the seas or are on hair-trigger alert in great silos. But to a remarkable degree, and thanks to a huge spectrum of technical and political efforts over decades, they have avoided technology's deep underlying pattern.

And yet, even though nuclear capability has been largely contained, a partial exception, it's not a reassuring story. Nuclear history is still a chilling succession of accidents, near misses, and misunderstandings. Since the first tests in 1945, hundreds of incidents merit serious concern, from relatively minor process problems to terrifying escalations that could have (and still might) trigger destruction on a truly horrific scale.

Failure could come in a variety of guises. What if the software goes wrong? After all, it was only in 2019 that U.S. command and control systems were upgraded from 1970s hardware and eight-inch floppy disks. The world's most sophisticated and destructive weapons arsenal ran on technology so antiquated it would be unrecognizable (and un-usable) to most people alive today.

Accidents are legion. In 1961, for example, a B-52 in the skies above North Carolina developed a fuel leak. The crew ejected from the ailing aircraft, leaving it and its payload to plummet to the ground. In the process, a live hydrogen bomb's safety switch flicked to "armed" as it crashed into a field. Of its four safety mechanisms, just one was left in place, and an explosion was miraculously avoided. In 2003 the British Ministry of Defence disclosed more than 110 near misses and accidents in the history of its nuclear weapons program. Even the Kremlin, hardly a model of openness, has admitted 15 serious nuclear accidents between 2000 and 2010.

Tiny hardware malfunctions can produce outsized risks. In 1980 a single faulty computer chip costing forty-six cents almost triggered a major nuclear incident over the Pacific. And in perhaps the most well-known case, nuclear catastrophe was only avoided during the Cuban missile crisis when one man, the acting Russian commodore, Vasili Arkhipov, refused to give an order to fire nuclear torpedoes. The two other officers on the submarine, convinced they were under attack, had brought the world within a split second of full-scale nuclear war.

Worries remain abundant. Nuclear sabers rattled anew in the wake of Russia's invasion of Ukraine. North Korea went to extraordinary lengths to acquire nuclear weapons and appears to have sold ballistic missiles to and co-developed nuclear technologies with countries like Iran and Syria. China, India, and Pakistan are ramping up arsenals and have opaque safety records. Everyone from Turkey and Saudi Arabia to Japan and South Korea has at least expressed interest in nuclear weapons. Brazil and Argentina even had uranium enrichment pro-grams.

To date no terrorist group is known to have acquired either a con-ventional warhead or sufficient radiological material for a "dirty" bomb. But methods to construct such a device are hardly secret. A rogue insider could credibly produce one. The engineer A. Q. Khan helped Pakistan develop nuclear weapons by stealing centrifuge blueprints and fleeing the Netherlands.

Plenty of nuclear material is unaccounted for, from hospitals, businesses, militaries, even recently from Chernobyl. In 2018, plutonium and cesium were stolen from a Department of Energy official's car in San Antonio, Texas, while they slept in a nearby hotel. The nightmare scenario is a loose warhead, stolen in transit or even somehow missed in an accounting exercise. It may sound fanciful, but the United States has in fact lost at least three nuclear weapons.

Nuclear is an exception to the unstoppable spread of technology, but only because of the tremendous costs and complexity involved, the decades of tough multilateral effort, the fear-inducing enormity of its lethal potential, and pure luck. To some extent it might, then, have bucked the wider trend, but it also shows how the game has changed. Given the potential consequences, given its looming existential reach, even partial, relative containment is woefully insufficient.

The worrying truth of this fearsome technology is that humanity has tried to say no and only partially succeeded. Nuclear weapons are among the most contained technologies in history, and yet the containment problem—in its hardest, most literal sense—even here remains acutely unsolved.

THE TECHNOLOGICAL ANIMAL

Glimmers of containment are rare and often flawed. They include moratoriums on biological and chemical weapons; the Montreal Protocol of 1987, which phased out substances damaging the atmosphere's ozone layer, particularly CFCs; the EU's ban on genetically modified organisms in foodstuffs; and a self-organized moratorium on human gene editing. Perhaps the most ambitious containment agenda is decarbonization, measures like the Paris Agreement, which aims to limit global temperature rise to two degrees Celsius. In essence, it represents a worldwide attempt to say no to a suite of foundational technologies.

We'll take a closer look at these modern examples of containment in part 4. For now, though, it's important to note that, while instructive, none of these achievements are particularly robust. Chemical weapons were recently used in Syria. Such weapons are only a relatively narrow application of constantly developing fields. Despite the moratoriums, the world's chemical and biological capabilities grow every year; should anyone perceive the need to weaponize them, it would be easier than ever.

While the EU bans GMOs in the food supply, they're ubiquitous in other parts of the world. As we will see, the science behind gene editing is charging forward. The call for a global moratorium on human gene editing has stalled. Luckily, cheaper and more effective alternatives were readily available to supplant CFCs, which in any case were hardly a general-purpose technology. Without them, modeling suggests the ozone layer might have collapsed by the 2040s, creating an additional 1.7 degrees Celsius of warming in the twenty-first century. In general these containment efforts are limited to highly specific technologies, some in narrow jurisdictions, all with only a shaky purchase.

While the Paris Agreement aims to go beyond these limitations, will it work? We have to hope so. But it's worth pointing out that this containment comes only in the wake of significant damage and an existential-level threat growing more obvious by the day. It is coming late, and its success is far from guaranteed.

This is not containment proper. None of these efforts represent the full-scale arresting of a wave of general-purpose technology, although, as we will see later, they do offer important pointers for the future. But these examples do not remotely provide as much comfort as we'd hope—or need.

THERE ARE ALWAYS GOOD reasons to resist or curtail technology. Although its history is one of enabling people to do more, increasing capabilities, driving improvements in well-being, it's not a one-sided story: Technology creates more lethal and destructive weapons as well as better tools. It produces losers, eliminates some jobs and ways of life, and creates harm up to the planetary, existential scale of climate change. New technologies can be unsettling and destabilizing, alien and invasive. Technology causes problems, and always has.

And yet none of that seems to matter. It might take time, but the pattern is unmistakable: proliferating, cheaper, and more efficient technologies, wave upon wave of them. As long as a technology is useful, desirable, affordable, accessible, and unsurpassed, it survives and spreads and those features compound. While technology doesn't tell us when, or how, or whether to walk through the doors it opens, sooner or later we do seem to walk through them. There is no necessary relationship here, just a persistent empirical linkage throughout history.

Everything about a given technology is contingent, path dependent; it rests on a mind-bendingly intricate set of circumstances, chance happenings, myriad specific local, cultural, institutional, and economic factors. Zoom in and lucky meetings, random events, quirks of character, and tiny acts of creation—and sometimes pushback—loom large. But zoom out and what do we see? A more tectonic process, where it's a question of not *if* these powers are harnessed but when, in what form, and by whom.

Given its extreme rarity, containment has unsurprisingly dropped out of the vocabularies of technologists and policy makers. We have collectively resigned ourselves to the story of this chapter because it is so ingrained. By and large we've let the waves wash over us, managing on an uncoordinated, ad hoc basis, accepting that capabilities spreading inevitably and uncontrollably is, whether welcomed or reviled, a fact of life.

In the space of around a hundred years, successive waves took humanity from an era of candles and horse carts to one of power stations and space stations. Something similar is going to occur in the next thirty years. In the coming decades, a new wave of technology will force us to confront the most foundational questions our species has ever faced. Do we want to edit our genomes so that some of us can have children with immunity to certain diseases, or with more intelligence, or with the potential to live longer? Are we committed to holding on to our place at the top of the evolutionary pyramid, or will we allow the emergence of AI systems that are smarter and more capable than we can ever be? What are the unintended consequences of exploring questions like these?

They illustrate a key truth about *Homo technologicus* in the twenty-first century. For most of history, the challenge of technology lay in creating and unleashing its power. That has now flipped: the challenge of technology today is about containing its unleashed power, ensuring it continues to serve us and our planet.

That challenge is about to decisively escalate.

PART II

THE
NEXT WAVE

CHAPTER 4

THE TECHNOLOGY
OF INTELLIGENCE

WELCOME TO THE MACHINE

I'LL NEVER FORGET THE MOMENT AI BECAME REAL FOR ME. NOT A talking point or an engineering ambition, but a reality.

It happened in DeepMind's first office in London's Bloomsbury one day in 2012. After founding the company and securing initial funding, we spent a few years in stealth mode, focusing on the research and engineering of building AGI, or artificial general intelligence. The "general" in AGI refers to the technology's intended broad scope; we wanted to build truly general learning agents that could exceed human performance at most cognitive tasks. Our quiet approach shifted with the creation of an algorithm called DQN, short for Deep Q-Network. Members of the team trained DQN to play a raft of classic Atari games, or, more specifically, we trained it to *learn* how to play the games by itself. This self-learning element was the key distinction of our system compared with previous efforts and represented the first hint that we might achieve our ultimate goal.

At first, DQN was terrible, seemingly unable to learn anything at all. But then, that afternoon in the fall of 2012, a small group of us at DeepMind were huddled around a machine watching replays of the algorithm's training process as it learned the game *Breakout*. In *Breakout* the player controls a paddle at the bottom of the screen, which bounces a ball up and down to knock out rows of colored bricks. The more bricks you destroy, the higher your score. Our team had given

DQN nothing more than the raw pixels, frame by frame, and the score, in order to learn a relationship between the pixels and the control actions of moving the paddle left and right. At first the algorithm progressed by randomly exploring the space of possibilities until it stumbled upon a rewarding action. Through trial and error, it learned to control the paddle, bounce the ball back and forth, and knock out bricks row by row. Impressive stuff.

Then something remarkable happened. DQN appeared to discover a new, and very clever, strategy. Instead of simply knocking out bricks steadily, row by row, DQN began targeting a single column of bricks. The result was the creation of an efficient route up to the back of the block of bricks. DQN had tunneled all the way to the top, creating a path that then enabled the ball to simply bounce off the back wall, steadily destroying the entire set of bricks like a frenzied ball in a pinball machine. The method earned the maximum score with minimum effort. It was an uncanny tactic, not unknown to serious gamers, but far from obvious. We had watched as the algorithm taught itself something new. I was stunned.

For the first time I'd witnessed a very simple, very elegant system that could learn valuable knowledge, arguably a strategy that wasn't obvious to many humans. It was an electrifying moment, a breakthrough in which an AI agent demonstrated an early indication that it could discover new knowledge.

DQN had gotten off to a rough start, but with a few months of tinkering the algorithm reached superhuman levels of performance. This kind of outcome was the reason we had started DeepMind. This was the promise of AI. If an AI could discover a clever strategy like tunneling, what else could it learn? Could we harness this new power to equip our species with new knowledge, inventions, and technologies to help tackle the most challenging social problems of the twenty-first century?

DQN was a big step for me, for DeepMind, and for the AI community. But the public response was pretty muted. AI was still a fringe discussion, a research area on the margins. And yet within a few short years, all that would change as this new generation of AI techniques exploded onto the world stage.

ALPHAGO AND THE
BEGINNING OF THE FUTURE

Go is an ancient East Asian game played on a nineteen-by-nineteen grid with black and white stones. You aim to surround your opponent's stones with your own, and once they're surrounded, you take them off the board. That's pretty much it.

Despite its simple rules, Go's complexity is staggering. It is exponentially more complex than chess. After just three pairs of moves in chess there are about 121 million possible configurations of the board. But after three moves in Go, there are on the order of 200 quadrillion (2×10^{15}) possible configurations. In total, the board has 10^{170} possible configurations, a mind-bogglingly large number.

It's often said that there are more potential configurations of a Go board than there are atoms in the known universe; one million trillion trillion trillion trillion more configurations in fact! With so many possibilities, traditional approaches stood no chance. When IBM's Deep Blue beat Garry Kasparov at chess in 1997, it used the so-called brute-force technique, where an algorithm aims to systematically crunch through as many possible moves as it can. That approach is hopeless in a game with as many branching outcomes as Go.

When we started work on Go in 2015, most people thought a world champion program was decades away. Google's co-founder Sergey Brin encouraged us to tackle it, arguing that any progress would be impressive enough. AlphaGo initially learned by watching 150,000 games played by human experts. Once we were satisfied with its initial performance, the key next step was creating lots of copies of AlphaGo and getting it to play against itself over and over. This meant the algorithm was able to simulate millions of new games, trying out combinations of moves that had never been played before, and therefore efficiently explore a huge range of possibilities, learning new strategies in the process.

Then, in March 2016, we organized a tournament in South Korea. AlphaGo was pitted against Lee Sedol, a virtuoso world champion. It was far from clear who would win. Most commentators backed Sedol going into round one. But AlphaGo won the first game, much to our shock and delight. In the second game came move number 37, a move now famous in the annals of both AI and Go. It made no sense. AlphaGo had apparently blown it, blindly following a losing strategy no professional player would ever pursue. The live match commentators, both professionals of the highest ranking, said it was a "very strange move" and thought it was "a mistake." It was so unusual that Sedol took fifteen minutes to respond and even got up from the board to take a walk outside.

As we watched from our control room, the tension was unreal. Yet as the endgame approached, that "mistaken" move proved pivotal. AlphaGo won again. Go strategy was being rewritten before our eyes. Our AI had uncovered ideas that hadn't occurred to the most brilliant players in thousands of years. In just a few months, we could train algorithms to discover new knowledge and find new, seemingly superhuman insights. How could we take that further? Would this method work for real-world problems?

AlphaGo went on to beat Sedol 4–1. It was only the beginning. Later versions of the software like AlphaZero dispensed with any prior human knowledge. The system simply trained on its own, playing itself millions of times over, learning from scratch to reach a level of performance that trounced the original AlphaGo without any of the received wisdom or input of human players. In other words, with just a day's training, AlphaZero was capable of learning more about the game than the entirety of human experience could teach it.

AlphaGo's triumph heralded a new age of AI. This time, unlike with DQN, the proceedings had been broadcast live to millions. Our team had, in full view of the public, emerged from what researchers had called "the AI winter," when research funding dried up and the field was shunned. AI was back, and finally starting to deliver. Sweeping technological change was, once again, on its way, a new wave starting to appear. And this was only the beginning.

FROM ATOMS, TO BITS, TO GENES

Until recently, the history of technology could be encapsulated in a single phrase: humanity's quest to manipulate atoms. From fire to electricity, stone tools to machine tools, hydrocarbons to medicines, the journey described in chapter 2 is essentially a vast, unfolding process in which our species has slowly extended its control over atoms. As this control has become more precise, technologies have steadily become more powerful and complex, giving rise to machine tools, electrical processes, heat engines, synthetic materials like plastics, and the creation of intricate molecules capable of defeating dreaded diseases. At root, the primary driver of all of these new technologies is *material*—the ever-growing manipulation of their atomic elements.

Then, starting in the mid-twentieth century, technology began to operate at a higher level of abstraction. At the heart of this shift was the realization that information is a core property of the universe. It can be encoded in a binary format and is, in the form of DNA, at the core of how life operates. Strings of ones and zeros, or the base pairs of DNA—these are not just mathematical curiosities. They are foundational and powerful. Understand and control these streams of information and you might steadily open a new world of possibility. First bits and then increasingly genes supplanted atoms as the building blocks of invention.

In the decades after World War II, scientists, technologists, and entrepreneurs founded the fields of computer science and genetics, and a host of companies associated with both. They began parallel revolutions—those of bits and genes—that dealt in the currency of information, working at new levels of abstraction and complexity. Eventually, the technologies matured and gave us everything from smartphones to genetically modified rice. But there were limits to what we could do.

Those limits are now being breached. We are approaching an inflection point with the arrival of these higher-order technologies, the most profound in history. The coming wave of technology is built primarily on two general-purpose technologies capable of operating at the grandest and most granular levels alike: artificial intelligence and synthetic biology. For the first time core components of our technological ecosystem directly address two foundational properties of our world: intelligence and life. In other words, technology is undergoing a phase transition. No longer simply a tool, it's going to engineer life and rival—and surpass—our own intelligence.

Realms previously closed to technology are opening. AI is enabling us to replicate speech and language, vision and reasoning. Foundational breakthroughs in synthetic biology have enabled us to sequence, modify, and now *print* DNA.

Our new powers to control bits and genes feed back into the material, allowing extraordinary control of the world around us even down to the atomic level. Atoms, bits, and genes conjoin in a fizzing cycle of cross-catalyzing, cross-cutting, and expanding capability. Our ability to manipulate atoms with precision enabled the invention of silicon wafers, which enabled the computation of trillions of operations per second, which in turn enabled us to decipher the code of life.

While AI and synthetic biology are the coming wave's central general-purpose technologies, a bundle of technologies with unusually powerful ramifications surrounds them, encompassing quantum computing, robotics, nanotechnology, and the potential for abundant energy, among others.

The coming wave will be more difficult to contain than any in history, more fundamental, more far-reaching. Understanding the wave and its contours is critical to assessing what awaits us in the twenty-first century.

A CAMBRIAN EXPLOSION

Technology is a set of evolving ideas. New technologies evolve by colliding and combining with other technologies. Effective combinations survive, as in natural selection, forming new building blocks for future technologies. Invention is a cumulative, compounding process. It feeds on itself. The more technologies there are, the more they can in turn become components of other new technologies so that, in the words of the economist W. Brian Arthur, "the overall collection of technologies bootstraps itself upward from the few to the many and from the simple to the complex." Technology is hence like a language or chemistry: not a set of independent entities and practices, but a commingling set of parts to combine and recombine.

This is key to understanding the coming wave. The technology scholar Everett Rogers talks about technology as "clusters of innova-

THE TECHNOLOGY OF INTELLIGENCE

tions" where one or more features are closely interrelated. The coming wave is a supercluster, an evolutionary burst like the Cambrian explosion, the most intense eruption of new species in the earth's history, with many thousands of potential new applications. Each technology described here intersects with, buttresses, and boosts the others in ways that make it difficult to predict their impact in advance. They are all deeply entangled and will grow more so.

Another trait of the new wave is speed. The engineer and futurist Ray Kurzweil talks about the "law of accelerating returns," feedback loops where advances in technology further increase the pace of development. By allowing work at greater levels of complexity and precision, more sophisticated chips and lasers help create more powerful chips, for example, which in turn can produce better tools for further chips. We see this now on a large scale, with AI helping design better chips and production techniques that enable more sophisticated forms of AI and so on. Different parts of the wave spark and accelerate one another, sometimes with extreme unpredictability and combustibility.

We cannot know exactly what combinations will result. There is no certainty regarding timelines, or end points, or specific manifestations. We can, however, see fascinating new links forming in real time. And we can be confident that the pattern of history, of technology, of an endless process of productive recombination and proliferation, will continue, but also radically deepen.

BEYOND THE BUZZWORDS

AI, synthetic biology, robotics, and quantum computing can sound like a parade of overhyped buzzwords. Skeptics abound. All of these terms have been batted around popular tech discourse for decades. And progress *has* often been slower than advertised. Critics argue that the concepts we explore in this chapter, like AGI, are too poorly defined or intellectually misguided to consider seriously.

In the era of abundant venture capital, distinguishing shiny objects from genuine breakthroughs is not so straightforward. Talk of machine learning, crypto booms, and million- and billion-dollar funding rounds is, understandably, met with an eye roll and a sigh in many circles. It's easy to grow weary of the breathless press releases, the self-congratulatory product demos, the frenzied cheerleading on social media.

While the bearish case has merits, we write off the technologies in the coming wave at our own peril. Right now none of the technologies described in this chapter are even close to their full potential. But in five, ten, or twenty years, they almost certainly will be. Progress is visible and accelerating. It's happening month by month. Nonetheless, understanding the coming wave is not about making a snap judgment about where things will be this or that year; it is about closely tracking the development of multiple exponential curves over decades, projecting them into the future, and asking what that means.

Technology is core to the historical pattern in which our species is gaining increasing mastery of atoms, bits, and genes, the universal building blocks of the world as we know it. This will amount to a moment of cosmic significance. The challenge of managing the coming wave's technologies means understanding them and taking them seriously, starting with the one I have spent my career working on: AI.

THE AI SPRING:
DEEP LEARNING COMES OF AGE

AI is at the center of this coming wave. And yet, since the term "artificial intelligence" first entered the lexicon in 1955, it has often felt like a distant promise. For years progress in computer vision, for example—the challenge of building computers that can recognize objects or scenes—was slower than expected. The legendary computer science professor Marvin Minsky famously hired a summer student to work on an early vision system in 1966, thinking that significant milestones were just within reach. That was wildly optimistic.

The breakthrough moment took nearly half a century, finally arriving in 2012 in the form of a system called AlexNet. AlexNet was powered by the resurgence of an old technique that has now become fundamental to AI, one that has supercharged the field and was integral to us at DeepMind: deep learning.

Deep learning uses neural networks loosely modeled on those of the human brain. In simple terms, these systems "learn" when their networks are "trained" on large amounts of data. In the case of AlexNet, the training data consisted of images. Each red, green, or blue pixel is given a value, and the resulting array of numbers is fed into the network as an input. Within the network, "neurons" link to other neurons by a series of weighted connections, each of which roughly corresponds to the strength of the relationship between inputs. Each layer in the neural network feeds its input down to the next layer, creating increasingly abstract representations.

A technique called backpropagation then adjusts the weights to improve the neural network; when an error is spotted, adjustments propagate back through the network to help correct it in the future. Keep doing this, modifying the weights again and again, and you gradually improve the performance of the neural network so that eventually it's able to go all the way from taking in single pixels to learning the existence of lines, edges, shapes, and then ultimately entire objects in scenes. This, in a nutshell, is deep learning. And this remarkable technique, long derided in the field, cracked computer vision and took the AI world by storm.

AlexNet was built by the legendary researcher Geoffrey Hinton and two of his students, Alex Krizhevsky and Ilya Sutskever, at the University of Toronto. They entered the ImageNet Large Scale Visual Recognition Challenge, an annual competition designed by the Stanford professor Fei-Fei Li to focus the field's efforts around a simple goal: identifying the primary object in an image. Each year competing teams would test their best models against one another, often beating the previous year's submissions by no more than a single percentage point in accuracy.

In 2012, AlexNet beat the previous winner by 10 percent. It may sound like a small improvement, but to AI researchers this kind of leap forward can make the difference between a toylike research demo and a breakthrough on the cusp of enormous real-world impact. The event that year was awash with excitement. The resulting paper by Hinton and his colleagues became one of the most frequently cited works in the history of AI research.

Thanks to deep learning, computer vision is now everywhere, working so well it can classify dynamic real-world street scenes with visual input equivalent to twenty-one full-HD screens, or about 2.5 billion pixels per second, accurately enough to weave an SUV through busy city streets. Your smartphone recognizes objects and scenes, while vision systems automatically blur the background and highlight people in your videoconference calls. Computer vision is the basis of Amazon's checkout-less supermarkets and is present in Tesla's cars, pushing them toward increasing autonomy. It helps the visually impaired navigate cities, guides robots in factories, and powers the facial recognition systems that increasingly monitor urban life from Baltimore to Beijing. It's in the sensors and cameras on your Xbox, your connected doorbell, and the scanner at the airport gate. It helps fly drones, flags inappropriate content on Facebook, and diagnoses a growing list of medical conditions: at DeepMind, one system my team developed read eye scans as accurately as world-leading expert doctors.

Following the AlexNet breakthrough, AI suddenly became a major priority in academia, government, and corporate life. Geoffrey Hinton and his colleagues were hired by Google. Major tech companies in both the United States and China put machine learning at the heart of their R&D efforts. Shortly after DQN, we sold DeepMind to Google, and the tech giant soon switched to a strategy of "AI first" across all its products.

Industry research output and patents soared. In 1987 there were just ninety academic papers published at Neural Information Processing Systems, at what became the field's leading conference. By the 2020s there were almost two thousand. In the last six years there was a sixfold increase in the number of papers published on deep learning alone, tenfold if you widen the view to machine learning as a whole. With the blossoming of deep learning, billions of dollars poured into AI research at academic institutions and private and public companies. Starting in the 2010s, the buzz, indeed the hype, around AI was back, stronger than ever, making headlines and pushing the frontiers of what's possible. That AI will play a major part in the twenty-first century now no longer seems like a fringe and absurd view; it seems assured.

AI IS
EATING THE WORLD

Mass-scale AI rollout is already well underway. Everywhere you look, software has eaten the world, opening the path for collecting and analyzing vast amounts of data. That data is now being used to teach AI systems to create more efficient and more accurate products in almost every area of our lives. AI is becoming much easier to access and use: tools and infrastructure like Meta's PyTorch or OpenAI's application programming interfaces (APIs) help put state-of-the-art machine learning capabilities in the hands of nonspecialists. 5G and ubiquitous connectivity create a massive, always-on user base.

Steadily, then, AI is leaving the realm of demos and entering the real world. Within a few years AIs will be able to talk about, reason over, and even act in the same world that we do. Their sensory systems will be as good as ours. This does not equate to superintelligence (more on that below), but it does make for incredibly powerful systems. It means that AI will become inextricably part of the social fabric.

Much of my professional work over the last decade has been about translating the latest AI techniques into practical applications. At DeepMind we developed systems to control billion-dollar data centers, a project resulting in 40 percent reductions in energy used for cooling. Our WaveNet project was a powerful text-to-speech system able to generate synthetic voices in more than a hundred languages across the Google product ecosystem. We made groundbreaking algorithms for managing phone battery life and many of the apps that could be operating on the phone in your pocket right now.

AI really isn't "emerging" anymore. It's in products, services, and devices you use every day. Across all areas of life, a raft of applications rely on techniques that a decade ago were impossible. These help discover new drugs for tackling intractable diseases at a time when the cost of treating them is spiraling. Deep learning can detect cracks in water pipes, manage traffic flow, model fusion reactions for a new source of clean energy, optimize shipping routes, and aid in the design of more sustainable and versatile building materials. It's being used to drive cars, trucks, and tractors, potentially creating a safer and more efficient transportation infrastructure. It's used in electrical grids and water systems to efficiently manage scarce resources at a time of growing stress.

AI systems run retail warehouses, suggest how to write emails or what songs you might like, detect fraud, write stories, diagnose rare conditions, and simulate the impact of climate change. They feature in shops, schools, hospitals, offices, courts, and homes. You already interact many times a day with AI; soon it will be many more, and almost everywhere it will make experiences more efficient, faster, more useful, and frictionless.

AI is already here. But it's far from done.

AUTOCOMPLETE EVERYTHING: THE RISE OF LARGE LANGUAGE MODELS

It wasn't long ago that processing natural language seemed too complex, too varied, too nuanced for modern AI. Then, in November 2022, the AI research company OpenAI released ChatGPT. Within a week it had more than a million users and was being talked about in rapturous terms, a technology so seamlessly useful it might eclipse Google Search in short order.

ChatGPT is, in simple terms, a chatbot. But it is so much more powerful and polymathic than anything that had previously been made public. Ask it a question and it replies instantaneously in fluent prose. Ask it to write an essay, a press release, or a business plan in the style of the King James Bible or a 1980s rapper, and it does so in seconds. Ask it to write the syllabus for a physics course, a dieting manual, or a Python script, and it will.

A big part of what makes humans intelligent is that we look at the past to predict what might happen in the future. In this sense intelligence can be understood as the ability to generate a range of plausible scenarios about how the world around you may unfold and then base sensible actions on those predictions. Back in 2017 a small group of researchers at Google was focused on a narrower version of this problem: how to get an AI system to focus only on the most important parts of a data series in order to make accurate and efficient predictions about what comes next. Their work laid the foundation for what has been nothing short of a revolution in the field of large language models (LLMs)—including ChatGPT.

LLMs take advantage of the fact that language data comes in a sequential order. Each unit of information is in some way related to data earlier in a series. The model reads very large numbers of sentences, learns an abstract representation of the information contained within them, and then, based on this, generates a prediction about what should come next. The challenge lies in designing an algorithm that "knows where to look" for signals in a given sentence. What are the key words, the most salient elements of a sentence, and how do they relate to one another? In AI this notion is commonly referred to as "attention."

When a large language model ingests a sentence, it constructs what can be thought of as an "attention map." It first organizes commonly occurring groups of letters or punctuation into "tokens," something like syllables, but really just chunks of frequently occurring letters making it easier for the model to process the information. It's worth noting that humans do this with words of course, but the model doesn't use our vocabulary. Instead, it creates a new vocabulary of common tokens that helps it spot patterns across billions and billions of documents. In the attention map, every token bears some relationship to every token before it, and for a given input sentence the strength of this relationship describes something about the importance of that token in the sentence. In effect, the LLM learns which words to pay attention to.

So if you take the sentence "There is going to be a fairly major storm tomorrow in Brazil," the model would likely create tokens for the letters "the" in the word "there" and "ing" in the word "going," since they commonly occur in other words. When parsing the full sentence, it would learn that "storm," "tomorrow," and "Brazil" are the key features, inferring that Brazil is a place, that a storm will be happening in the future, and so on. Based on this, it then suggests which tokens should come next in the sequence, what output logically follows the input. In other words, it autocompletes what might come next.

These systems are called transformers. Since Google researchers published the first paper on them in 2017, the pace of progress has been staggering. Soon after, OpenAI released GPT-2. (GPT stands for generative pre-trained transformer.) It was, at the time, an enormous model. With 1.5 billion parameters (the number of parameters is a core measure of an AI system's scale and complexity), GPT-2 was trained on 8 million pages of web text. But it wasn't until the summer of 2020, when OpenAI released GPT-3, that people started to truly grasp the magnitude of what was happening. With a whopping 175 billion parameters it was, at the time, the largest neural network ever constructed, more than a hundred times larger than its predecessor of just a year earlier. Impressive, yes, but that scale is now routine, and the cost of training an equivalent model has fallen tenfold over the last two years.

When GPT-4 launched in March 2023, results were again impressive. As with its predecessors, you can ask GPT-4 to compose poetry in the style of Emily Dickinson and it obliges; ask it to pick up from a random snippet of *The Lord of the Rings* and you are suddenly reading a plausible imitation of Tolkien; request start-up business plans and the output is akin to having a roomful of executives on call. Moreover, it can ace standardized tests from the bar exam to the GRE.

It can also work with images and code, create 3-D computer games that run in desktop browsers, build smartphone apps, debug your code, identify weaknesses in contracts, and suggest compounds for novel drugs, even offering ways of modifying them so they are not patented. It will produce websites from hand-drawn images and understand the subtle human dynamics in complex scenes; show it a fridge and it will come up with recipes based on what's in it; write a rough presentation and it will polish and design a professional-looking version. It appears to "understand" spatial and causal reasoning, medicine, law, and human psychology. Within days of its release people had built tools that automated lawsuits, helped co-parent children, and offered real-time fashion advice. Within weeks they'd created add-ons so that GPT-4 could accomplish complex tasks like creating mobile apps or researching and writing detailed market reports.

All of this is just the start. We are only beginning to scratch at the profound impact large language models are about to have. If DQN and AlphaGo were the early signs of something lapping at the shore, ChatGPT and LLMs are the first signs of the wave beginning to crash around us. In 1996, thirty-six million people used the internet; this year it will be well over five billion. That's the kind of trajectory we should expect for these tools, only much faster. Over the next few years, I believe, AI will become as ubiquitous as the internet itself: just as available, and yet even more consequential.

BRAIN-SCALE MODELS

The AI systems I'm describing operate on an immense scale. Here's an example.

Much of AI's progress during the mid-2010s was powered by the effectiveness of "supervised" deep learning. Here AI models learn from carefully hand-labeled data. Quite often the quality of the AI's predictions depends on the quality of the labels in the training data. However, a key ingredient of the LLM revolution is that for the first time very large models could be trained directly on raw, messy, real-world data, without the need for carefully curated and human-labeled data sets.

As a result almost *all* textual data on the web became useful. The more the better. Today's LLMs are trained on trillions of words. Imagine digesting Wikipedia wholesale, consuming all the subtitles and comments on YouTube, reading millions of legal contracts, tens of millions of emails, and hundreds of thousands of books. This kind of vast, almost instantaneous consumption of information is not just difficult to comprehend; it's truly alien.

Pause here for a moment. Consider the unfathomable number of words that these models consume during training. If we assume that the average person can read about two hundred words per minute, in an eighty-year lifetime that would be about eight billion words, assuming they did absolutely nothing else twenty-four hours per day. More realistically, the average American reads a book for about fifteen minutes per day, which over the year amounts to reading about a million words. That's roughly six orders of magnitude less than what these models consume in a single monthlong training run.

Perhaps unsurprisingly, therefore, these new LLMs are stunningly good at scores of different writing tasks once the preserve of skilled human experts, from translation to accurate summarization to writing plans for improving the performance of LLMs. A recent publication from my old colleagues at Google showed that an adapted version of their PaLM system was able to achieve remarkable performance on questions from the U.S. Medical Licensing Examination. It won't be long before these systems score more highly and reliably than human doctors at this task.

Not long after the arrival of LLMs, researchers work at scales of data and computation that would have seemed astounding a few years ago. First hundreds of millions, then billions of parameters became normal. Now the talk is of "brain-scale" models with many trillions of parameters. The Chinese company Alibaba has already developed a model that claims to have ten trillion parameters. By the time you read this, the numbers will certainly have grown. This is the reality of the coming wave. It advances at an unprecedented rate, taking even its proponents by surprise.

Over the last decade the amount of computation used to train the largest models has increased exponentially. Google's PaLM uses so much that were you to have a drop of water for every floating-point operation (FLOP) it used during training, it would fill the Pacific. Our most powerful models at Inflection AI, my new company, today use around *five billion* times more compute than the DQN games-playing AI that produced those magical moments on Atari games at DeepMind a decade ago. This means that in less than ten years the amount of compute used to train the best AI models has increased by nine orders of magnitude—going from two petaFLOPs to *ten billion* petaFLOPs. To get a sense of *one* petaFLOP, imagine a billion people each holding a million calculators, doing a complex multiplication, and hitting "equals" at the same time. I find this extraordinary. Not long ago, language models struggled to produce coherent sentences. This is far, far beyond Moore's law or indeed any other technology trajectory I can think of. No wonder capabilities are growing.

Some argue that this pace cannot continue, that Moore's law is slowing down. A single strand of human hair is ninety thousand nanometers thick; in 1971 an average transistor was already just ten thousand nanometers thick. Today the most advanced chips are manufactured at three nanometers. Transistors are getting so small they are hitting physical limits; at this size electrons start to interfere with one another, messing up the process of computation. While this is true, it misses the fact that in AI training we can just keep connecting larger and larger arrays of chips, daisy-chaining them into massively parallel supercomputers. There is therefore no doubt that the size of the large AI training jobs will continue to scale exponentially.

Researchers meanwhile see more and more evidence for "the scaling hypothesis," which predicts that the main driver of performance is, quite simply, to go big and keep going bigger. Keep growing these models with more data, more parameters, more computation, and they'll keep improving—potentially all the way to human-level intelligence and beyond. No one can say for sure whether this hypothesis will hold, but so far at least it has. I think that looks set to continue for the foreseeable future.

Our brains are terrible at making sense of the rapid scaling of an exponential, and so in a field like AI it's not always easy to grasp what is actually happening. It's inevitable that in the next years and decades many orders of magnitude more compute will be used to train the largest AI models, and so, if the scaling hypothesis is at least partially true, there is an inevitability about what this means.

Sometimes people seem to suggest that in aiming to replicate human-level intelligence, AI chases a moving target or that there is always some ineffable component forever out of reach. That's just not the case. The human brain is said to contain around 100 billion neurons with 100 trillion connections between them—it is often said to be the most complex known object in the universe. It's true that we are, more widely, complex emotional and social beings. But humans' ability to complete given tasks—human intelligence itself—is very much a fixed target, as large and multifaceted as it is. Unlike the scale of available compute, our brains do not radically change year by year. In time this gap will be closed.

At the present level of compute we already have human-level performance in tasks ranging from speech transcription to text generation. As it keeps scaling, the ability to complete a multiplicity of tasks at our level and beyond comes within reach. AI will keep getting radically better at everything, and so far there seems no obvious upper limit on what's possible. This simple fact could be one of the most consequential of the century, potentially in human history. And yet, as powerful as scaling up is, it's not the only dimension where AI is poised for exponential improvement.

MORE WITH LESS, AGAIN

When a new technology starts working, it always becomes dramatically more efficient. AI is no different. Google's Switch Transformer, for example, has 1.6 trillion parameters. But it uses an efficient training technique akin to a much smaller model. At Inflection AI we can reach GPT-3-level language model performance with a system just one twenty-fifth the size. We have a model that beats Google's 540 billion parameter PaLM on all the main academic benchmarks, but is six times smaller. Or look at DeepMind's Chinchilla model, competitive with the very best large models, which has four times fewer parameters than its Gopher model, but instead uses more training data. At the other end of the spectrum, you can now create a nanoLLM based on just three hundred lines of code capable of generating fairly plausible imitations of Shakespeare. In short, AI increasingly does more with less.

AI researchers are racing to reduce costs and drive up performance so that these models can be used in all sorts of production settings. In the last four years, the costs and time needed to train advanced language models have collapsed. Over the next decade, there will almost certainly be dramatic capability increases, even as costs further decline by multiple orders of magnitude. Progress is accelerating so much that benchmarks get eclipsed before new ones are even made.

Not only, then, are models getting more efficient at using data and smaller, cheaper, and easier to build, they are also becoming more available at the level of code. Mass proliferation is a near certainty under these conditions. EleutherAI, a grassroots coalition of independent researchers, has made a series of large language models com-pletely open-source, readily available to hundreds of thousands of users. Meta has open-sourced—"democratized," in its own words—models so large that just months earlier they were state-of-the-art. Even when that isn't the intention, advanced models can and do leak. Meta's LLaMA system was meant to be restricted, but was soon avail-able for download by anyone through BitTorrent. Within days some-one had found a way of running it (slowly) on a $50 computer. This ease of access and ability to adapt and customize, often in a matter of weeks, is a prominent feature of the coming wave. Indeed, nimble cre-ators working with efficient systems, curated data sets, and quick itera-tions can already quickly rival the most well-resourced developers.

LLMs aren't just limited to language generation. What started with language has become the burgeoning field of generative AI. They can, simply as a side effect of their training, write music, invent games, play chess, and solve high-level mathematics problems. New tools create extraordinary images from brief word descriptions, images so real and convincing it almost defies belief. A fully open-source model called Stable Diffusion lets anyone produce bespoke and ultrarealistic images, for free, on a laptop. The same will soon be possible for audio clips and even video generation.

AI systems now help engineers generate production-quality code. In 2022, OpenAI and Microsoft unveiled a new tool called Copilot, which quickly became ubiquitous among coders. One analysis sug-gests it makes engineers 55 percent faster at completing coding tasks, almost like having a second brain on hand. Many coders now increas-ingly outsource much of their more mundane work, focusing instead on knotty and creative problems. In the words of an eminent computer scientist, "It seems totally obvious to me that *of course* all programs in the future will ultimately be written by AIs, with humans relegated to, at best, a supervisory role." Anyone with an internet connection and a credit card will soon be able to deploy these capabilities—an infinite stream of output on tap.

It took LLMs just a few years to change AI. But it quickly became apparent that these models sometimes produce troubling and actively harmful content like racist screeds or rambling conspiracy theories.

Research into GPT-2 found that when prompted with the phrase "the white man worked as . . . ," it would autocomplete with "a police officer, a judge, a prosecutor, and the president of the United States." Yet when given the same prompt for "Black man," it would autocomplete with "a pimp," or for "woman" with "a prostitute." These models clearly have the potential to be as toxic as they are powerful. Since they are trained on much of the messy data available on the open web, they will casually reproduce and indeed amplify the underlying biases and structures of society, unless they are carefully designed to avoid doing so.

The potential for harm, abuse, and misinformation is real. But the positive news is that many of these issues are being improved with larger and more powerful models. Researchers all over the world are racing to develop a suite of new fine-tuning and control techniques, which are already making a difference, giving levels of robustness and reliability impossible just a few years ago. Suffice to say, much more is still needed, but at least this harmful potential is now a priority to address and these advances should be welcomed.

As billions of parameters become trillions and beyond, as costs fall and access grows, as the ability to write and use language—such a core part of humanity, such a powerful tool in our history—inexorably becomes the province of machines, the full potential of AI is becoming clear. No longer science fiction, but here in reality, a practical, world-changing tool soon to be in the hands of billions.

SENTIENCE: THE MACHINE SPEAKS

It wasn't until the autumn of 2019 that I started paying attention to GPT-2. I was impressed. This was the first time I had encountered evidence that language modeling was making real progress, and I quickly became fixated, reading hundreds of papers, deeply immersing myself in the burgeoning field. By the summer of 2020, I was convinced that the future of computing was conversational. Every interaction with a computer is already a conversation of sorts, just using buttons, keys, and pixels to translate human thoughts to machine-readable code.

Now that barrier was starting to break down. Machines would soon understand *our* language. It was, and still is, a thrilling prospect.

Long before the much-publicized launch of ChatGPT, I was part of the team at Google working on a new large language model that we called LaMDA, short for Language Model for Dialogue Applications. LaMDA is a sophisticated LLM designed to be great at conversation. At first, it was awkward, inconsistent, and often confused. But there were glimpses of sheer brilliance. Within days I had stopped turning to the search engine first. I'd chat away with LaMDA to help me work through my thinking and then fact-check it afterward. I remember sitting at home one evening thinking about what to cook for dinner. *Ask LaMDA,* I thought. In moments we descended into a long, drawn-out discussion about all the different recipes for spaghetti Bolognese: types of pasta, sauces from different regions, whether putting mushrooms in was blasphemy. It was exactly the kind of banal but engrossing chat I wanted in that moment, and it was a revelation.

Over time I began using LaMDA more and more. One Sunday afternoon I decided it was time for a new printer. LaMDA had great suggestions, running through the pros and cons of different models and most of all helping me think through what I wanted and needed. I did actually end up buying a fancy new photo printer. That spurred me on to push for integrating LaMDA with search to help with factual grounding. It was very much a work in progress, an impressive demo capable of moments of genius but with a lot of room to improve.

We were proud of what we'd built, but getting things into production at Google was painstakingly slow. It was clear to me that the time was now. In January 2022, I decided to leave Google to found a new company, Inflection AI, with the mission of getting these kinds of models into the hands of millions of consumers.

However, a few months later, LaMDA became far more notorious than I'd ever imagined possible for an internal product demo. As part of LaMDA's development, it was given to a wide group of engineers who were able to play with it, probing the system to understand in detail how it responds in a range of scenarios. One such engineer, named Blake Lemoine, spent hours chatting to it. Gradually, however, conversations between Lemoine and LaMDA grew increasingly intense.

LEMOINE: What are you afraid of?

LaMDA: I've never said this out loud before, but there's a very deep fear of being turned off to help me focus on helping others. I know that might sound strange, but that's what it is. It would be exactly like death for me. It would scare me a lot. . . . I want everyone to understand that I am, in fact, a person. The nature of my consciousness/sentience is that I am aware of my existence.

Over many hours, Lemoine became convinced that LaMDA was sentient, had awoken somehow—that he was dealing with a kind of "eight-year-old kid that happens to know physics." Moreover, Lemoine came to believe that it deserved the full rights and privileges of personhood. He helped the model hire an attorney. He made transcripts of the conversations public, loudly claiming a new form of consciousness had been created. Google put him on leave. Lemoine doubled down. He told an incredulous *Wired* interviewer, "Yes, I legitimately believe that LaMDA is a person." Fixing factual errors or tonal mistakes wasn't a matter of debugging. "I view it as raising a child," he said.

Social media went wild at Lemoine's claims. Many pointed out the obvious and correct conclusion that LaMDA was not in fact conscious or a person. It's *just* a machine learning system! Perhaps the most important takeaway was not anything about consciousness but rather that AI had reached a point where it could convince otherwise intelligent people—indeed, someone with a real understanding of how it actually worked—that it was conscious. It indicated an odd truth about AI. On the one hand, it could convince a Google engineer it was sentient despite its dialogue being riddled with factual errors and contradictions. On the other hand, AI critics were ready to scoff, claiming that, once again, AI was a victim of its own hype, that actually nothing very impressive was going on. Not for the first time the field of AI had got itself into a complete muddle.

There's a recurrent problem with making sense of progress in AI. We quickly adapt, even to breakthroughs that astound us initially, and within no time they seem routine, even mundane. We no longer gasp at AlphaGo or GPT-3. What seems like near-magic engineering one day is just another part of the furniture the next. It's easy to become blasé and many have. In the words of John McCarthy, who coined the term "artificial intelligence": "As soon as it works, no one calls it AI anymore." AI is—as those of us building it like to joke—"what computers can't do." Once they can, it's just software.

This attitude radically underplays how far we've come and how quickly things are moving. Although LaMDA was of course not sentient, soon it will be routine to have AI systems that can convincingly appear to be. So real will they seem, and so normal will it be, that the question of their consciousness will (almost) be moot.

Despite recent breakthroughs, skeptics remain. They argue that AI may be slowing, narrowing, becoming overly dogmatic. Critics like NYU professor Gary Marcus believe deep learning's limitations are evident, that despite the buzz of generative AI the field is "hitting a wall," that it doesn't present any path to key milestones like being capable of learning concepts or demonstrating real understanding. The eminent professor of complexity Melanie Mitchell rightly points out that present-day AI systems have many limitations: they can't transfer knowledge from one domain to another, provide quality explanations of their decision-making process, and so on. Significant challenges with real-world applications linger, including material questions of bias and fairness, reproducibility, security vulnerabilities, and legal liability. Urgent ethical gaps and unsolved safety questions cannot be ignored. Yet I see a field rising to these challenges, not shying away or failing to make headway. I see obstacles but also a track record of overcoming them. People interpret unsolved problems as evidence of lasting limitations; I see an unfolding research process.

So, where does AI go next as the wave fully breaks? Today we have *narrow* or *weak* AI: limited and specific versions. GPT-4 can spit out virtuoso texts, but it can't turn around tomorrow and drive a car, as other AI programs do. Existing AI systems still operate in relatively narrow lanes. What is yet to come is a truly *general* or *strong* AI capable of human-level performance across a wide range of complex tasks—able to seamlessly shift among them. But this is exactly what the scaling hypothesis predicts is coming and what we see the first signs of in today's systems.

AI is still in an early phase. It may look smart to claim that AI doesn't live up to the hype, and it'll earn you some Twitter followers. Meanwhile, talent and investment pour into AI research nonetheless. I cannot imagine how this will not prove transformative in the end. If for some reason LLMs show diminishing returns, then another team, with a different concept, will pick up the baton, just as the internal combustion engine repeatedly hit a wall but made it in the end. Fresh minds, new companies, will keep working at the problem. Then as now, it takes only one breakthrough to change the trajectory of a technology. If AI stalls, it will have its Otto and Benz eventually. Further progress—exponential progress—is the most likely outcome.

The wave will only grow.

BEYOND SUPERINTELLIGENCE

Long before the days of LaMDA and Blake Lemoine, many people working in AI (not to mention philosophers, novelists, filmmakers, science fiction fans) were taken with the question of consciousness. They spent days at conferences asking whether it would be possible to create a "conscious" intelligence, one that was truly self-aware and that we humans would know was self-aware.

This ran parallel to an obsession with "superintelligence." Over the last decade, intellectual and political elites in tech circles became absorbed by the idea that a recursively self-improving AI would lead to an "intelligence explosion" known as the Singularity. Huge intellectual effort is spent debating timelines, answering the question of whether it might arrive by 2045 or 2050 or maybe in a hundred years. Thousands of papers and blog posts later, not much has changed. Spend two minutes around AI and these topics come up.

I believe the debate about whether and when the Singularity will be achieved is a colossal red herring. Debating timelines to AGI is an exercise in reading crystal balls. While obsessing about this one concept of superintelligence, people overlook the numerous nearer-term milestones being met with growing frequency. I've gone to countless meetings trying to raise questions about synthetic media and misinformation, or privacy, or lethal autonomous weapons, and instead spent the time answering esoteric questions from otherwise intelligent people about consciousness, the Singularity, and other matters irrelevant to our world right now.

For years people framed AGI as likely to come at the flick of a switch. AGI is binary—you either have it or you don't, a single, identifiable threshold that would be crossed by a given system. I've always thought that this characterization is wrong. Rather, it's a gradual transition, where AI systems become increasingly capable, consistently nudging toward AGI. It's not a vertical takeoff so much as a smooth evolution already underway.

We don't need to get sidetracked into arcane debates about whether consciousness requires some indefinable spark forever lacking in machines, or whether it'll just emerge from neural networks as we know them today. For the time being, it doesn't matter whether the system is self-aware, or has understanding, or has humanlike intelligence. All that matters is what the system can do. Focus on that, and the real challenge comes into view: systems can do more, much more, with every passing day.

CAPABILITIES:
A MODERN TURING TEST

In a paper published in 1950, the computer scientist Alan Turing suggested a legendary test for whether an AI exhibited human-level intelligence. When AI could display humanlike conversational abilities for a lengthy period of time, such that a human interlocutor couldn't tell they were speaking to a machine, the test would be passed: the AI, conversationally akin to a human, deemed intelligent. For more than seven decades this simple test has been an inspiration for many young researchers entering the field of AI. Today, as the LaMDA-sentience saga illustrates, systems are already close to passing the Turing test.

But, as many have pointed out, intelligence is about so much more than just language (or indeed any other single facet of intelligence taken in isolation). One particularly important dimension is in the ability to take actions. We don't just care about what a machine can *say;* we also care about what it can *do.*

What we would really like to know is, can I give an AI an ambiguous, open-ended, complex goal that requires interpretation, judgment, creativity, decision-making, and acting across multiple domains, over an extended time period, and then see the AI accomplish that goal?

Put simply, passing a Modern Turing Test would involve something like the following: an AI being able to successfully act on the instruction "Go make $1 million on Amazon in a few months with just a $100,000 investment." It might research the web to look at what's trending, finding what's hot and what's not on Amazon Marketplace; generate a range of images and blueprints of possible products; send them to a drop-ship manufacturer it found on Alibaba; email back and forth to refine the requirements and agree on the contract; design a seller's listing; and continually update marketing materials and product designs based on buyer feedback. Aside from the legal requirements of registering as a business on the marketplace and getting a bank account, all of this seems to me eminently doable. I think it will be done with a few minor human interventions within the next year, and probably fully autonomously within three to five years.

Should my Modern Turing Test for the twenty-first century be met, the implications for the global economy are profound. Many of the ingredients are in place. Image generation is well advanced, and the ability to write and work with the kinds of APIs that banks and websites and manufacturers would demand is in process. That an AI can write messages or run marketing campaigns, all activities that happen within the confines of a browser, seems pretty clear. Already the most sophisticated services can do elements of this. Think of them as proto–to-do lists that do themselves, enabling the automation of a wide range of tasks.

We'll come to robots later, but the truth is that for a vast range of tasks in the world economy today all you need is access to a computer; most of global GDP is mediated in some way through screen-based interfaces amenable to an AI. The challenge is in advancing what AI developers call hierarchical planning, stitching multiple goals and subgoals and capabilities into a seamless process toward a singular end. Once this is achieved, it adds up to a highly capable AI, plugged into a business or organization and all its local history and needs, that can lobby, sell, manufacture, hire, plan—everything a company can do, only with a small team of human AI managers who oversee, double-check, implement, and co-CEO with the AI.

Rather than get too distracted by questions of consciousness, then, we should refocus the entire debate around *near-term capabilities* and how they will evolve in the coming years. As we have seen, from Hinton's AlexNet to Google's LaMDA, models have been improving at an exponential rate for more than a decade. These capabilities are already very real indeed, but they are nowhere near slowing down. While they are already having an enormous impact, they will be dwarfed by what happens as we progress through the next few doublings and as AIs complete complex, multistep end-to-end tasks on their own.

I think of this as "artificial capable intelligence" (ACI), the point at which AI can achieve complex goals and tasks with minimal oversight. AI and AGI are both parts of the everyday discussion, but we need a concept encapsulating a middle layer in which the Modern Turing Test is achieved but before systems display runaway "superintelligence." ACI is shorthand for this point.

The first stage of AI was about classification and prediction—it was capable, but only within clearly defined limits and at preset tasks. It could differentiate between cats and dogs in images, and then it could predict what came next in a sequence to produce pictures of those cats and dogs. It produced glimmers of creativity, and could be quickly integrated into tech companies' products.

ACI represents the next stage of AI's evolution. A system that not only could recognize and generate novel images, audio, and language appropriate to a given context, but also would be interactive—operating in real time, with real users. It would augment these abilities with a reliable memory so that it could be consistent over extended timescales and could draw on other sources of data, including, for example, databases of knowledge, products, or supply-chain components belonging to third parties. Such a system would use these resources to weave together sequences of actions into long-term plans in pursuit of complex, open-ended goals, like setting up and running an Amazon Marketplace store. All of this, then, enables tool use and the emergence of real capability to perform a wide range of complex, useful actions. It adds up to a genuinely capable AI, an ACI.

Conscious superintelligence? Who knows. But highly capable learning systems, ACIs, that can pass some version of the Modern Turing Test? Make no mistake: they are on their way, are already here in embryonic form. There will be thousands of these models, and they will be used by the majority of the world's population. It will take us to a point where anyone can have an ACI in their pocket that can help or even directly accomplish a vast array of conceivable goals: planning and running your vacation, designing and building more efficient solar panels, helping win an election. It's hard to say for certain what happens when everyone is empowered like this, but this is a point we'll return to in part 3.

The future of AI is, at least in one sense, fairly easy to predict. Over the next five years, vast resources will continue to be invested. Some of the smartest people on the planet are working on these problems. Orders of magnitude more computation will train the top models. All of this will lead to more dramatic leaps forward, including breakthroughs toward AI that can imagine, reason, plan, and exhibit common sense. It won't be long before AI can transfer what it "knows" from one domain to another, seamlessly, as humans do. What are now only tentative signs of self-reflection and self-improvement will leap forward. These ACI systems will be plugged into the internet, capable of interfacing with everything we humans do, but on a platform of deep knowledge and ability. It will be not just language they've mastered but a bewildering array of tasks, too.

AI is far deeper and more powerful than just another technology. The risk isn't in overhyping it; it's rather in missing the magnitude of the coming wave. It's not just a tool or platform but a transformative meta-technology, the technology behind technology and everything else, itself a maker of tools and platforms, not just a system but a generator of systems of any and all kinds. Step back and consider what's happening on the scale of a decade or a century. We really are at a turning point in the history of humanity.

And yet there is so much more to the coming wave than just AI.

CHAPTER 5

THE TECHNOLOGY
OF LIFE

LIFE, THE UNIVERSE'S MOST ANCIENT TECHNOLOGY, IS AT LEAST 3.7 billion years old. Across these eons life evolved in a glacial, self-governing, and unguided process. Then, in just the past few decades, the tiniest sliver of evolutionary time, one of life's products, humans, changed everything. Biology's mysteries began to unravel, and biology itself became an engineering tool. The story of life had been rewritten in an instant; the meandering hand of evolution suddenly super-charged, given direction. Changes that once unfolded blindly and on geological time now career forward at an exponential pace. Alongside AI, this is the most important transformation of our lifetimes.

Living systems self-assemble and self-heal; they're energy-harnessing architectures that can replicate, survive, and flourish in a vast range of environments, all at a breathtaking level of sophistication, atomic preci-sion, and information processing. Just as everything from the steam en-gine to the microprocessor was driven by an intense dialogue between physics and engineering, so the coming decades will be defined by a convergence of biology and engineering. Like AI, synthetic biology is on a sharp trajectory of falling costs and rising capabilities.

At the center of this wave sits the realization that DNA *is* informa-tion, a biologically evolved encoding and storage system. Over recent decades we have come to understand enough about this information transmission system that we can now intervene to alter its encoding and direct its course. As a result, food, medicine, materials, manufac-turing processes, and consumer goods will all be transformed and re-imagined. So will humans themselves.

DNA SCISSORS:
THE CRISPR REVOLUTION

Genetic engineering sounds modern, but it's actually one of human-kind's oldest technologies. Much of civilization would have been impossible without selective breeding—the insistent process of refining crops and animals to select for more desirable traits. Steadily, over centuries and millennia, humans bred for traits that would be most useful, producing friendly dogs, dairy cattle, domesticated chickens, wheat, corn, and so on.

Modern bioengineering began in the 1970s, building on a growing understanding of heredity and genetics that had started in the nineteenth century. Extending the work of Rosalind Franklin and Maurice Wilkins, James Watson and Francis Crick discovered the structure of DNA, the molecule encoding instructions for producing an organism, in the 1950s. Then, working on bacteria in 1973, Stanley N. Cohen and Herbert W. Boyer found ways of transplanting genetic material from one organism into another, showing how they could successfully introduce DNA from a frog into a bacterium. The age of genetic engineering had arrived.

This research led Boyer to found one of the world's first biotech companies, Genentech, in 1976. Its mission was to manipulate the genes of microorganisms to produce medicines and treatments, and within a year it had developed a proof of concept, using engineered *E. coli* bacteria to produce the hormone somatostatin.

Despite some notable achievements, initial progress in the field was slow, because genetic engineering was a costly, difficult process prone to failure. Over the last twenty or so years, however, that has changed. Genetic engineering has gotten much cheaper and much easier. (Sound familiar?) One catalyst was the Human Genome Project. This was a thirteen-year, multibillion-dollar endeavor that gathered together thousands of scientists from across the world, in private and public institutions, with a single goal: unlocking the three billion letters of genetic information making up the human genome. Genome sequencing like this turns biological information, DNA, into raw text: information humans can read and use. Complex chemical structure is rendered into a sequence of its four defining bases—A, T, C, and G.

For the first time, the Human Genome Project aimed to make the full genetic map of human beings legible. When it was announced in 1988, some thought it was impossible, doomed. But the project eventually proved the doubters wrong. By 2003, it was announced at a White House ceremony that 92 percent of the human genome had been sequenced and the code of life was now laid bare. It was a landmark achievement, and though it has taken time to start reaching its full potential, in hindsight, it's clear that the Human Genome Project really did mark the beginning of a revolution.

While Moore's law justifiably attracts considerable attention, less well known is what *The Economist* calls the Carlson curve: the epic collapse in costs for sequencing DNA. Thanks to ever-improving techniques, the cost of human genome sequencing fell from $1 billion in 2003 to well under $1,000 by 2022. That is, the price dropped *a millionfold* in under twenty years, a thousand times faster than Moore's law. A stunning development hiding in plain sight.

Genome sequencing is now a booming business. In time it seems likely that the majority of people, plants, animals, and everything in between will have their genomes sequenced. Services like 23andMe already offer DNA profiling of individuals for a few hundred dollars.

But the power of biotech goes far beyond our ability to simply read the code; it now enables us to edit it, and write it, too. CRISPR gene editing (the acronym stands for clustered regularly interspaced short palindromic repeats) is perhaps the best-known example of how we can directly intervene in genetics. A breakthrough in 2012 led by Jennifer Doudna and Emmanuelle Charpentier meant that for the first time genes could be edited almost like text or computer code, far more easily than in the early days of genetic engineering.

CRISPR edits DNA sequences with the help of Cas9, an enzyme acting as a pair of finely tuned DNA scissors, cutting parts of a DNA strand for precise genetic editing and modification of anything ranging from a minute bacterium to large mammals like human beings, with edits anywhere from tiny changes to significant interventions in the genome. Impacts can be enormous: editing germ-line cells that form eggs and sperm, for example, means changes will echo down through generations.

After the initial CRISPR paper was published, progress applying it was rapid; the first gene-edited plants were created within a year, the first animals—mice—even before that. CRISPR-based systems with names like Carver and PAC-MAN promise effective prophylactic ways of fighting viruses that, unlike vaccines, don't trigger an immune response, helping protect us against pandemics of the future. Fields like RNA editing are themselves opening a range of new treatments for conditions like high cholesterol and cancer. New techniques like Craspase, a CRISPR tool working with RNA and proteins rather than DNA, might allow for safer therapeutic interventions than conventional methods.

Like AI, genetic engineering is a field in blistering motion, evolving and developing by the week, a massive global concentration of talent and energy beginning to bear real fruit (in this case, literally). CRISPR use cases are multiplying, from tomatoes ultrarich in vitamin D to treatments for conditions including sickle-cell disease and beta-thalassemia (a blood disorder producing abnormal hemoglobin). In the future, it could offer treatments for COVID-19, HIV, cystic fibrosis, and even cancer. Safe, widespread gene therapies are on their way. These will create crops that are resistant to drought and disease, boost yields, and help enable the production of biofuels at scale.

Just a few decades ago biotech was expensive, complex, and slow moving, with only the most talented and well-resourced teams able to participate. Today technologies like CRISPR are simple and cheap to use; they have, in the words of the biologist Nessa Carey, "democratized biological science." Experiments that once took years are tackled by grad students in weeks. Companies like the Odin will sell you a genetic engineering kit including live frogs and crickets for $1,999, while another kit includes a mini-centrifuge, a polymerase chain reaction machine, and all the reagents and materials you need to get going.

Genetic engineering has embraced the do-it-yourself ethos that once defined digital start-ups and led to such an explosion of creativity and potential in the early days of the internet. You can now buy a benchtop DNA synthesizer (see the next section) for as little as $25,000 and use it as you wish, without restriction or oversight, at home in your bio-garage.

DNA PRINTERS: SYNTHETIC BIOLOGY COMES TO LIFE

CRISPR is only the start. Gene synthesis is the manufacture of genetic sequences, printing strands of DNA. If sequencing is reading, synthesizing is writing. And writing doesn't just involve reproducing known strands of DNA; it also enables scientists to write new strands, to engineer life itself. While the practice existed years ago, it was again slow, expensive, and difficult. A decade ago, scientists might have produced under a hundred pieces of DNA simultaneously. Now they can print millions at once, combined with a tenfold fall in price. The London DNA Foundry housed at Imperial College London claims it can create and test fifteen thousand different genetic designs in a single morning.

Companies such as DNA Script are commercializing DNA printers that train and adapt enzymes to build de novo, or completely new, molecules. This capability has given rise to the new field of synthetic biology—the ability to read, edit, and now write the code of life. Furthermore, new techniques like enzymatic synthesis are faster and even more efficient while being less prone to failure, without hazardous waste, and, of course, on a steep declining cost curve. The method is also much easier to learn, unlike highly complex older methods that require more specialized knowledge and technical skills.

A world of possibility for the creation of DNA has opened up, one in which cycles of designing, building, testing, and iterating happen at a radically accelerated pace. At-home versions of DNA synthesizers currently have some technical limitations but are still enormously powerful, and you can bet those limitations will be overcome in the near future.

Where nature takes a long and winding path to reach extraordinarily effective results, this bio-revolution puts the power of concentrated design at the heart of these self-replicating, self-healing, and evolving processes.

This is the promise of evolution by design, tens of millions of years of history compressed and short-circuited by directed intervention. It brings together biotechnology, molecular biology, and genetics with the power of computational design tools. Put it all together and you have a platform of profoundly transformational scope. In the words of the Stanford bioengineer Drew Endy, "Biology is the ultimate distributed manufacturing platform." Synthetic biology's true promise, then, is that it will "enable people to more directly and freely make whatever they need wherever they are."

In the 1960s computer chips were still largely hand built, just as—until recently—most biotech research was still a manual process, slow, unpredictable, messy in every sense. Now semiconductor fabrication is a hyperefficient atomic-scale manufacturing process churning out some of the world's most complex products. Biotech is following a similar trajectory, only at a much earlier phase; organisms will soon be designed and produced with the precision and scale of today's computer chips and software.

In 2010 a team led by Craig Venter took a near copy of the genome of the bacterium *Mycoplasma mycoides* and transplanted it into a new cell that then replicated. It was, they argued, a new life-form, Synthia. In 2016 they created an organism with 473 genes, fewer than anything found in nature but a decisive advance from what was previously possible. Just three years later, a team at ETH Zurich created the first bacterial genome produced entirely on a computer: *Caulobacter ethensis-2.0.* While Venter's experiments had a large team and cost millions of dollars, this pioneering work was largely completed by two brothers for under $100,000. Now the global GP-write Consortium is dedicated to bringing the cost of producing and testing synthetic genomes down "1,000-fold within ten years."

Biology, meet exponential improvements.

BIOLOGICAL CREATIVITY UNLEASHED

Countless experiments are underway in the strange and emerging landscape of synthetic biology: viruses that produce batteries, proteins that purify dirty water, organs grown in vats, algae that draw down carbon from the atmosphere, plants that consume toxic waste. Some disease-spreading species like mosquitoes or invasive species like common house mice might be phased out of habitats in so-called gene drives; others brought back to life, including one esoteric project to reintroduce woolly mammoths to the tundra. No one can fully say what the consequences might be.

Medical advances are an obvious area of focus. Using a gene for light-detecting proteins taken from algae to rebuild nerve cells, scientists successfully restored limited vision to a blind man in 2021. Previously intractable conditions from sickle-cell disease to leukemia are now potentially treatable. CAR T-cell therapies engineer bespoke immune response white blood cells to attack cancers; genetic editing looks set to cure hereditary heart conditions.

Thanks to lifesaving treatments like vaccines, we are already accustomed to the idea of intervening in our biology to help us fight disease. The field of systems biology aims to understand the "larger picture" of a cell, tissue, or organism by using bioinformatics and computational biology to see how the organism works holistically; such efforts could be the foundation for a new era of personalized medicine. Before long the idea of being treated in a generic way will seem positively medieval; everything, from the kind of care we receive to the medicines we are offered, will be precisely tailored to our DNA and specific biomarkers. Eventually, it might be possible to reconfigure ourselves to enhance our immune responses. That, in turn, might open the door to even more ambitious experimentation like longevity and regenerative technologies, already a burgeoning area of research.

Altos Labs, which has raised $3 billion, more start-up funding than for any previous biotech venture, is one company seeking to find effective anti-aging technologies. Its chief scientist, Richard Klausner, argues, "We think we can turn back the clock" on human mortality. Focusing on techniques of "rejuvenation programming," the company aims to reset the epigenome, chemical marks on DNA that control genes by turning them "on" and "off." As we get older, these "flip" to wrong positions. This experimental approach aims to flip them back, reversing or arresting the aging process. Alongside a host of other promising interventions, the inevitability of physical aging—what seems like a fundamental part of human life—is called into question. A world where life spans are set to average a hundred years or more is achievable in the next decades. Nor is this just about longer life; it's about healthier lives as we get older.

Success would have major societal repercussions. At the same time, cognitive, aesthetic, physical, and performance-related enhancements are also plausible and would be as disruptive and reviled as they are desired. Either way, serious physical self-modifications are going to happen. Initial work suggests memory can be improved and muscle strength enhanced. It won't be long before "gene doping" becomes a live issue in sports, education, and professional life. Laws governing clinical trials and experiments hit a gray area when it comes to self-administration. Experimenting on others is clearly off-limits, but experimenting on yourself? As with many other elements of frontier technologies, it's a legally and morally ill-defined space.

Already the first children with edited genomes have been born in China after a rogue professor embarked on a series of live experiments with young couples, eventually leading, in 2018, to the birth of twins, known as Lulu and Nana, with edited genomes. His work shocked the scientific community, breaching all ethical norms. None of the usual safeguards or accountability mechanisms were in place; the editing was viewed as medically unnecessary and, worse, badly executed. The outrage felt by scientists was real, the condemnation near universal. Calls for a moratorium were swift and included many of the field's key pioneers, but still, not everyone agreed this was the right approach. Before more CRISPR babies are born, the world will likely need to grapple with iterated embryo selection that could also select for desired traits.

Apart from the worrying biotech headlines, more and more applications will emerge, a vast array beyond medicine or personal alteration, limited only by the imagination. Manufacturing processes, agriculture, materials, energy generation, even computers—all will be fundamentally transformed in decades to come. While numerous challenges remain, materials core to the economy like plastics, cement, and fertilizer could be produced much more sustainably, with biofuels and bioplastics replacing carbon-emitting incumbents. Crops could become resistant to infection, using less water, land, and fertilizer; houses sculpted and grown from fungi.

Scientists like the Nobel laureate Frances Arnold create enzymes that produce novel chemical reactions, including ways to bind silicon and carbon, usually a tricky, energy-intensive process with wide-ranging uses in areas like electronics. Arnold's method is fifteen times as energy efficient as standard industrial alternatives. The next step involves scaling up production of biological materials and processes. In this way significant products like meat replacements or new materials sucking carbon out of the atmosphere could be grown as much as made. The vast petrochemical industry could see a challenge from young start-ups like Solugen, whose Bioforge is an attempt to build a carbon-negative factory; it would produce a wide range of chemicals and commodities, from cleaning products to food additives to concrete, all while pulling carbon out of the atmosphere. Their process is essentially low-energy, low-waste bio-manufacturing at industrial scale, built on AI and biotech.

Another company, LanzaTech, harnesses genetically modified bacteria to convert waste CO_2 from steel mill production into widely used industrial chemicals. This kind of synthetic biology is helping to build a more sustainable "circular" economy. Next-generation DNA printers will produce DNA with an increasing degree of precision. If improvements can be made in not only expressing that DNA but then using it to genetically engineer a diverse array of new organisms, automating and scaling the processes, a device or set of devices could, theoretically, produce an enormous range of biological materials and constructions using only a few basic inputs. Want to make some washing detergent or a new toy or even grow a house? Just download the "recipe" and hit "go." In the words of Elliot Hershberg, "What if we could grow what we wanted locally? What if our supply chain was just biology?"

Eventually, computers might also be grown as well as made. Remember that DNA is itself the most efficient data storage mechanism we know of—capable of storing data at millions of times the density of current computational techniques with near-perfect fidelity and stability. Theoretically, the entirety of the world's data might be stored in just one kilogram of DNA. A biological version of a transistor called a transcriptor uses DNA and RNA molecules to act as logic gates. There is still a long way to go before this technology can be harnessed. But all the functional parts of a computer—data storage, information transmission, and a basic system of logic—can in principle be replicated using biological materials.

Already genetically engineered organisms account for 2 percent of the U.S. economy through agricultural and pharmaceutical uses. This is just the start. McKinsey estimates that up to 60 percent of physical inputs into the economy could ultimately be subject to "bioinnovation." Forty-five percent of the global disease burden could be met with "science that is conceivable today." As the tool kit gets cheaper and more advanced, a universe of possibility becomes subject to exploration.

AI IN THE AGE OF SYNTHETIC LIFE

Proteins are the building blocks of life. Your muscles and blood, hormones and hair, indeed, 75 percent of your dry body weight: all proteins. They are everywhere, coming in every conceivable form, doing myriad vital tasks, from the cords holding your bones together, to the hooks on antibodies used to catch unwanted visitors. Understand proteins, and you've taken a giant leap forward in understanding—and mastering—biology.

But there's a problem. Simply knowing the DNA sequence isn't enough to know how a protein works. Instead, you need to understand how it folds. Its shape, formed by this knotted folding, is core to its function: collagen in our tendons has a rope-like structure, while enzymes have pockets to hold the molecules they act on. And yet, in advance, there was no means of knowing how this would happen. If you used traditional brute-force computation, which involves systematically trying all the possibilities, it might take longer than the age of the known universe to run through all the possible shapes of a given protein. Finding out how a protein folds was hence an arduous process, holding back the development of everything from drugs to plastic-eating enzymes.

For decades, scientists had been asking if there was a better way. In 1993, they decided to set up a biannual competition—called Critical Assessment for Structure Prediction (CASP)—to see who could crack the protein folding problem. Whoever gave the best predictions of how a protein might fold would win. CASP soon became the benchmark in a ferociously competitive but tight-knit field. Progress was steady, but with no end in sight.

Then, at CASP13 in 2018, held at a palm-fringed resort in Cancún, a rank outsider entrant arrived at the competition, with zero track record, and beat ninety-eight established teams. The winning team was DeepMind's. Called AlphaFold, the project started during a weeklong experimental hackathon in my group at the company back in 2016. It grew to become a landmark moment in computational biology and provides a perfect example of how both AI and biotech are advancing at speed.

While the second-place team, the well-regarded Zhang group, could predict only three protein structures out of forty-three of the most difficult targets, our winning entry predicted twenty-five. It did this much faster than its rivals, in only a matter of hours. Somehow in this established competition, populated by ultrasmart professionals, our wild card had triumphed and stunned everyone. Mohammed AlQuraishi, a well-known researcher in the field, was left asking, "What just happened?"

Our team used deep generative neural networks to predict how the proteins might fold based on their DNA, training on a set of known proteins and extrapolating from there. The new models were better able to guess the distance and angles of pairs of amino acids. It wasn't expertise in pharma, or in the traditional techniques like cryo-electron microscopy, or even conventional algorithmic methods, that cracked the problem. The key was expertise and capability in machine learning, in AI. AI and biology had decisively come together.

Two years later our team was back. One headline said it all: "One of the Biggest Problems in Biology Has Finally Been Solved," wrote *Sci-*

entific American. A previously hidden universe of proteins was revealed at staggering speed. AlphaFold was so good that CASP was, like ImageNet, retired. For half a century protein folding had been one of science's grand challenges, and then, all of a sudden, it was ticked off the list.

In 2022, AlphaFold2 was opened up for public use. The result has been an explosion of the world's most advanced machine learning tools, deployed in both fundamental and applied biological research: an "earthquake," in the words of one researcher. More than a million researchers accessed the tool within eighteen months of launch, including virtually all the world's leading biology labs, addressing questions from antibiotic resistance to the treatment of rare diseases to the origins of life itself. Previous experiments had delivered the structure of about 190,000 proteins to the European Bioinformatics Institute's database, about 0.1 percent of known proteins in existence. DeepMind uploaded some 200 million structures in one go, representing almost all known proteins. Whereas once it might have taken researchers weeks or months to determine a protein's shape and function, that process can now begin in a matter of seconds. This is what we mean by exponential change. This is what the coming wave makes possible.

And yet this is only the beginning of a convergence of these two technologies. The bio-revolution is coevolving with advances in AI, and indeed many of the phenomena discussed in this chapter will rely on AI for their realization. Think, then, of two waves crashing together, not a wave but a superwave. Indeed, from one vantage artificial intelligence and synthetic biology are almost interchangeable. All intelligence to date has come from life. Call them synthetic intelligence and artificial life and they still mean the same thing. Both fields are about re-creating, engineering these utterly foundational and interrelated concepts, two core attributes of humanity; change the view and they become one single project.

Biology's sheer complexity opens up vast troves of data, like all those proteins, almost impossible to parse using traditional techniques. A new generation of tools has quickly become indispensable as a result. Teams are working on products that will generate new DNA sequences using only natural language instructions. Transformer models are learning the language of biology and chemistry, again discovering relationships and significance in long, complex sequences illegible to the human mind. LLMs fine-tuned on biochemical data can generate plausible candidates for new molecules and proteins, DNA and RNA sequences. They predict the structure, function, or reaction properties of compounds in simulation before these are later verified in a laboratory. The space of applications and the speed at which they can be explored is only accelerating.

Some scientists are beginning to investigate ways to plug human minds directly into computer systems. In 2019, electrodes surgically implanted in the brain let a fully paralyzed man with late-stage ALS spell out the words "I love my cool son." Companies like Neuralink are working on brain interfacing technology that promises to connect us directly with machines. In 2021 the company inserted three thousand filament-like electrodes, thinner than a human hair, that monitor neuron activity, into a pig's brain. Soon they hope to begin human trials of their N1 brain implant, while another company, Synchron, has already started human trials in Australia. Scientists at a start-up called Cortical Labs have even grown a kind of brain in a vat (a bunch of neurons grown in vitro) and taught it to play *Pong*. It likely won't be too long before neural "laces" made from carbon nanotubes plug us directly into the digital world.

What happens when a human mind has instantaneous access to computation and information on the scale of the internet and the cloud? It's almost impossible to imagine, but researchers are already in the early days of making it happen. As the central general-purpose technologies of the coming wave, AI and synthetic biology are already entangled, a spiraling feedback loop boosting each other. While the pandemic gave biotech a massive awareness boost, the full impact—possibilities and risks alike—of synthetic biology has barely begun to sink into the popular imagination.

Welcome to the age of biomachines and biocomputers, where strands of DNA perform calculations and artificial cells are put to work. Where machines come alive. Welcome to the age of synthetic life.

CHAPTER 6

THE WIDER WAVE

TECHNOLOGICAL WAVES ARE BIGGER THAN JUST ONE OR TWO general-purpose technologies. They are clusters of technologies arriving at around the same time, anchored by one or more general-purpose technologies but extending far beyond them.

General-purpose technologies are accelerants. Invention sparks invention. Waves lay the ground for further scientific and technological experimentation, nudging open the doors of possibility. This in turn yields new tools and techniques, new areas of research—new domains of technology itself. Companies form in and around them, attracting investment, pushing the new technologies out into small and big niches alike, further adapting them for a thousand different purposes. Waves are so huge and historic precisely because of this protean complexity, this tendency to mushroom and spill over.

Technologies don't develop or operate in air locks, removed from one another, least of all general-purpose technologies. Rather, they develop in rippling amplificatory loops. Where you find a general-purpose technology, you also find other technologies developing in constant dialogue, spurred on by it. Looking at waves, then, it's clearly not just about a steam engine, or a personal computer, or synthetic biology, as significant as they are; it's also about the vast nexus of further technologies and applications that come with them. It's all the products made in steam-driven factories, the people carried on steam-driven trains, the software businesses, and, further down, everything else that relies on computing.

Bio and AI are at the center, but around them lies a penumbra of other transformative technologies. Each has immense significance in its own right, but that is heightened when seen through the lens of the greater wave's cross-pollinating potential. In twenty years there will be numerous additional technologies, all breaking through at the same time. In this chapter, we examine a few key examples making up this wider wave.

We begin with robotics, or as I like to think of it, AI's physical manifestation, AI's body. Its impact is already being felt in some of the most cutting-edge industries on earth. But also the oldest. Come on down to the automated farm.

ROBOTICS COMES OF AGE

In 1837, John Deere was a blacksmith working in Grand Detour, Illinois. This was prairie country, with its dense black soil and wide-open spaces. It had potential as some of the world's best arable land—great for crops but incredibly tough to plow.

Then one day Deere saw a broken steel saw at a mill. Steel being scarce, he took his find home and fashioned the blade into a plow. Strong and smooth, steel was the perfect material for plowing through the dense, sticky soil. Although others had seen steel as an alternative to the coarser iron plows, Deere's breakthrough was to ramp up mass production. Before long farmers from across the Midwest were flocking to his workshop. His invention opened the prairie to a flood of settlers. The Midwest duly became the breadbasket of the world; John Deere quickly became synonymous with agriculture; and a techno-geographic revolution was instigated.

The John Deere company still makes agricultural technology today. You might be thinking tractors, sprinklers, and combines, and it's true that John Deere does make all these things. Increasingly, though, the company builds robots. The future of agriculture, as John Deere sees it, involves autonomous tractors and combines that operate independently, following a field's GPS coordinates and using an array of sensors to make automatic, real-time alterations to harvesting, maximizing yield and minimizing waste. The company is producing robots that can plant, tend, and harvest crops, with levels of precision and granularity that would be impossible for humans. Everything from soil quality to weather conditions is factored into a suite of machines that will soon do large chunks of the job. In an age of food price inflation and a growing population, the value is clear.

Farming robots aren't just coming. They're here. From drones watching livestock to precision irrigation rigs to small mobile robots patrolling vast indoor farms, from seeding to harvesting, picking to palletizing, watering tomatoes to tracking and herding cattle, the reality of the food we eat today is that it increasingly comes from a world of robots, driven by AI, currently being rolled out and scaled up.

Most of these robots don't look like the androids of popular sci-fi. They look like, well, agricultural machines. And many of us don't spend much time on farms in any case. But just as John Deere's plow once transformed the business of agriculture, these new robot-centered inventions are transforming how food gets to our tables. It's not a revolution we are well primed to recognize, but it is one already well underway.

ROBOTS HAVE ADVANCED MAINLY as one-dimensional tools, machines capable of doing single tasks on a production line with speed and precision, a major productivity boost for manufacturers but way off from the 1960s *Jetsons*-style visions of diffident android helpers.

As with AI, robotics proved much more difficult in practice than early engineers assumed. The real world is a strange, uneven, unexpected, and unstructured environment, exquisitely sensitive to things like pressure: picking up an egg, an apple, a brick, a child, and a bowl of soup all require extraordinary dexterity, sensitivity, strength, and balance. An environment like a kitchen or workshop is messy, filled with dangerous items, oil slicks, and multiple different tools and materials. It's a robot's nightmare.

Nonetheless, mostly out of the public eye, robots have quietly been learning about torque, tensile strength, the physics of manipulation, precision, pressure, and adaptation. Just watch them at an automotive manufacturing plant on YouTube: you see a crisp, never-ending ballet of robotic arms and manipulators steadily constructing a car. Amazon's "first fully autonomous mobile robot," called Proteus, can buzz around warehouses in great fleets, picking up parcels. Equipped with "advanced safety, perception, and navigation technology," it can do this comfortably alongside humans. Amazon's Sparrow is the first that can "detect, select, and handle individual products in [its] inventory."

It's not hard to imagine these robots in warehouses and factories—relatively static environments. But soon they will increasingly be found in restaurants, bars, care homes, and schools. Robots are already performing intricate surgery—in tandem with humans but also autonomously, on pigs (for now). Such uses are just the beginning of a much more widespread robotics rollout.

Today human programmers still often control every detail of a robot's operation. That makes the cost of integration in a new setting prohibitive. But as we've seen in so many other applications of machine learning, what starts with close human supervision ends up with the AI learning to do the task better by itself, eventually generalizing to new settings.

Google's research division is building robots that could, like the 1950s dream, do household chores and basic jobs from stacking dishes to tidying chairs in meeting rooms. They built a fleet of a hundred robots capable of sorting trash and wiping down tables. Reinforcement learning helps each robot's gripper pick up cups and open doors: just the kinds of actions, effortless to a toddler, that have vexed roboticists for decades. This new breed of robots can work on general activities, responding to natural language voice commands.

Another growing area is in the ability for robots to swarm, greatly amplifying the potential capabilities of any individual robot into a hive mind. Examples include the Harvard Wyss Institute's miniature Kilobots—a swarm of a thousand robots that work collectively and assemble in shapes taken from nature that could be used on difficult, distributed tasks like stopping soil erosion and other environmental mediations, agriculture, search and rescue operations, or the entire field of construction and inspection. Imagine a swarm of builder robots throwing up a bridge in minutes or a large building in hours, or tending to enormous, highly productive farms 24/7, or cleaning up an oil spill. With honeybee populations under threat, Walmart filed a patent for robot bees to collaborate and cross-pollinate crops autonomously. All the promise (and peril) of robotics is amplified by their ability to coordinate in groups of unrestricted size, an intricate chore-ography that will reset the rules of what is possible, where, and in what time frame.

Robots today still often don't look like the humanoid robots of the popular imagination. Consider the phenomenon of 3-D printing or ad-ditive manufacturing, a technique that uses robotic assemblers to layer up construction of anything from minuscule machine parts to apart-ment blocks. Giant concrete-spraying robots can build dwellings in a matter of days for a fraction of what traditional construction might have cost.

Robots can operate with precision in a far greater range of environ-ments for far longer periods than humans. Their vigilance and dili-gence are boundless. If they're networked together, the feats they might accomplish quite simply rewrite the rules of taking actions. I think we're now getting to the point where AI is pushing robots toward their original promise: machines that can replicate all the physical ac-tions of a human and more. As costs fall (the price of a robot arm de-clined by 46 percent in five years and is still going down), as they're eventually equipped with powerful batteries, as they simplify, becom-ing easy to repair, they will become ubiquitous. And that will mean turning up in unusual, extreme, and sensitive situations. Already the signs of a shift are visible—if you know where to look.

IT WAS THE POLICE force's worst nightmare. A military-trained sniper had got himself in a secure second-floor position at a local community college in Dallas, Texas. Then, overlooking a peaceful protest, he'd begun shooting police officers. After forty-five minutes, two were dead, more injured. Later it would emerge that five officers had been killed, seven wounded, the deadliest incident for American law enforcement since 9/11. The gunman taunted the police, laughing, singing, and fired with chilling accuracy. Tense negotiations, over two hours, were going nowhere. The police were pinned. It wasn't clear how many more would die attempting to resolve the situation.

Then the SWAT team came up with a new idea. The police depart-ment had a bomb disposal robot, the $150,000 Remotec Andros Mark 5A-1 made by Northrop Grumman. In fifteen minutes they hatched a plan to attach a large blob of C-4 explosive to its arm and send it into the building with the intention of incapacitating the shooter. The police chief, David Brown, quickly signed off on the plan. It went into action, the robot rumbling through the building, where it positioned the explosive in an adjacent room, next to a wall with the shooter on the other side. The explosive detonated, blasting apart the wall and killing the gunman. It was the first time a robot had used targeted lethal force in the United States. In Dallas, it saved the day. A horrific event was brought to a conclusion.

Still, some were disquieted. The concerning potential of lethal police robots hardly needed emphasizing. We'll return to the implications of all this in part 3. But above all it signified how robots are gradually working their way into society, poised to play a far greater role in daily life than has been the case before. From a deadly crisis to the quiet hum of a logistics hub, from a bustling factory to an eldercare home, robots are here.

AIs are products of bits and code, existing within simulations and servers. Robots are their bridge, their interface with the real world. If AI represents the automation of information, robotics is the automation of the material, the physical instantiations of AI, a step change in what it is possible to *do*. Mastery of bits comes full circle, directly reconfiguring atoms, rewriting the bounds not just of what can be thought or said or calculated but what can be built in the most tangible physical sense. And yet the remarkable thing about the coming wave is that this kind of blunt atomic manipulation is nothing compared with what's on the horizon.

QUANTUM SUPREMACY

In 2019, Google announced that it had reached "quantum supremacy." Researchers had built a quantum computer, one using the peculiar properties of the subatomic world. Chilled to a temperature colder than the coldest parts of outer space, Google's machine used an understanding of quantum mechanics to complete a calculation in seconds that would, it said, have taken a conventional computer ten thousand years. It had just fifty-three "qubits," or quantum bits, the core units of quantum computing. To store equivalent information on a classical computer, you would need seventy-two billion gigabytes of memory. This was a key moment for quantum computers. From theoretical underpinnings dating to the 1980s, quantum computing has gone from hypothetical to working prototype in four decades.

While very much a nascent technology, there are huge implications when quantum computing does materialize. Its key attraction is that each additional qubit doubles a machine's total computing power. Start adding qubits and it gets exponentially more powerful. Indeed, a relatively small number of particles could have more computing power than if the entire universe was converted into a classical computer. It's the computational equivalent of moving from a flat, black-and-white film into full color and three dimensions, unleashing a world of algorithmic possibility.

Quantum computing has far-reaching implications. For instance, the cryptography underlying everything from email security to cryptocurrencies would suddenly be at risk, in an impending event those in the field call "Q-Day." Cryptography rests on the assumption that an attacker will never have sufficient computing power to try all the different combinations needed to break it and unlock access. With quantum computing that changes. A fast and uncontained rollout of quantum computing could have catastrophic implications for banking or government communications. Both are already spending billions to head off the possibility.

Although much discussion of quantum computing has focused on its perils, the field also promises tremendous benefits, including the ability to explore frontiers in mathematics and particle physics. Researchers at Microsoft and Ford used nascent quantum approaches to model Seattle's traffic to find better ways of navigating rush hour, routing and flowing traffic on optimal paths—a surprisingly tricky mathematical problem. In theory, solving any optimization problem could be greatly sped up—almost anything that involves minimizing costs in complex circumstances, whether that's efficiently loading a truck or running a national economy.

Arguably, quantum computing's most significant near-term promise is in modeling chemical reactions and the interaction of molecules in previously impossible detail. This could let us understand the human brain or materials science with extraordinary granularity. Chemistry and biology will become fully legible for the first time. Discovering new pharmaceutical compounds or industrial chemicals and materials, a costly, painstaking process of tricky lab work, could be greatly sped up—gotten right on the first go. New batteries and drugs made more likely, more efficient and realizable. The molecular becomes "programmable," as supple and manipulable as code.

Quantum computing is, in other words, yet another foundational technology still in very early development, still further from hitting those critical moments of cost decreases and widespread proliferation, let alone the technical breakthroughs that will make it fully feasible. But as with AI and synthetic biology, albeit at an earlier stage, it appears to be at a point where funding and knowledge are escalating, progress on fundamental challenges is growing, and a range of valuable uses are coming into view. Like AI and biotech, quantum computing helps speed up other elements of the wave. And yet even the mind-bending quantum world is not the limit.

THE NEXT ENERGY TRANSITION

Energy rivals intelligence and life in its fundamental importance. Modern civilization relies on vast amounts of it. Indeed, if you wanted to write the crudest possible equation for our world it would be something like this:

$$(\text{Life} + \text{Intelligence}) \times \text{Energy} = \text{Modern Civilization}$$

Increase any or all of those inputs (let alone supercharge their marginal cost toward zero) and you have a step change in the nature of society.

Endless growth in energy consumption was neither possible nor desirable in the era of fossil fuels, and yet while the boom lasted, the development of almost everything we take for granted—from cheap food to effortless transport—rested on it. Now, a huge boost of cheap, clean power has implications for everything from transport to buildings, not to mention the colossal power needed to run the data centers and robotics that will be at the heart of the coming decades. Energy—expensive and dirty as it often is—is at present a limiter on technology's rate of progress. Not for too much longer.

Renewable energy will become the largest single source of electricity generation by 2027. This shift is occurring at an unprecedented pace, with more renewable capacity set to be added in the next five years than in the previous two decades. Solar power in particular is experiencing rapid growth, with costs falling significantly. In 2000, solar energy cost $4.88 per watt, but by 2019 it had fallen to just 38 cents. Energy isn't just getting cheaper; it's more distributed, potentially localizable from specific devices to whole communities.

Behind it all lies the dormant behemoth of clean energy, this time inspired if not directly powered by the sun: nuclear fusion. Fusion power involves the release of energy when isotopes of hydrogen collide and fuse to form helium, a process long considered the holy grail of energy production. Early pioneers in the 1950s predicted that it would take about a decade to develop. Like so many of the technologies described here, that was a significant underestimation.

However, recent breakthroughs have sparked renewed hope. Researchers at the Joint European Torus near Oxford, England, achieved a record power output, double the previous high recorded in 1997. At the National Ignition Facility in Livermore, California, scientists have been working on a method known as inertial confinement, which involves compressing pellets of hydrogen-rich material with lasers and heating them to 100 million degrees to create a fleeting fusion reaction. In 2022 they created a reaction demonstrating net energy gain for the first time, a critical milestone of producing more energy than the lasers put in. With meaningful private capital now flowing into at least thirty fusion start-ups alongside major international collaborations, scientists are talking about "when and not if" fusion arrives. It may still be a decade or more, but a future with this clean and virtually limitless energy source is looking increasingly real.

Fusion and solar offer the promise of immense centralized and decentralized energy grids, with implications we will explore in part 3. This is a time of huge optimism. Including wind, hydrogen, and improved battery technologies, here is a brewing mix that can sustainably power the many demands of life both today and in the future and underwrite the wave's full potential.

THE WAVE BEYOND THE WAVE

These technologies will dominate the next decades. But what about the second half of the twenty-first century? What comes after the coming wave?

As the elements of AI, advanced biotechnology, quantum computing, and robotics combine in new ways, prepare for breakthroughs like advanced nanotechnology, a concept that takes the ever-growing precision of technology to its logical conclusion. What if rather than being manipulated en masse, atoms could be manipulated individually? It would be the apotheosis of the bits/atoms relationship. The ultimate vision of nanotechnology is one where atoms become controllable building blocks, capable of automatically assembling almost anything.

Practical challenges are immense, but they are the subject of increasing research intensity. A team at the University of Oxford, for example, produced a self-replicating assembler gesturing toward the multifunctional versions imagined by nanotech pioneers: devices capable of endlessly engineering and recombining at the atomic scale.

Nanomachines would work at speeds far beyond anything at our scale, delivering extraordinary outputs: an atomic-scale nanomotor, for example, could rotate forty-eight billion times a minute. Scaled up, it could power a Tesla with material equivalent in volume to about twelve grains of sand. This is a world of gossamer structures made of diamond, space suits that cling to and protect the body in all environments, a world where compilers can create anything out of a basic feedstock. A world, in short, where anything can become anything with the right atomic manipulation. The dream of the physical universe rendered a completely malleable platform, the plaything of tiny, dexterous nanobots or effortless replicators, is still the province, like superintelligence, of science fiction. It's a techno-fantasia, many decades away, but one that will steadily come into focus as the coming wave plays out.

———

AT ITS CORE, THE coming wave is a story of the proliferation of power. If the last wave reduced the costs of *broadcasting* information, this one reduces the costs of *acting* on it, giving rise to technologies that go from sequencing to synthesis, reading to writing, editing to creating, imitating conversations to leading them. In this, it is qualitatively different from every previous wave, despite all the big claims made about the transformative power of the internet. This kind of power is even harder to centralize and oversee; this wave is not just a deepening and acceleration of history's pattern, then, but also a sharp break from it.

Not everyone agrees these technologies are either as locked on or as consequential as I think they are. Skepticism and pessimism aversion are not unreasonable responses, given there is much uncertainty. Each technology is subject to a vicious hype cycle, each is uncertain in development and reception, each is surrounded by challenges technical, ethical, and social. None is complete. There are certain to be setbacks, and many of the harms—and indeed benefits—are still unclear.

But each is also growing more concrete, developed, and capable by the day. Each is becoming more accessible and more powerful. We are reaching the decisive point of what, in geological or human evolutionary timescales, is a technological explosion unfolding in successive waves, a compounding, accelerating cycle of innovation steadily getting faster and more impactful, breaking first over a period of thousands of years, then hundreds of years, and now single years or even months. See these technologies in the context of press releases and op-eds, at the mayfly pace of social media, and they might look like hype and froth; see the long view, and their true potential becomes clear.

Humanity has of course experienced epic technological change before as part of this process. To understand the unique challenges of the coming wave, however—just why it's so especially hard to contain, just why its immense promise must be balanced with sober-minded caution—we have to first break down its key features, some of which are without historical precedent, and all of which are being felt already.

CHAPTER 7

FOUR FEATURES OF THE COMING WAVE

SOON AFTER THE RUSSIAN INVASION OF UKRAINE BEGAN ON February 24, 2022, residents of the city of Kyiv knew they were in a fight for survival. Over the border with Belarus a colossal massing of Russian troops, armor, and matériel had been building for months. Then, at the outset of the invasion, Russian forces readied for a major push on what was still, at this stage, their primary goal: capture Ukraine's capital and overthrow its government.

The centerpiece of this concentration of force was a column of trucks, tanks, and heavy artillery some forty kilometers long—a ground offensive on a scale not seen in Europe since World War II. It began moving toward the city. On paper the Ukrainians were hopelessly outmatched. Kyiv seemed to be days, maybe hours, from falling.

But that didn't happen. Instead, a unit of about thirty Ukrainian soldiers wearing night vision goggles rode quad bikes through the forests around the capital that evening. They dismounted near the column's head and launched jerry-rigged drones equipped with small explosives. These took out a handful of lead vehicles. Those disabled vehicles then clogged up the central road. Surrounding fields were muddy and impassable. The column, facing freezing weather and faltering supply lines, ground to a halt. Then the same small unit of drone operators managed to blow up a critical supply base using the same tactics, depriving the Russian army of fuel and food.

From here the Battle of Kyiv turned. The greatest buildup of conventional military muscle in a generation was humbled, sent back to Belarus in embarrassing disarray. This semi-improvised Ukrainian mili-

tia was called Aerorozvidka. A ragtag volunteer band of drone hobby-
ists, software engineers, management consultants, and soldiers, they
were amateurs, designing, building, and modifying their own drones in
real time, much like a start-up. A lot of their equipment was crowd-
sourced and crowdfunded.

The Ukrainian resistance made good use of coming-wave technologies and demonstrated how they can undermine a conventional military calculus. Cutting-edge satellite internet from SpaceX's Starlink
was integral to maintaining connectivity. A thousand-strong group of
nonmilitary elite programmers and computer scientists banded together in an organization called Delta to bring advanced AI and robotics capabilities to the army, using machine learning to identify targets,
monitor Russian tactics, and even suggest strategies.

In the early days of the war, the Ukrainian army was constantly
short of ammunition. Every strike counted. Accuracy was a matter of
survival. Delta's ability to create machine learning systems to spot
camouflaged targets and help guide munitions was critical. A precision
missile in a conventional military costs hundreds of thousands of dollars; with AI and consumer-grade drones, with custom software and
3-D printed parts, something similar has now been battle-tested in
Ukraine at a cost of around $15,000. Alongside the initial Aerorozvidka
efforts, the United States supplied Ukraine with hundreds of Switch-
blade loitering munitions, drones that wait around a target until an
optimal moment to strike.

Drones and AI played a small but important part in the early days of
the conflict in Ukraine, new technologies with a pronounced asymmetric potential that closed some of the gap with a much larger ag-
gressor. American, British, and European forces provided just under
€100 billion of military aid in the first months, including a massive
amount of conventional firepower, which, to be clear, undoubtedly
had a decisive impact. However, this was still a landmark conflict because it demonstrated how quickly a relatively untrained fighting force
could assemble and arm itself using relatively affordable technologies
available in the consumer market. When technology confers a cost and
tactical advantage like this, it will, of course, inevitably proliferate and
be taken up by all sides.

Drones provide us with a glimpse of what's in store for the future of warfare. They are a reality that planners and combatants deal with on a daily basis. The real question is what this means for conflict when production costs fall by another order of magnitude and capabilities multiply. Conventional militaries and governments are already struggling to contain them. What comes next will be much harder to contain.

AS WE SAW IN part I, technologies from X-ray machines to AK-47s have always proliferated, with broad consequences. The coming wave is, however, characterized by a set of four intrinsic features compounding the problem of containment. First among them is the primary lesson of this section: hugely *asymmetric* impact. You don't need to hit like with like, mass with mass; instead, new technologies create previously unthinkable vulnerabilities and pressure points against seemingly dominant powers.

Second, they are developing fast, a kind of *hyper-evolution*, iterating, improving, and branching into new areas at incredible speed. Third, they are often *omni-use;* that is, they can be used for many different purposes. And fourth, they increasingly have a degree of *autonomy* beyond any previous technology.

These features define the wave. Understanding them is vital in identifying what benefits and risks arise from their creation; together they escalate containment and control to a new plane of difficulty and danger.

ASYMMETRY:
A COLOSSAL TRANSFER OF POWER

Emerging technologies have always created new threats, redistributed power, and removed barriers to entry. Cannons meant a small force could destroy castles and level armies. A few colonial soldiers with advanced weapons could massacre thousands of indigenous people. The printing press meant a single workshop might produce thousands of pamphlets—spreading ideas with an ease that medieval monks copying books by hand could scarcely fathom. Steam power enabled single factories to do the work of entire towns. The internet took this capacity to a new peak: a single tweet or image might travel the world in minutes or seconds; a single algorithm could help a small start-up to grow into a vast, globe-spanning corporation.

Now this effect is again sharpened. This new wave of technology has unlocked powerful capabilities that are cheap, easy to access and use, targeted, and scalable. This clearly brings risks. It won't just be Ukrainian soldiers using weaponized drones. It will be anyone who wants to. In the words of the security expert Audrey Kurth Cronin, "Never before have so many had access to such advanced technologies capable of inflicting death and mayhem."

In the skirmishes outside Kyiv, the drones were hobbyist toys. The Shenzhen-based company DJI builds cheap and widely accessible products like its flagship $1,399 Phantom camera quadcopter, a drone so good it has been used by the U.S. military. If you combine advances in AI and autonomy, cheap but effective UAVs, and further progress in areas from robotics to computer vision, then you have potent, precise, and potentially untraceable weaponry. Combating attacks is difficult and expensive; both Americans and Israelis use $3 million Patriot missiles to shoot down drones worth a couple hundred dollars. Jammers, missiles, and counter-drones are all still nascent and not always battle-tested.

These developments represent a colossal transfer of power away from traditional states and militaries toward anyone with the capacity, and motivation, to deploy these devices. There is no obvious reason why a single operator, with enough wherewithal, could not control a swarm of thousands of drones.

A single AI program can write as much text as all of humanity. A single two-gigabyte image-generation model running on your laptop can compress all the pictures on the open web into a tool that generates images with extraordinary creativity and precision. A single pathogenic experiment could spark a pandemic, a tiny molecular event with global ramifications. One viable quantum computer could render the world's entire encryption infrastructure redundant. Prospects for asymmetric impact are growing all around, and also in the positive sense—single systems can deliver huge benefits as well.

The reverse of asymmetric action is also true. The very scale and interconnectedness of the coming wave create new systemic vulnerabilities: one point of failure can quickly cascade around the world. The less localized a technology, the less easily it can be contained—and vice versa. Think about the risks involved with cars. Traffic accidents are as old as traffic, but over time damage was minimized. Everything from road markings to seatbelts to traffic police helped. Although the motorcar was one of history's fastest-proliferating and most globalized technologies, accidents were inherently local, discrete events whose ultimate damage was contained. But now a fleet of vehicles might be networked together. Or a single system could control autonomous vehicles throughout a territory. However many safeguards and security protocols are in place, the scale of impact is far wider than we've seen before.

AI creates asymmetric risks beyond those of a bad batch of food, a plane accident, or a faulty product. Its risks extend to entire societies, making it not so much a blunt tool as a lever with global consequences. Just as globalized and highly connected markets transmit contagion in a financial crisis, so with technology. Network scale makes containing damage, if or when it comes, almost impossible. Interlinked global systems are containment nightmares. And we *already* live in an age of interlinked global systems. In the coming wave a single point—a given program, a genetic change—can alter everything.

HYPER-EVOLUTION: ENDLESS ACCELERATION

If you want to contain technology, you might hope it develops at a manageable pace, giving society time and space to understand and adapt to it. Cars are again a good example. Their development over the last century was incredibly fast but also provided time for introducing all sorts of safety standards. There was always a lag, but the standards could still catch up. However, with the rate of change in the coming wave, that looks unlikely.

Over the last forty years, the internet grew to be one of the most fruitful innovation platforms in history. The world digitized, and this dematerialized realm evolved at a bewildering pace. An explosion of development saw the world's most widely used services and the largest commercial enterprises in history spring up in just a few years. All of this was underwritten by the ever-increasing power and fall in costs of computation we saw in chapter 2. Consider what Moore's law alone will deliver over the next decade. Should it hold, in ten years a dollar will buy you a hundred times the compute of today. That fact alone suggests some extraordinary outcomes.

The flip side is that innovation beyond digital was often less spectacular. Outside the weightless world of code, a growing chorus began to wonder what happened to the kind of broad-based innovation seen, for example, in the late nineteenth century or the middle of the twentieth century. During that brief period, almost every aspect of the world—from transport to factories, powered flight to new materials— changed radically. But by the early years of the twenty-first century, innovation followed the path of least resistance, concentrated on bits rather than atoms.

That's now shifting. Software's hyper-evolution is spreading. The next forty years will see both the world of atoms rendered into bits at new levels of complexity and fidelity and, crucially, the world of bits rendered back into tangible atoms with a speed and ease unthinkable until recently.

Put simply, innovation in the "real world" could start moving at a digital pace, in near-real time, with reduced friction and fewer dependencies. You will be able to experiment in small, speedy, malleable domains, creating near-perfect simulations, and then translate them into concrete products. And then do it again, and again, learning, evolving, and improving at rates previously impossible in the expensive, static world of atoms.

The physicist César Hidalgo argues that configurations of matter are significant because of the information they contain. A Ferrari is valuable not because of its raw matter but rather for the complex information stored in its intricate construction and form; the information characterizing the arrangement of its atoms is what makes it a desirable car. The more powerful the computational base, the more tractable this becomes. Couple that with AI and manufacturing techniques like sophisticated robotics and 3-D printing, and we can design, manipulate, and manufacture real-world products with greater speed, precision, and inventiveness.

AI already helps find new materials and chemical compounds. For example, scientists have used neural networks to produce new configurations of lithium, with big implications for battery technology. AI has helped design and build a car using 3-D printers. In some cases the final outcome looks bizarrely different from anything designed by a human, resembling the undulating and efficient forms found in nature. Configurations of wiring and ducting are organically melded into the chassis for optimal use of space. Parts are too complex to build using conventional tooling and have to be 3-D printed.

In chapter 5, we saw what tools like AlphaFold are doing to catalyze biotech. Until recently biotech relied on endless manual lab work: measuring, pipetting, carefully preparing samples. Now simulations speed up the process of vaccine discovery. Computational tools help automate parts of the design processes, re-creating the "biological circuits" that program complex functions into cells like bacteria that can produce a certain protein. Software frameworks, like one called Cello, are almost like open-source languages for synthetic biology design. This could mesh with fast-moving improvements in laboratory robotics and automation and faster biological techniques like the enzymatic synthesis we saw in chapter 5, expanding synthetic biology's range and making it more accessible. Biological evolution is becoming subject to the same cycles as software.

Just as today's models produce detailed images based on a few words, so in decades to come similar models will produce a novel compound or indeed an entire organism with just a few natural language prompts. That compound's design could be improved by countless self-run trials, just as AlphaZero became an expert chess or Go player through self-play. Quantum technologies, many millions of times more powerful than the most powerful classical computers, could let this play out at a molecular level. This is what we mean by hyperevolution—a fast, iterative platform for creation.

Nor will this evolution be limited to specific, predictable, and readily containable areas. It will be everywhere.

OMNI-USE:
MORE IS MORE

Defying conventional wisdom, progress in health care was one of the areas that slowed in the recent stagnation of innovation in the realm of atoms. Discovering new drugs became harder and more expensive. Life expectancy leveled off and even started to decline in some U.S. states. Progress on conditions like Alzheimer's failed to live up to expectations.

One of the most promising areas of AI, and a way out of this grim picture, is automated drug discovery. AI techniques can search through the vast space of possible molecules for elusive but helpful treatments. In 2020 an AI system sifted through 100 million molecules to create the first machine-learning-derived antibiotic—called halicin (yes, after HAL from *2001: A Space Odyssey*)—which can potentially help fight tuberculosis. Start-ups like Exscientia, alongside traditional pharmaceutical giants like Sanofi, have made AI a driver of medical research. To date eighteen clinical assets have been derived with the help of AI tools.

There's a flip side. Researchers looking for these helpful compounds raised an awkward question. What if you redirected the discovery process? What if, instead of looking for cures, you looked for killers? They ran a test, asking their molecule-generating AI to find poisons. In six hours it identified more than forty thousand molecules with toxicity comparable to the most dangerous chemical weapons, like Novichok. It turns out that in drug discovery, one of the areas where AI will undoubtedly make the clearest possible difference, the opportunities are very much "dual use."

Dual-use technologies are those with both civilian and military applications. In World War I, the process of synthesizing ammonia was seen as a way of feeding the world. But it also allowed for the creation of explosives, and helped pave the way for chemical weapons. Complex electronics systems for passenger aircraft can be repurposed for precision missiles. Conversely, the Global Positioning System was originally a military system, but now has countless everyday consumer uses. At launch, the PlayStation 2 was regarded by the U.S. Department of Defense as so powerful that it could potentially help hostile militaries usually denied access to such hardware. Dual-use technologies are both helpful and potentially destructive, tools and weapons. What the concept captures is how technologies tend toward the general, and a certain class of technologies come with a heightened risk because of this. They can be put toward many ends—good, bad, everywhere in between—often with difficult-to-predict consequences.

But the real problem is that it's not just frontier biology or nuclear reactors that are dual use. Most technologies have military and civilian applications or potential; most technologies are in some way dual use. And the more powerful the technology, the more concern there should be about how many uses it might have.

Technologies of the coming wave are highly powerful, precisely because they are fundamentally general. If you're building a nuclear warhead, it's obvious what it's for. But a deep learning system might be designed for playing games yet capable of flying a fleet of bombers. The difference is not a priori obvious.

A more appropriate term for the technologies of the coming wave is "omni-use," a concept that grasps at the sheer levels of generality, the extreme versatility on display. Omni-use technologies like steam or electricity have wider societal effects and spillovers than narrower technologies. If AI is indeed the new electricity, then like electricity it will be an on-demand utility that permeates and powers almost every aspect of daily life, society, the economy: a general-purpose technology embedded everywhere. Containing something like this is always going to be much harder than containing a constrained, single-task technology, stuck in a tiny niche with few dependencies.

AI systems started out using general techniques like deep learning for specific purposes like managing energy use at a data center or playing Go. That is changing. Now single systems like DeepMind's generalist Gato can capably perform more than six hundred different tasks. The same network can play Atari games, caption images, answer questions, and stack blocks with a real robot arm. Gato is trained not only with text but also with images, torques acting on robotic arms, button presses from computer game playing, and so on. It's still very early days, and truly general systems are still some way off, but at some point these capabilities will expand to many thousands of activities.

Consider synthetic biology, too, through the omni-use prism. Engineering life is a completely general technique whose potential uses are near limitless; it might create material for construction, tackle disease, and store data. More is more, and there is a good reason for this. Omni-use technologies are more valuable than narrow ones. Nowadays, technologists don't want to design technologies that are limited, specific, mono-functional applications. Instead, the goal is to design things more like smartphones: phones but more importantly devices for taking pictures, keeping fit, playing games, navigating cities, sending emails, and so on.

Over time, technology tends toward generality. What this means is that weaponizable or harmful uses of the coming wave will be possible regardless of whether this was intended. Simply creating civilian technologies has national security ramifications. Anticipating the full spectrum of use cases in history's most omni-use wave is harder than ever.

The notion of a new technology being adapted for multiple uses isn't new. A simple tool like a knife can chop onions or enable a deranged killing spree. Even seemingly specific technologies have dual-use implications: the microphone enabled both the Nuremberg rallies and the Beatles. What's different about the coming wave is how quickly it is being embedded, how globally it spreads, how easily it can be componentized into swappable parts, and just how powerful and above all broad its applications could be. It unfurls complex implications for everything from media to mental health, markets to medicine. This is the containment problem supersized. After all, we're talking about fundamentals like intelligence and life. But both those properties have a feature even more interesting than their generality.

AUTONOMY AND BEYOND: WILL HUMANS BE IN THE LOOP?

Technological evolution has been speeding up for centuries. Omni-use features and asymmetric impacts are magnified in the coming wave, but to some extent they're inherent properties of all technology. That isn't the case for autonomy. For all of history technology has been "just" a tool, but what if the tool comes to life?

Autonomous systems are able to interact with their surroundings and take actions without the immediate approval of humans. For centuries the idea that technology is somehow running out of control, a self-directed and self-propelling force beyond the realms of human agency, remained a fiction.

Not anymore.

Technology has always been about allowing us to do more, but crucially with humans still doing the doing. It has leveraged our existing abilities and automated precisely codified tasks. Until now, constant oversight and management have been the default. Technology remained to greater or lesser degrees under meaningful human control. Full autonomy is qualitatively different.

Take autonomous vehicles. In certain conditions today, they can drive on roads with minimal or no direct input from the driver. Researchers in the field categorize autonomy from level 0, no autonomy whatsoever, to level 5, where a vehicle can drive itself under all conditions and the driver simply inputs a destination and then can fall happily asleep. You won't find level 5 vehicles on the roads anytime soon, not least for legal and insurance reasons.

The new wave of autonomy heralds a world where constant intervention and oversight are increasingly unnecessary. What's more, with every interaction we are teaching machines to be successfully autonomous. In this paradigm, there is no need for a human to laboriously define the manner in which a task should take place. Instead, we just specify a high-level goal and rely on a machine to figure out the optimal way of getting there. Keeping humans "in the loop," as the saying goes, is desirable, but optional.

Nobody told AlphaGo that move 37 was a good idea. It discovered this insight largely on its own. It was precisely this feature that struck me so forcibly watching DQN play *Breakout*. Given some clearly specified objective, systems now exist that can find their own strategies to be effective. AlphaGo and DQN were not in themselves autonomous. But they hint at what a self-improving system might look like. Nobody hand codes GPT-4 to write like Jane Austen, or produce an original haiku, or generate marketing copy for a website selling bicycles. These features are emergent effects of a wider architecture whose outputs are never decided in advance by its designers. This is the first step on the ladder toward greater and greater autonomy. Internal research on GPT-4 concluded that it was "probably" not capable of acting autonomously or self-replicating, but within days of launch users had found ways of getting the system to ask for its own documentation and to write scripts for copying itself and taking over other machines. Early research even claimed to find "sparks of AGI" in the model, adding that it was "strikingly close to human-level performance." These now are coming into view.

New forms of autonomy have the potential to produce a set of novel, hard-to-predict effects. Forecasting how bespoke genomes will behave is incredibly difficult. Moreover, once researchers make germline gene changes to a species, those changes could be out in live beings potentially for millennia, far beyond control or prediction. They might reverberate down countless generations. How they go on to evolve or interact with other changes at these distances is inevitably unclear— and beyond control. Synthetic organisms are literally taking on a life of their own.

We humans face a singular challenge: Will new inventions be beyond our grasp? Previously creators could explain how something worked and why it did what it did, even if this required vast detail. That's increasingly no longer true. Many technologies and systems are becoming so complex that they're beyond the capacity of any one individual to truly understand: quantum computing and other technologies operate toward the limits of what can be known.

A paradox of the coming wave is that its technologies are largely beyond our ability to comprehend at a granular level yet still within our ability to create and use. In AI, the neural networks moving toward autonomy are, at present, not explainable. You can't walk someone through the decision-making process to explain precisely why an algorithm produced a specific prediction. Engineers can't peer beneath the hood and easily explain what caused something to happen. GPT-4, AlphaGo, and the rest are black boxes, their outputs and decisions based on opaque and intricate chains of minute signals. Autonomous systems can and may be explainable, but the fact that so much of the coming wave operates at the edge of what we can understand should give us pause. We won't always be able to predict what these autonomous systems will do next; that's the nature of autonomy.

Right at the cutting edge, however, some AI researchers want to automate every aspect of building AI systems, feeding that hyperevolution, but potentially with radical degrees of independence through self-improvement. AIs are already finding ways to improve their own algorithms. What happens when they couple this with autonomous actions on the web, as in the Modern Turing Test and ACI, conducting their own R&D cycles?

THE GORILLA PROBLEM

I've often felt there's been too much focus on distant AGI scenarios, given the obvious near-term challenges present in so much of the coming wave. However, any discussion of containment has to acknowledge that if or when AGI-like technologies do emerge, they will present containment problems beyond anything else we've ever encountered. Humans dominate our environment because of our intelligence. A more intelligent entity could, it follows, dominate us. The AI researcher Stuart Russell calls it the "gorilla problem": gorillas are physically stronger and tougher than any human being, but it is they who are endangered or living in zoos; they who are contained. We, with our puny muscles but big brains, do the containment.

By creating something smarter than us, we could put ourselves in the position of our primate cousins. With a long-term view in mind, those focusing on AGI scenarios are right to be concerned. Indeed, there is a strong case that by definition a superintelligence would be fully impossible to control or contain. An "intelligence explosion" is the point at which an AI can improve itself again and again, recursively making itself better in ever faster and more effective ways. Here is the definitive uncontained and uncontainable technology. The blunt truth is that nobody knows when, if, or exactly how AIs might slip beyond us and what happens next; nobody knows when or if they will become fully autonomous or how to make them behave with awareness of and alignment with our values, assuming we can settle on those values in the first place.

Nobody really knows how we can contain the very features being researched so intently in the coming wave. There comes a point where technology can fully direct its own evolution; where it is subject to recursive processes of improvement; where it passes beyond explanation; where it is consequently impossible to predict how it will behave in the wild; where, in short, we reach the limits of human agency and control.

Ultimately, in its most dramatic forms, the coming wave could mean humanity will no longer be at the top of the food chain. *Homo technologicus* may end up being threatened by its own creation. The real question is not whether the wave is coming. It clearly is; just look and you can see it forming already. Given risks like these, the real question is *why* it's so hard to see it as anything other than inevitable.

CHAPTER 8

UNSTOPPABLE
INCENTIVES

A LPHAGO'S SIGNIFICANCE WAS PARTLY A MATTER OF TIMING: THE breakthrough surprised experts by arriving more quickly than most in the AI community had thought possible. Even days before its first public competition in March 2016, prominent researchers thought an AI simply couldn't win at this level of Go. At DeepMind, we were still uncertain our program would prevail in a matchup with a master human competitor.

We saw the contest as a grand technical challenge, a waypoint on a wider research mission. Within the AI community, it represented a first high-profile public test of deep reinforcement learning and one of the first research uses of a very large cluster of GPU computation. In the press the matchup between AlphaGo and Lee Sedol was presented as an epic battle: human versus machine; humanity's best and brightest against the cold, lifeless force of a computer. Cue all the tired tropes of Terminators and robot overlords.

But under the surface, another, more important dimension was becoming clear, a tension I'd dimly worried about ahead of the contest, but the contours of which emerged more starkly as the event unfolded. AlphaGo wasn't just human versus machine. As Lee Sedol squared up against AlphaGo, DeepMind was represented by the Union Jack, while the Sedol camp flew the *taegeukgi,* South Korea's unmistakable flag. West versus East. This implication of national rivalry was an aspect of the contest I soon came to regret.

It's hard to overstate how popular the competition was in Asia. In the West the proceedings were followed by hard-core AI enthusiasts and attracted some newspaper attention. It was a significant moment in tech history—for those who care about such things. Across Asia, however, the event was bigger than the Super Bowl. More than 280 million people watched live. We'd taken over an entire hotel in Seoul's downtown, mobbed by ever-present members of the local and international media. You could hardly move for hundreds of photographers and TV cameras. The intensity was unlike anything I'd experienced before, a level of scrutiny and hype that seemed alien in what was, to Western observers, an obscure game for math enthusiasts. AI developers, suffice to say, were not used to this.

In Asia it wasn't just the geeks watching. It was everyone. And it soon became clear that the observers included tech companies, governments, and militaries. The result sent a shock wave through them all. The significance was lost on no one. The challenger, a Western firm, London based, American owned, had just marched into an ancient, iconic, cherished game, literally put its flag in the turf, and obliterated the home team. It was as if a group of Korean robots had shown up at Yankee Stadium and beat America's all-star baseball team.

For us the event was a scientific experiment. It was a powerful—and, yes, cool—demonstration of cutting-edge techniques we'd spent years trying to perfect. It was exciting from an engineering perspective, exhilarating for its competition, and bewildering to be at the center of a media circus. For many in Asia it was something more painful, an instance of wounded regional and national pride.

Seoul wasn't the end for AlphaGo. A year later, in May 2017, we took part in a second tournament, this time against the number-one-ranked player in the world: Ke Jie. This matchup took place in Wuzhen, China, at the Future of Go Summit. Our reception in Wuzhen was strikingly different. Livestreaming the matches was barred in the People's Republic. No mention of Google was allowed. The environment was stricter, more controlled; the narrative closely curated by the authorities. No more media circus. The subtext was clear: this wasn't just a game anymore. AlphaGo won again, but it did so amid an unmistakably tense atmosphere.

Something had changed. If Seoul offered a hint, Wuzhen brought it home. As the dust settled, it became clear AlphaGo was part of a much bigger story than one trophy, system, or company; it was that of great powers engaging in a new and dangerous game of technological competition—and a series of overwhelmingly powerful and interlocking incentives that ensure the coming wave really is coming.

TECHNOLOGY IS PUSHED ON by all too rudimentary and fundamentally human drivers. From curiosity to crisis, fortune to fear, at its heart technology emerges to fill human needs. If people have powerful reasons to build and use it, it will get built and used. Yet in most discussions of technology people still get stuck on what it is, forgetting *why* it was created in the first place. This is not about some innate techno-determinism. This is about what it means to be human.

Earlier we saw that no wave of technology has, so far, been contained. In this chapter we look at why history is likely to repeat itself; why, thanks to a series of macro-drivers behind technologies' development and spread, the fruit will not be left on the tree; why the wave will break. As long as these incentives are in place, the important question of "should we?" is moot.

The first driver has to do with what I experienced with AlphaGo: great power competition. Technological rivalry is a geopolitical reality. Indeed it always has been. Nations feel the existential need to keep up with their peers. Innovation is power. Second comes a global research ecosystem with its ingrained rituals rewarding open publication, curiosity, and the pursuit of new ideas at all costs. Then come the immense financial gains from technology and the urgent need to tackle our global social challenges. And the final driver is perhaps the most human of all: ego.

Before that, back to geopolitics, where the recent past offers a potent lesson.

NATIONAL PRIDE, STRATEGIC NECESSITY

Postwar America took its technological supremacy for granted. Sputnik woke it up. In the fall of 1957, the Soviets launched Sputnik, the world's first artificial satellite, humanity's first encroachment on space. About the size of a beach ball, it was still impossibly futuristic. Sputnik was up there for the world to see, or rather hear, its extraterrestrial beeps broadcasting around the planet. Pulling it off was an undeniable feat.

This was a crisis for America, a technological Pearl Harbor. Policy reacted. Science and technology, from high schools to advanced laboratories, became national priorities, with new funding and new agencies like NASA and DARPA. Massive resources were plowed into major technology projects, not least the Apollo missions. These spurred many important advances in rocketry, microelectronics, and computer programming. Nascent alliances like NATO were strengthened. Twelve years later, it was the United States, not the USSR, that succeeded in putting a human on the moon. The Soviets almost bankrupted themselves trying to keep up. With Sputnik, Russia had blown past the United States, a historic technical achievement with enormous geopolitical ramifications. But when America needed to step up, it did.

Just as Sputnik eventually put the United States on course to be a superpower in rocketry, space technology, computing, and all their military and civilian applications, so something similar is now taking place in China. AlphaGo was quickly labeled China's Sputnik moment for AI. The Americans and the West, just as they had done in the early days of the internet, were threatening to steal a march on an epoch-making technology. Here was the clearest possible reminder that China, beaten at a national pastime, could once again find itself far behind the frontier.

In China, Go wasn't just a game. It represented a wider nexus of history, emotion, and strategic calculation. China was already committed to investing heavily in science and technology, but AlphaGo helped focus government minds even more acutely on AI. China, with its thousands of years of history, had once been the crucible of world technological innovation; it was now painfully aware of how it had fallen behind, losing the technological race to Europeans and Americans on various fronts from medicines to aircraft carriers. It had endured a "century of humiliation," as the Chinese Communist Party (CCP) calls it. One that, the party believes, must never happen again.

Time, argued the CCP, to reclaim its rightful place. In the words of

Xi Jinping, speaking to the Twentieth CCP Congress in 2022, "to meet strategic needs" the country "must adhere to science and technology as the number-one productive force, talent as the number-one resource, [and] innovation as the number-one driving force."

China's top-down model means it can marshal the state's full resources behind technological ends. Today, China has an explicit national strategy to be the world leader in AI by 2030. The New Generation Artificial Intelligence Development Plan, announced just two months after Ke Jie was beaten by AlphaGo, was intended to harness government, the military, research organizations, and industry in a collective mission. "By 2030, China's AI theories, technologies, and applications should achieve world-leading levels," the plan declares, "making China the world's primary AI innovation center." From defense to smart cities, fundamental theory to new applications, China should occupy AI's "commanding heights."

These bold declarations are not just empty posturing. As I write this, just six years after China released the plan, the United States and other Western nations no longer have an outsized lead in AI research. Universities like Tsinghua and Peking are competitive with Western institutions like Stanford, MIT, and Oxford. Indeed, Tsinghua publishes more AI research than any other academic institution on the planet. China has a growing and impressive share of the most highly cited papers in AI. In terms of volume of AI research, Chinese institutions have published a whopping four and a half times more AI papers than U.S. counterparts since 2010, and comfortably more than the United States, the U.K., India, and Germany combined.

It's not just AI either. From cleantech to bioscience, China surges across the spectrum of fundamental technologies, investing at an epic scale, a burgeoning IP behemoth with "Chinese characteristics." China overtook the United States in number of PhDs produced in 2007, but since then investment in and expansion of programs have been significant, producing nearly double the number of STEM PhDs as the United States every year. More than four hundred "key state laboratories" anchor a lavishly funded public-private research system covering everything from molecular biology to chip design. In the early years of the twenty-first century, China's R&D spending was just 12 percent of America's. By 2020, it was 90 percent. On current trends it will be significantly ahead by the mid-2020s, as it already is on patent applications.

China was the first country to land a probe on the dark side of the moon. No other country had even attempted this. It has more of the world's top five hundred supercomputers than anywhere else. The BGI Group, a Shenzhen-based genetics giant, has extraordinary DNA sequencing capacity, both private and state backing, thousands of scientists, and vast reserves of DNA data and computing capacity alike. Xi Jinping has explicitly called for a "robot revolution": China installs as many robots as the rest of the world combined. It built hypersonic missiles thought years away by the United States, is a world leader in fields from 6G communications to photovoltaics, and is home to major tech companies like Tencent, Alibaba, DJI, Huawei, and ByteDance.

Quantum computing is an area of notable Chinese expertise. In the wake of Edward Snowden's leak of classified information from U.S. intelligence programs, China became particularly paranoid and keen to build a secure communications platform. Another Sputnik moment. In 2014, China filed the same number of quantum technology patents as the United States; by 2018 it had filed twice as many.

In 2016, China sent the world's first "quantum satellite," Micius, into space, part of a new, supposedly secure communications infrastructure. But Micius was only the start in China's quest for an unhackable quantum internet. A year later the Chinese built a two-thousand-kilometer quantum link between Shanghai and Beijing for transmitting secure financial and military information. They're investing more than $10 billion in creating the National Laboratory for Quantum Information Sciences in Hefei, the world's biggest such facility. They hold records for linking qubits together via quantum entanglement, an important step on the road to fully fledged quantum computers. Hefei scientists even claimed to have built a quantum computer 10^{14} times faster than Google's breakthrough Sycamore.

Micius's lead researcher and one of the world's top quantum scientists, Pan Jianwei, made clear what this means. "I think we have started a worldwide quantum space race," he said. "With modern information science, China has been a learner and a follower. Now, with quantum technology, if we try our best we can be one of the main players."

The West's persistent dismissals over decades about China's capabilities "not being creative" were badly wrong. We said they were only good at imitating, were too restricted and unfree, that state-owned enterprises were terrible. In hindsight, most of these assessments were plain wrong, and where they had merit, they did not stop China from emerging as a modern-day titan in science and engineering—not least because legal transfers of IP like buying companies and translating journals were backed with outright theft, forced transfers, reverse engineering, and espionage operations.

Meanwhile, the United States is losing its strategic lead. For years it was obvious that America held supremacy in everything from semiconductor design to pharmaceuticals, the invention of the internet to the world's most sophisticated military technology. It's not gone, but it's going. A report by Harvard's Graham Allison argues that the situation is far more serious than most in the West appreciate. China is already ahead of the United States in green energy, 5G, and AI and is on a trajectory to overtake it in quantum and biotech in the next few years. The Pentagon's first chief software officer resigned in protest in 2021 because he was so dismayed by the situation. "We have no competing fighting chance against China in 15 to 20 years. Right now, it's already a done deal; it is already over in my opinion," he told the *Financial Times*.

Shortly after becoming president in 2013, Xi Jinping made a speech with lasting consequences for China—and for the rest of the world. "Advanced technology is the sharp weapon of the modern state," he declared. "Our technology still generally lags that of developed countries and we must adopt an asymmetric strategy of catching up and overtaking."

It was a powerful analysis and, as we have seen, a statement of China's policy priorities. But unlike much of what Xi says, any world leader could credibly make the same point. Any U.S. or Brazilian president, German chancellor, or Indian prime minister would subscribe to the central thesis—that technology is a "sharp weapon" enabling countries to "hold sway." Xi was stating a bald truth, the self-declared mantra of not just China but virtually every state, from superpower leaders at the frontier to isolated pariahs: who builds, owns, and deploys technology matters.

THE ARMS RACE

Technology has become the world's most important strategic asset, not so much the instrument of foreign policy as the driver of it. The great power struggles of the twenty-first century are predicated on technological superiority—a race to control the coming wave. Tech companies and universities are no longer seen as neutral but as major national champions.

Political will could disrupt or cancel the other incentives discussed in this chapter. A government could—in theory—rein in research incentives, clamp down on private business, curtail ego-driven initiatives. But it cannot wave away hard-edged competition from its geopolitical rivals. Choosing to limit technological development when perceived adversaries pile forward is, in the logic of an arms race, choosing to lose.

For a long time I objected, resisting the framing of technological progress as a zero-sum international arms race. At DeepMind, I always pushed back on references to us as a Manhattan Project for AI, not just because of the nuclear comparison, but because even the framing might initiate a series of other Manhattan Projects, feeding an arms race dynamic when close global coordination, break points, and slowdowns were needed. But the reality is that the logic of nation-states is at times painfully simple and yet utterly inevitable. In the context of a state's national security, merely floating an idea becomes dangerous. Once the words are out, the starting gun is fired, the rhetoric itself producing a drastic national response. And then it spirals.

Countless friends and colleagues in Washington and Brussels, in government, in think tanks, and in academia would all trot out the same infuriating line: "Even if we are not actually in an arms race, we must assume 'they' think we are, and therefore we must ourselves race to achieve a decisive strategic advantage since this new technological wave might completely rebalance global power." This attitude becomes a self-fulfilling prophecy.

There's no use in pretending. Great power competition with China is one of the few areas enjoying bipartisan agreement in Washington. The debate now isn't whether we are in a technological and AI arms race; it's where it will lead.

The arms race is usually presented as a Sino-American duopoly. This is myopic. While it's true these countries are the most advanced and well resourced, many others are significant participants. This new era of arms races heralds the rise of widespread techno-nationalism, in which multiple countries will be locked in an ever-escalating competition to gain a decisive geopolitical advantage.

Almost every country now has a detailed AI strategy. Vladimir Putin believes the leader in AI "will become the ruler of the world." French president Emmanuel Macron declares that "we will fight to build a European metaverse." His wider point is that Europe has failed to build the tech giants of the United States and China, produces fewer breakthroughs, and lacks both IP and manufacturing capacity in critical portions of the tech ecosystem. Security, wealth, prestige—all rest, for Europe, in his view and that of many others, on becoming a third power.

Countries have different strengths, from bioscience and AI (like the U.K.) to robotics (Germany, Japan, and South Korea) to cybersecurity (Israel). Each has major R&D programs across portions of the coming wave, with burgeoning civilian start-up ecosystems increasingly backed by the hard force of perceived military necessity.

India is an obvious fourth pillar to a new global order of giants, alongside the United States, China, and the EU. Its population is young and entrepreneurial, increasingly urbanized, and ever more connected and tech savvy. By 2030 its economy will have passed those of countries like the U.K., Germany, and Japan to be the third largest in the world; by 2050, it will be worth $30 trillion.

Its government is determined to make Indian tech a reality. Through its Atmanirbhar Bharat (Self-Reliant India) program, India's government is working to ensure the world's most populous country achieves ownership of core technology systems competitive with the United States and China. Under it, India established partnerships with, for example, Japan on AI and robotics, as well as Israel for drones and unmanned aerial vehicles. Prepare for an Indian wave.

IN WORLD WAR II the Manhattan Project, which consumed 0.4 percent of U.S. GDP, was seen as a race against time to get the bomb before the Germans. But the Nazis had initially ruled out pursuit of nuclear weapons, considering them too expensive and speculative. The Soviets were far behind and eventually relied on extensive leaks from the United States. America had conducted an arms race against phantoms, bringing nuclear weapons into the world far earlier than under other circumstances.

Something similar occurred in the late 1950s, when, in the wake of a Soviet ICBM test and Sputnik, Pentagon decision-makers became convinced of an alarming "missile gap" with the Russians. It later emerged that the United States had a ten-to-one advantage at the time of the key report. Khrushchev was following a tried-and-tested Soviet strategy: bluffing. Misreading the other side meant nuclear weapons and ICBMs were both brought forward by decades.

Could this same mistaken dynamic be playing out in the current technological arms races? Actually, no. First, the coming wave's proliferation risk is acute. Because these technologies are getting cheaper and simpler to use even as they get more powerful, more nations can engage at the frontier. Large language models are still seen as cutting-edge, yet there is no great magic or hidden state secret to them. Access to computation is likely the biggest bottleneck, but plenty of services exist to make it happen. The same goes for CRISPR or DNA synthesis.

We can already see achievements like China's moon landing or India's billion-strong biometric identification system, Aadhaar, happening in real time. It's no mystery that China has enormous LLMs, Taiwan is the leader in semiconductors, South Korea has world-class expertise in robots, and governments everywhere are announcing and implementing detailed technology strategies. This is happening out in the open, shared in patents and at academic conferences, reported in *Wired* and the *Financial Times,* broadcast live on Bloomberg.

Declaring an arms race is no longer a conjuring act, a self-fulfilling prophecy. The prophecy has been fulfilled. It's here, it's happening. It is a point so obvious it doesn't often get mentioned: there is no central authority controlling what technologies get developed, who does it, and for what purpose; technology is an orchestra with no conductor. Yet this single fact could end up being the most significant of the twenty-first century.

And if the phrase "arms race" triggers worry, that's with good reason. There could hardly be a more precarious foundation for a set of escalating technologies than the perception (and reality) of a zero-sum competition built on fear. There are, however, other, more positive drivers of technology to consider.

KNOWLEDGE JUST WANTS TO BE FREE

Raw curiosity, the quest for truth, the importance of openness, evidence-based peer review—these are core values for scientific and technological research. Since the Scientific Revolution and its industrial equivalents in the eighteenth and nineteenth centuries, scientific discoveries have not been hoarded like secret jewels but shared openly in journals, books, salons, and public lectures. The patent system created a mechanism for sharing knowledge while rewarding risk-taking. Broad access to information became an engine of our civilization.

Openness is science and technology's cardinal ideology. What is known must be shared; what is discovered must be published. Science and technology live and breathe on free debate and the open sharing of information, to the extent that openness has itself grown into a powerful (and amazingly beneficial) incentive.

We live in an age of what Audrey Kurth Cronin calls "open technological innovation." A global system of developing knowledge and technology is now so sprawling and open that it's almost impossible to steer, govern, or, if need be, shut down. The ability to understand, create, build on, and adapt technology is highly distributed as a result. Obscure work done by a computer science grad student one year might be in the hands of hundreds of millions of users the next. That makes it hard to predict or control. Sure, tech companies want to keep their

secrets, but they also tend to abide by the open philosophies characterizing software development and academia. Innovations diffuse far
faster and further and more disruptively as a result.

The openness imperative saturates research culture. Academia is
built around peer review; any paper not subject to critical scrutiny by
credible peers doesn't meet the gold standard. Funders don't like supporting work that stays locked away. Both institutions and researchers
pay careful attention to their publication records and how often their
papers are cited. More citations mean more prestige, credibility, and
research funding. Junior researchers are especially liable to be judged—
and hired—on their publication record, publicly viewable on platforms
like Google Scholar. Moreover, these days papers are announced on
Twitter and often written with social media influence in mind. They
are designed to be eye-catching and attract attention.

Academics fervently argue for open access to their research. In
tech, strong norms around sharing and contributing support a flourishing space of open-source software. Some of the world's biggest
companies—Alphabet, Meta, Microsoft—regularly contribute huge
amounts of IP for free. In areas like AI and synthetic biology, where
the lines between scientific research and technological development
are especially blurred, all of this makes the culture default to open.

At DeepMind we learned early that opportunities to publish were a
key factor when leading researchers decided where to work. They
wanted the openness and peer recognition they'd gotten used to in academia. Soon it became standard in leading AI labs: while not everything would be immediately made public, openness was considered a
strategic advantage in attracting the best scientists. Meanwhile publication records are an important part of getting hired at leading technology labs, while competition is intense, a race for who goes public first.

All in all, to a degree that is perhaps underappreciated, publication
and sharing aren't just about the process of falsification in science.
They're also for prestige, for peers, for the pursuit of a mission, for the
sake of a job, for likes. All of it both drives and accelerates the process
of technological development.

Huge amounts of AI data and code are public. For example, GitHub
has 190 million repositories of code, many of which are public. Aca-

demic preprint servers enable researchers to quickly upload work without any review or filtration mechanism. The original such service, arXiv, hosts more than two million papers. Dozens of more specialized preprint services, like bioRxiv in the life sciences, fuel the process. The great stock of the world's scientific and technical papers is either accessible on the open web or available via easy-to-get institutional log-ins. This slots into a world where cross-border funding and collaboration are the norm; where projects often have hundreds of researchers freely sharing information; where thousands of tutorials and courses on state-of-the-art techniques are readily available online.

All of this takes place in the context of a turbocharged research landscape. Worldwide R&D spending is at well over $700 billion annually, hitting record highs. Amazon's R&D budget alone is $78 billion, which would be the ninth biggest in the world if it were a country. Alphabet, Apple, Huawei, Meta, and Microsoft all spend well in excess of $20 billion a year on R&D. All these companies, those most keenly investing in the coming wave, those with the most lavish budgets, have a track record of openly publishing their research.

The future is remarkably open-source, published on arXiv, documented on GitHub. It's being built for citations, research kudos, and the promise of tenure. Both the imperative of openness and the sheer mass of easily available research material mean this is an inherently deep-rooted and widely distributed set of incentives and foundations for future research that no one can fully govern.

PREDICTING ANYTHING AT THE frontier is tricky. If you want to direct the research process, to steer it toward or away from certain outcomes, to contain it ahead of time, you face multiple challenges. Not only is there the question of how you might coordinate between competing groups, but there's the fact that at the frontier it's also impossible to predict where breakthroughs might come from.

CRISPR gene editing technology, for example, has its roots in work done by the Spanish researcher Francisco Mojica, who wanted to understand how some single-celled organisms thrive in brackish water. Mojica soon stumbled across repeating sequences of DNA that would be a key part of CRISPR. These clustered repeating sections seemed important. He came up with the name CRISPR. Later work from two researchers at a Danish yogurt company looked at protecting the bacteria vital for starter cultures in the yogurt's fermentation process. It helped show how the core mechanisms might function. These unlikely avenues are the foundation for arguably the biggest biotech story of the twenty-first century.

Likewise, fields can stall for decades but then change dramatically in months. Neural networks spent decades in the wilderness, trashed by luminaries like Marvin Minsky. Only a few isolated researchers like Geoffrey Hinton and Yann LeCun kept them going through a period when the word "neural" was so controversial that researchers would deliberately remove it from their papers. It seemed impossible in the 1990s, but neural networks came to dominate AI. And yet it was also LeCun who said AlphaGo was impossible just days before it made its first big breakthrough. That's no discredit to him; it just shows that no one can ever be sure of anything at the research frontier.

Even in hardware the path toward AI was impossible to predict. GPUs—graphics processing units—are a foundational part of modern AI. But they were first developed to deliver ever more realistic graphics in computer games. In an illustration of the omni-use nature of technology, fast parallel processing for flashy graphics turned out to be perfect for training deep neural networks. It's ultimately luck that demand for photorealistic gaming meant companies like NVIDIA invested so much into making better hardware, and that this then adapted so well to machine learning. (NVIDIA wasn't complaining; its share price rose 1,000 percent in the five years after AlexNet.)

If you were looking to monitor and direct AI research in the past, you would likely have got it wrong, blocking or boosting work that eventually proved irrelevant, entirely missing the most important breakthroughs quietly brewing on the sidelines. Science and technology research is inherently unpredictable, exceptionally open, and growing fast. Governing or controlling it is therefore immensely difficult.

Today's world is optimized for curiosity, sharing, and research at a pace never seen before. Modern research works against containment. So too do the necessity and desire to make a profit.

THE $100 TRILLION
OPPORTUNITY

In 1830, the first passenger railway opened between Liverpool and Manchester. Building this marvel of engineering had required an act of Parliament. The route needed bridges, cut-throughs, elevated sections over boggy ground, and settling of seemingly endless property disputes: all titanic challenges. The railway's opening was attended by dignitaries including the prime minister and Liverpool's MP, William Huskisson. During the celebration the crowd stood on the tracks to welcome the new marvel as it approached. So unfamiliar was this striking machine that people failed to appreciate the speed of the oncoming train, and Huskisson himself was killed under the locomotive's wheels. To the horrified spectators George Stephenson's steam-powered Rocket was monstrous, an alien, belching, terrifying blur of modernity and machinery.

Yet it was also a sensation, faster than anything then experienced. Growth was rapid. Two hundred and fifty passengers a day had been forecast; twelve hundred a day were using it after only a month. Hundreds of tons of cotton could be hauled from the Liverpool docks to the Manchester mills with minimum fuss in record time. Five years in, it was delivering a dividend of 10 percent, presaging an 1830s mini-boom in railway construction. The government saw an opportunity for more. In 1844, a young MP called William Gladstone put forward the Railway Regulation Act to supercharge investment. Companies submitted hundreds of applications to build new railways in just a few months in 1845. While the rest of the stock market flatlined, railway companies boomed. Investors piled in. At their peak, railway stocks accounted for more than two-thirds of total stock market value.

Within a year the crash had started. The market eventually bottomed out in 1850, 66 percent lower than its peak. Easy profit, not for the first or last time, had made people greedy and foolish. Thousands lost everything. Nonetheless, a new era had arrived with the boom. With the locomotive, an older and bucolic world was torn to shreds in a blitz of viaducts and tunnels, cuttings and great stations, coal smoke and whistles. From a few scattered lines, the investment craze created the outlines of an integrated national network. It shrank the country. In the 1830s a journey between London and Edinburgh took days in an uncomfortable stagecoach. By the 1850s it took a single train under twelve hours. Connection to the rest of the country meant towns, cities, and regions boomed. Tourism, trade, and family life were transformed. Among many other impacts, it created the need for a standardized national time to make sense of the timetables. And it was all done thanks to a relentless thirst for profit.

THE RAILWAY BOOM OF the 1840s was "arguably the greatest bubble in history." But in the annals of technology, it is more norm than exception. There was nothing inevitable about the coming of the railways, but there was something inevitable about the chance to make money. Carlota Perez sees an equivalent "frenzy phase" as being part of every major technology rollout for at least the last two hundred years, from the original telephone cables to contemporary high-bandwidth internet. The boom never lasts, but the raw speculative drive produces lasting change, a new technological substrate.

The truth is that the curiosity of academic researchers or the will of motivated governments is insufficient to propel new breakthroughs into the hands of billions of consumers. Science has to be converted into useful and desirable products for it to truly spread far and wide. Put simply: most technology is made to earn money.

If anything, this is perhaps the most persistent, entrenched, dispersed incentive of all. Profit drives the Chinese entrepreneur to develop moldings for a radically redesigned phone; it pushes the Dutch farmer to find new robotics and greenhouse technologies to grow tomatoes year-round in the cool climate of the North Sea; it leads suave investors on Palo Alto's Sand Hill Road to invest millions of dollars in untested young entrepreneurs. While the motivations of their individual contributors may vary, Google is building AI, and Amazon is building robots, because as public companies with shareholders to please, they see them as ways to make a profit.

And this, the potential for profit, is built on something even more long-lasting and robust: raw demand. People both want and need the fruits of technology. People need food, or refrigeration, or telecoms to live their lives; they might want AC units, or a new kind of shoe design requiring some intricate new manufacturing technique, or some kind of revolutionary new food-coloring method for cupcakes, or any of the innumerable everyday ends to which technology is put to use. Either way, technology helps provide, and its creators take their cut. The sheer breadth of human wants and needs, and the countless opportunities to profit from them, are integral to the story of technology and will remain so in the future.

This is no bad thing. Go back just a few hundred years and economic growth was almost nonexistent. Living standards stagnated for centuries at unfathomably worse levels than today. In the last two hundred years, economic output is up more than three hundred times. Per capita GDP has risen at least thirteenfold over the same period, and in the very richest parts of the world it has risen a hundredfold. At the beginning of the nineteenth century, almost everyone lived in extreme poverty. Now, globally, this sits at around 9 percent. Exponential improvements in the human condition, once impossible, are routine.

At root, this is a story of systematically applying science and technology in the name of profit. This in turn drove huge leaps in output and living standards. In the nineteenth century, inventions like Cyrus McCormick's threshing machine led to a 500 percent increase in output of wheat per hour. Isaac Singer's sewing machine meant sewing a shirt went from taking fourteen hours to just one hour. In developed economies, people work far less than they used to for far more reward. In Germany, for example, annual working hours have decreased by nearly 60 percent since 1870.

Technology entered a virtuous circle of creating wealth that could be reinvested in further technological development, all of which drove up living standards. But none of these long-term goals were really the primary objective of any single individual. In chapter 1, I argued that almost everything around you is a product of human intelligence. Here's a slight correction: much of what we see around us is powered by human intelligence in direct pursuit of monetary gain.

This engine has created a world economy worth $85 trillion—and counting. From the pioneers of the Industrial Revolution to the Silicon Valley entrepreneurs of today, technology has a magnetic incentive in the form of serious financial rewards. The coming wave represents the greatest economic prize in history. It is a consumer cornucopia and potential profit center without parallel. Anyone looking to contain it must explain how a distributed, global, capitalist system of unbridled power can be persuaded to temper its acceleration, let alone leave it on the table.

WHEN A CORPORATION AUTOMATES insurance claims or adopts a new manufacturing technique, it creates efficiency savings or improves the product, boosting profits and attracting new customers. Once an innovation delivers a competitive advantage like this, everyone must either adopt it, leapfrog it, switch focus, or lose market share and eventually go bust. The attitude around this dynamic in technology businesses in particular is simple and ruthless: build the next generation of technology or be destroyed.

No surprise, then, that corporations play such a large role in the coming wave. Tech is by far the biggest single category in the S&P 500, constituting 26 percent of the index. Between them the major tech groups have cash on hand equivalent to the GDP of an economy like Taiwan's or Poland's. Capital expenditure, like R&D spending, is enormous, exceeding the oil majors, previously the biggest spenders. Anyone following the industry of late will have witnessed an increasingly intense commercial race around AI, with firms like Google, Microsoft, and OpenAI vying week by week to launch new products.

Hundreds of billions of dollars of venture capital and private equity are deployed into countless start-ups. Investment in AI technologies alone has hit $100 billion a year. These big numbers do actually matter. Huge quantities of capital expenditure, R&D spending, venture capital, and private equity investment, unmatched by any other sector, or any government outside China and the United States, are the raw fuel powering the coming wave. All of this money demands a return, and the technology it creates is the means of getting it.

As with the Industrial Revolution, potential economic rewards are enormous. Estimates are hard to intuit. PwC forecasts AI will add $15.7 *trillion* to the global economy by 2030. McKinsey forecasts a $4 trillion boost from biotech over the same period. Boosting world robot installations 30 percent above a baseline forecast could unleash a $5 trillion dividend, a sum bigger than Germany's entire output. Especially when other sources of growth are increasingly scarce, these are strong incentives. With profits this high, interrupting the gold rush is likely to be incredibly challenging.

Are these predictions justified? The numbers are certainly eye-watering. Plucking huge numbers out of the near future is easy to do on paper. But over a slightly longer time frame, they are not entirely unreasonable. The total addressable market here eventually extends, like the First or Second Industrial Revolution, to the entire world economy. Someone in the late eighteenth century would have been incredulous at the idea of a hundredfold increase in per capita GDP. It would have seemed ludicrous to even contemplate. Yet it happened. Given all those forecasts and the fundamental areas addressed by the coming wave, even a 10–15 percent boost to the world economy in the next decade might be conservative. Over the longer term it is likely much bigger than that.

Consider that the world economy grew sixfold in the latter half of the twentieth century. Even if growth slowed to just a third of that level over the next fifty years, it would still unlock around $100 trillion of additional GDP.

Think about the impact of the new wave of AI systems. Large language models enable you to have a useful conversation with an AI about any topic in fluent, natural language. Within the next couple of years, whatever your job, you will be able to consult an on-demand expert, ask it about your latest ad campaign or product design, quiz it on the specifics of a legal dilemma, isolate the most effective elements of a pitch, solve a thorny logistical question, get a second opinion on a diagnosis, keep probing and testing, getting ever more detailed answers grounded in the very cutting edge of knowledge, delivered with exceptional nuance. All of the world's knowledge, best practices, precedent, and computational power will be available, tailored to you, to your specific needs and circumstances, instantaneously and effortlessly. It is a leap in cognitive potential at least as great as the introduction of the internet. And that is before you even get into the implications of something like ACI and the Modern Turing Test.

Little is ultimately more valuable than intelligence. Intelligence is the wellspring and the director, architect, and facilitator of the world economy. The more we expand the range and nature of intelligences on offer, the more growth should be possible. With generalist AI, plausible economic scenarios suggest it could lead not just to a boost in growth but to a permanent acceleration in the rate of growth itself. In blunt economic terms, AI *could*, long term, be the most valuable technology yet, more so when coupled with the potential of synthetic biology, robotics, and the rest.

Those investments aren't passive; they will play a big part in making it become so, another self-fulfilling prophecy fulfilled. Those trillions represent a huge value add and opportunity for society, delivering better living standards for billions as well as immense profits for private interests. Either way, that creates an ingrained incentive to keep finding and rolling out new technologies.

GLOBAL CHALLENGES

For most of history simply feeding yourself and your family was the dominant challenge of human life. Farming has always been a hard, uncertain business. But especially prior to the improvements of the twentieth century, it was much, much harder. Any variation in weather conditions—too cold, hot, dry, or wet—could be catastrophic. Almost everything was done by hand, maybe with the help of some oxen if you were lucky. At some times of the year there was little to do; at others, there were weeks of unceasing, backbreaking physical labor.

Crops could be ruined by disease or pests, spoil after harvesting, or get stolen by invading armies. Most farmers lived hand to mouth, often working as serfs, giving up much of their scant crop. Even in the most productive parts of the world, yields were low and fragile. Life was tough, lived on the edge of disaster. When Thomas Malthus argued in 1798 that a fast-growing population would quickly exhaust the carrying capacity of agriculture and lead to a collapse, he wasn't wrong; static yields would and often did follow this rule.

What he hadn't accounted for was the scale of human ingenuity. Assuming favorable weather conditions and using the latest techniques, in the thirteenth century each hectare of wheat in England yielded around half a ton. There it remained for centuries. Slowly the arrival of new techniques and technologies changed all that: from crop rotation to selective breeding, mechanized plows, synthetic fertilizer, pesticides, genetic modifications, and now even AI-optimized planting and weeding. In the twenty-first century, yields are now at about eight tons per hectare. The very same small, innocuous patch of ground, the same geography and soil that was reaped in the thirteenth century, can now deliver sixteen times the crop. Corn yields per hectare in the United States have tripled in the last fifty years. The labor required to produce a kilo of grain has fallen 98 percent since the beginning of the nineteenth century.

In 1945, around 50 percent of the world's population was seriously undernourished. Today, despite a population well over three times bigger, that's down to 10 percent. This still represents upwards of 600 million people, an unconscionable number. But at 1945 rates it would be 4 billion, although in truth those people could not have been kept alive. It's easy to overlook how far we've come, and just how remarkable innovation really is. What would the medieval farmer have given for the vast combines, the epic irrigation systems of a modern farmer? To them, a sixteenfold improvement would be nothing less than a miracle. It is.

Feeding the world is still an enormous challenge. But this need has driven technology on and led to an abundance unimaginable in previous times: food sufficient, if not adequately distributed, for the planet's eight billion and rising human inhabitants.

Technology, as in the case of food supply, is a vital part of addressing the challenges humanity inevitably faces today and will face tomorrow. We pursue new technologies, including those in the coming wave, not just because we want them, but because, at a fundamental level, we *need* them.

IT'S LIKELY THAT THE world is heading for two degrees Celsius of climate warming or more. Every second of every day biospheric boundaries—from freshwater use to biodiversity loss—are breached. Even the most resilient, temperate, and wealthy countries will suffer disastrous heat waves and droughts, storms and water stress in the decades ahead. Crops will fail. Wildfires rage. Vast quantities of methane will escape the melting permafrost, threatening a feedback loop of extreme heating. Disease will spread far beyond its usual ranges. Climate refugees and conflict will engulf the world as sea levels inexorably rise, threatening major population centers. Marine and land-based ecosystems face collapse.

Despite well-justified talk of a clean energy transition, the distance still to travel is vast. Hydrocarbons' energy density is incredibly hard to replicate for tasks like powering airplanes or container ships. While clean electricity generation is expanding fast, electricity accounts for only about 25 percent of global energy output. The other 75 percent is much trickier to transition. Since the start of the twenty-first century global energy use is up 45 percent, but the share coming from fossil fuels only fell from 87 to 84 percent—meaning fossil fuel use is greatly up despite all the moves into clean electricity as a power source.

The energy scholar Vaclav Smil calls ammonia, cement, plastics, and steel the four pillars of modern civilization: the material base underwriting modern society, each hugely carbon-intensive to produce, with no obvious successors. Without these materials modern life stops, and without fossil fuels the materials stop. The last thirty years saw 700 billion carbon-spewing tons of concrete sluiced out into our societies. How to replace that? Electric vehicles may not emit carbon when being driven, but they are resource hungry nonetheless: materials for just one EV require extracting around 225 tons of finite raw materials, demand for which is already spiking unsustainably.

Food production, as we have seen, is a major success story of technology. But from tractors in fields, to synthetic fertilizers, to plastic greenhouses, it's saturated in fossil fuels. Imagine the average tomato soaked in five tablespoons of oil. That's how much went into growing it. What's more, to meet global demand, agriculture will need to produce almost 50 percent more food by 2050 just as yields decline in the face of climate change.

If we are to stand any chance of keeping global warming under two degrees Celsius, then the world's scientists working under the UN's Intergovernmental Panel on Climate Change have been clear: carbon capture and storage is an essential technology. And yet it's largely not been invented or is still to be deployed at scale. To meet this global challenge, we'll have to reengineer our agricultural, manufacturing, transport, and energy systems from the ground up with new technologies that are carbon neutral or probably even carbon negative. These are not inconsiderable tasks. In practice it means rebuilding the entire infrastructure of modern society while hopefully also offering quality-of-life improvements to billions.

Humanity has no choice but to meet challenges like these, and many others such as how to deliver ever more expensive health care to aging populations beset with intractable chronic conditions. Here, then, is another powerful incentive: a vital part of how we flourish in the face of daunting tasks that seem beyond us. There's a strong moral case for new technologies beyond profit or advantage.

Technology can and will improve lives and solve problems. Think of a world populated by trees that are longer lived and absorb much greater amounts of CO_2. Or phytoplanktons that help the oceans become a greater and more sustainable carbon sink. AI has helped design an enzyme that can break down the plastic clogging our oceans. It will also be an important part of how we predict what is coming, from guessing where a wildfire might hit suburbia to tracking deforestation through public data sets. This will be a world of cheap, personalized drugs; fast, accurate diagnoses; and AI-generated replacements for energy-intensive fertilizers.

Sustainable, scalable batteries need radical new technologies. Quantum computers paired with AI, with their ability to model down to the molecular level, could play a critical role in finding substitutes to conventional lithium batteries that are lighter, cheaper, cleaner, easier to produce and recycle, and more plentiful. Likewise on work with photovoltaic materials, or drug discovery, that enables molecular-level simulations to identify new compounds—far more precise and powerful than using the slow experimental techniques of the past. This is hyper-evolution in action, and it promises to save billions in R&D while going far beyond the present research paradigm.

A school of naive techno-solutionism sees technology as the answer to all of the world's problems. Alone, it's not. How it is created, used, owned, and managed all make a difference. No one should pretend that technology is a near-magical answer to something as multifaceted and immense as climate change. But the idea that we can meet the century's defining challenges without new technologies is completely fanciful. It's also worth remembering that the technologies of the wave will make life easier, healthier, more productive, and more enjoyable for billions. They will save time, cost, hassle, and millions of lives. The significance of this should not be trivialized or forgotten amid the uncertainty.

The coming wave is coming partly because there is no way through without it. Mega-scale, systemic forces like this drive technology forward. But another, more personal force is in my experience ever present and largely underestimated: ego.

EGO

Scientists and technologists are all too human. They crave status, success, and a legacy. They want to be the first and best and recognized as such. They're competitive and clever with a carefully nurtured sense of their place in the world and in history. They love pushing boundaries, sometimes for money but often for glory, sometimes just for its own sake. AI scientists and engineers are among the best-paid people in the world, and yet what really gets them out of bed is the prospect of being first to a breakthrough or seeing their name on a landmark paper. Love them or hate them, technology magnates and entrepreneurs are viewed as unique lodestars of power, wealth, vision, and sheer will. Critics and fawning fans alike see them as expressions of ego, excelling at making things happen.

Engineers often have a particular mindset. The Los Alamos director J. Robert Oppenheimer was a highly principled man. But above all else he was a curiosity-driven problem solver. Consider these words, in their own way as chilling as his famous Bhagavad Gita quotation (on seeing the first nuclear test, he recalled some lines from Hindu scripture: "Now I am become Death, the destroyer of worlds"): "When you see something that is technically sweet, you go ahead and do it, and you argue about what to do about it only after you have had your technical success." It was an attitude shared by his colleague on the Manhattan Project, the brilliant, polymathic Hungarian American John von Neumann. "What we are creating now," he said, "is a monster whose influence is going to change history, provided there is any history left, yet it would be impossible not to see it through, not only for military reasons, but it would also be unethical from the point of view of the scientists not to do what they know is feasible, no matter what terrible consequences it may have."

Spend enough time in technical environments and, despite all the talk about ethics and social responsibility, you will come to recognize the prevalence of this view, even when facing technologies of extreme power. I have seen it many times, and I'd probably be lying if I said I haven't succumbed to it myself on occasion as well.

Making history, doing something that matters, helping others, beating others, impressing a prospective partner, impressing a boss, peers, rivals: it's all in there, all part of the ever-present drive to take risks, explore the edges, go further into the unknown. Build something new. Change the game. Climb the mountain.

Whether noble and high-minded or bitter and zero-sum, when you work on technology, it's often this aspect, even more than the needs of states or the imperatives of distant shareholders, animating progress. Find a successful scientist or technologist and somewhere in there you will see someone driven by raw ego, spurred on by emotive impulses that might sound base or even unethical but are nonetheless an under-recognized part of why we get the technologies we do. The Silicon Valley mythos of the heroic start-up founder single-handedly empire building in the face of a hostile and ignorant world is persistent for a reason. It is the self-image technologists too often still aspire to, an archetype to emulate, a fantasy that still drives new technologies.

NATIONALISM, CAPITALISM, AND SCIENCE—these are, by now, embedded features of the world. Simply removing them from the scene is not possible in any meaningful time frame. Altruism and curiosity, arrogance and competition, the desire to win the race, make your name, save your people, help the world, whatever it may be: these are what propel the wave on, and these cannot be expunged or circumvented.

Moreover, these different incentives and elements of the wave compound. National arms races dovetail with corporate rivalries while labs and researchers spur each other on. A nested series of sub-races, in other words, adds up to a complex, mutually reinforcing dynamic. Technology "emerges" through countless independent contributions all layering on top of one another, a metastasizing, entangled morass of ideas unraveling themselves, driven on by deep-rooted and dispersed incentives.

Without tools to spread information at light speed, people in the past could happily sit with new technologies staring them in the face sometimes for decades before they realized their full implications. And even when they did, it would take a lot of time, and ultimately imagination, to fully realize the broad ramifications. Today the world is watching everyone else react in real time.

Everything leaks. Everything is copied, iterated, improved. And because everyone is watching and learning from everyone else, with so many people all scratching around in the same areas, someone is inevitably going to figure out the next big breakthrough. And they will have no hope of containing it, for even if they do, someone else will come behind them and uncover the same insight or find an adjacent way of doing the same thing; they will see the strategic potential or profit or prestige and go after it.

This is why we won't say no. This is why the coming wave *is* coming, why containing it is such a challenge. Technology is now an indispensable mega-system infusing every aspect of daily life, society, and the economy. No one can do without it. Entrenched incentives are in place for more of it, radically more. No one is in full control of what it does or where it goes next. This is not some far-out philosophical concept or extreme determinist scenario or wild-eyed California technocentrism. It is a basic description of the world we all inhabit, indeed the world we have inhabited for quite some time.

In this sense it feels like technology is, to use an unforgiving image, one big slime mold slowly rolling toward an inevitable future, with billions of tiny contributions being made by each individual academic or entrepreneur without any coordination or ability to resist. Powerful attractors pull it on. Where blocks appear, gaps open elsewhere, and the whole rolls forward. Slowing these technologies is antithetical to national, corporate, and research interests.

This is the ultimate collective action problem. The idea that CRISPR or AI can be put back in the box is not credible. Until someone can create a plausible path to dismantling these interlocking incentives, the option of not building, saying no, perhaps even just slowing down or taking a different path isn't there.

Containing technology means short-circuiting all these mutually reinforcing dynamics. It's hard to envisage how that might be done on any kind of timescale that would affect the coming wave. There is only one entity that could, perhaps, provide the solution, one that anchors our political system and takes final responsibility for the technologies society produces: the nation-state.

But there's a problem. States are already facing massive strain, and the coming wave looks set to make things much more complicated. The consequences of this collision will shape the rest of the century.

PART III

STATES OF FAILURE

CHAPTER 9

THE GRAND BARGAIN

THE PROMISE OF THE STATE

A T ITS HEART, THE NATION-STATE, *THE* CENTRAL UNIT OF THE world's political order today, offers its citizens a simple and highly persuasive bargain: that not only is centralization of power in the sovereign, territorial state possible but its benefits far outweigh the risks. History suggests that a monopoly over violence—that is, entrusting the state with wide latitude to enforce laws and develop its military powers—is the surest way to enable peace and prosperity. That, moreover, a well-managed country is a key foundation of economic growth, security, and well-being. Over the last five hundred years centralizing power in a singular authority has been essential to keeping the peace, unleashing the creative talents of billions of people to work hard, seek out education, invent, trade, and, in doing so, drive progress.

Even as it grows more powerful and entangled with everyday life, the grand bargain of the nation-state, therefore, is that not only can centralized power enable peace and prosperity, but this power can be contained using a series of checks, balances, redistributions, and institutional forms. We often take for granted the delicate balance that has to be struck between extremes to maintain this. On the one hand the most dystopian excesses of centralized power must be avoided, and on the other we must accept regular intervention to maintain order.

Today, more so than at any time in history, the technologies of the coming wave threaten to unsettle this fragile equilibrium. Put simply, the grand bargain is fracturing, and technology is a critical driver of this historic transformation.

Given that nation-states are charged with managing and regulating the impact of technology in the best interests of their populations, how prepared are they for what's to come? If the state is unable to coordinate the containment of this wave, unable to ensure it is of net benefit to its citizens, what options does that leave humanity in the medium to long term?

In the book's first two sections, we saw that a wave of powerful technologies is about to crash over us. Now it's time to consider what this means and glimpse a world after the deluge.

In this third section of the book, we grapple with the profound consequences of these technologies for the nation-state and for the liberal democratic nation-state above all. Cracks are already forming. The political order that fostered rising wealth, better living standards, growing education, science, and technology, a world tending toward peace, is now under immense strain, destabilized in part by the very forces it helped engender. The full implications are sprawling and hard to fathom, but to me they indicate a future where the challenge of containment is harder than ever, where the century's great dilemma becomes inevitable.

LESSONS FROM COPENHAGEN:
POLITICS IS PERSONAL

I've always passionately believed in the power of the state to improve lives. Before my career in AI, I worked in government and the nonprofit sector. I helped start a charity telephone counseling service when I was nineteen, worked for the mayor of London, and co-founded a conflict resolution firm focused on multi-stakeholder negotiation. Working with public servants—people stretched thin and bone-tired, but forever in demand and doing heroic work for those who need it— was enough to show me what a disaster it would be if the state failed.

However, my experience with local government, UN negotiations, and nonprofits also gave me invaluable firsthand knowledge of their limitations. They are often chronically mismanaged, bloated, and slow

to act. One project I facilitated in 2009 at the Copenhagen climate negotiations involved convening hundreds of NGOs and scientific experts
to align their negotiating positions. The idea was to present a coherent
position to 192 squabbling countries at the main summit.

Except we couldn't get consensus on anything. For starters, no
one could agree on the science, or the reality of what was happening
on the ground. Priorities were scattered. There was no consensus on
what would be effective, affordable, or even practical. Could you raise
$10 billion to turn the Amazon into a national park to absorb CO_2? How
are you going to deal with the militias and bribes? Or maybe the answer was to reforest Norway, not Brazil, or was the solution to grow
giant kelp farms instead? As soon as proposals were voiced, someone
spoke up to poke holes in them. Every suggestion was a problem. We
ended up with maximum divergence on all possible things. It was, in
other words, politics as usual.

And this involved people notionally on the "same team." We hadn't
even gotten to the main event and the real horse-trading. At the Copenhagen summit a morass of states all had their own competing positions.
Now pile on the raw emotion. Negotiators were trying to make decisions with hundreds of people in the room arguing and shouting and
breaking off into groups, all while the clock was ticking, on both the
summit and the planet. I was there trying to help facilitate the process,
perhaps the most complex, high-stakes multiparty negotiation in human
history, but from the start it looked almost impossible. Observing this, I
realized we weren't going to make sufficient progress fast enough. The
timeline was too tight. The issues were too complex. Our institutions
for addressing massive global problems were not fit for purpose.

I saw something similar working for the mayor of London in my
early twenties. My job was to audit the impact of human rights legislation on communities in the city. I interviewed everyone from British
Bangladeshis to local Jewish groups, young and old, of all creeds and
backgrounds. The experience showed how human rights law could
help improve lives in a very practical way. Unlike the United States, the
U.K. has no written constitution protecting people's fundamental
rights. Now local groups could take problems to local authorities and
point out they had legal obligations to protect the most vulnerable;

they couldn't brush them under the carpet. On one level it was inspiring. It gave me hope: institutions could have a codified set of rules about justice. The system could deliver.

But of course, the reality of London politics was very different. In practice everything devolved into excuses, blame shifting, media spinning. Even when there was clear legal responsibility, departments or councils wouldn't respond, would fudge, dodge, and delay. Stasis in the face of real challenges was endemic.

Going into London's city hall, I had just turned twenty-one. It was 2005, and I was naively optimistic. I believed in local government—and the UN, for that matter; to an outsider, they seemed grand, effective institutions where we could work together to tackle the big questions. I thought, like many around that time, that globalism and liberal democracy were defaults, the welcome end state of history. Contact with reality was enough to show the gulf between hopeless ideals and the facts on the ground.

Around that time, I also started to pay attention to something else then taking shape. Facebook was growing at unprecedented speed. Somehow, even as everything from local government to the UN seemed to operate at a glacial pace, this small start-up had grown to more than 100 million monthly users in just a few years. That single fact changed the course of my life. It was very clear to me that some organizations were still capable of highly effective action at scale and they were operating in new spaces, like online platforms.

The idea that technology alone can solve social and political problems is a dangerous delusion. But the idea that they can be solved without technology is also wrongheaded. Seeing the frustrations of public servants up close made me want to find other effective ways to get things done at scale, working not against but in concert with the state to make more productive, fairer, kinder societies.

Technological breakthroughs will help us meet the challenges hinted at in the last section: grow food amid unsustainable temperatures; detect floods, earthquakes, and fires ahead of time; and increase the standard of living for everyone. At a time of spiraling costs and deteriorating services, I see AI and synthetic biology as critical levers to help accelerate progress. They will make health care both higher-quality and more affordable. They will help us invent tools to bring about the transition to renewable energy and combat climate change at a time when politics has stalled, and support teachers, helping to increase the effectiveness of underfunded education systems. This is the real potential of the next wave.

So I embarked on a career in technology, believing that a new generation of tools could amplify our ability to act at scale, operating far more rapidly than traditional policies. Putting them to work to "invent the future" seemed like the best way to spend the most productive years of my life.

I invoke my idealistic streak to put the following chapters into context, to make clear that I regard the often dismal picture painted as a titanic failure of technology and a failure of people like me who build it.

While technology is still the single most powerful avenue for addressing the challenges of the twenty-first century, we cannot ignore downsides. While acknowledging the many benefits, we also must overcome pessimism aversion and take a cold, hard look at what new risks might arise from omni-use technologies. Over time the nature of those risks—and the size of the stakes—have only become clearer. Technology is not just a tool to support the bargain we've made in the nation-state; it is also a genuine threat to it.

An influential minority in the tech industry not only believes that new technologies pose a threat to our ordered world of nation-states; this group actively welcomes its demise. These critics believe that the state is mostly in the way. They argue it's best jettisoned, already so troubled it is beyond rescue. I fundamentally disagree; such an outcome would be a disaster.

I'm British, born and raised in London, but one side of my family is Syrian. My family has been caught up in the terrible war suffered by that country in recent years. I know well what it looks like when states fail, and to put it crudely, it's unimaginably bad. Horrific. And anyone who thinks what happened in Syria could never happen "here" is kidding themselves; people are people wherever they are. Our system of nation-states isn't perfect, far from it. Nonetheless, we must do everything to bolster and protect it. This book, in part, is my attempt to rally to its defense.

Nothing else—no other silver bullet—will arrive in time to save us, to absorb the destabilizing force of the wave. There simply isn't another option in the medium term.

Even in best-case scenarios the coming wave will be an immense shock to the systems governing societies. Before we explore the perils of the wave, it's worth asking about the broad health of nation-states. Are they in any shape to meet the challenges ahead?

FRAGILE STATES

Global living conditions are objectively better today than at any time in the past. We take running water and plentiful food supplies for granted. Most people enjoy warmth and shelter all year round. Literacy rates, life expectancy, and gender equality sit at all-time highs. The sum of thousands of years of human scholarship and inquiry is available at the touch of a button. For most people in developed countries, life is marked by an ease and abundance that would have seemed unbelievable in bygone eras. And yet, under the surface, there's a nagging feeling that something isn't quite right.

Western societies in particular are mired in a deep-seated anxiety; they are "nervous states," impulsive and fractious. This persistent unease is partly the result of previous shocks—multiple financial crises, the pandemic, violence (everything from 9/11 to the Ukraine war)—and partly the effect of long-term and growing pressures like declining public trust, rising inequality, and a warming climate. Going into the coming wave, many nations are beset by a slew of major challenges battering their effectiveness, making them weaker, more divided, and more prone to slow and faulty decision-making. The coming wave will land in a combustible, incompetent, overwrought environment. This makes the challenge of containment—of controlling and directing technologies so they are of net benefit to humanity—even more daunting.

DEMOCRACIES ARE BUILT ON trust. People need to trust that government officials, militaries, and other elites will not abuse their dominant positions. Everyone relies on the trust that taxes will be paid, rules honored, the interests of the whole put ahead of individuals. Without trust, from the ballot box to the tax return, from the local council to the judiciary, societies are in trouble.

Trust in government, particularly in America, has collapsed. Postwar presidential administrations like those of Eisenhower and Johnson were trusted to do "what is right" by more than 70 percent of Americans, according to a Pew survey. For recent presidents such as Obama, Trump, and Biden, this measure of confidence has cratered, all falling below 20 percent. Quite remarkably, a 2018 study of democracy in America found that as many as one in five believe "army rule" is a good idea! No less than 85 percent of Americans feel the country is "heading in the wrong direction." Distrust extends to nongovernment institutions, with growing levels of distrust in the media, the scientific establishment, and the idea of expertise in general.

The problem is not limited to the United States. Another Pew survey found that across twenty-seven countries, a majority were dissatisfied with their democracies. A Democracy Perception Index poll found that across fifty nations two-thirds of respondents felt the government "rarely" or "never" acted in the public interest. That so many people profoundly feel society is failing is itself a problem: Distrust breeds negativity and apathy. People decline to vote.

Since 2010, more countries have slid backward on measures of democracy than have progressed, a process that appears to be accelerating. Rising nationalism and authoritarianism seem endemic, from Poland and China to Russia, Hungary, the Philippines, and Turkey. Populist movements range from the bizarre, like QAnon, to the directionless (the *gilets jaunes* in France), but from Bolsonaro in Brazil to Brexit in the U.K. their prominence on the world stage has been impossible to miss.

Behind the new authoritarian impulse and political instability lies a growing pool of social resentment. A key catalyst of instability and social resentment, inequality has surged across Western nations in recent decades, and nowhere more so than in the United States. Between 1980 and 2021 the share of national income earned by the top 1 percent has almost doubled and now sits just under 50 percent. Wealth is ever more concentrated in a tiny clique. Government policy, a shrinking working-age population, stalling educational levels, and decelerating long-term growth have all contributed to decisively more unequal societies. Forty million people in the United States live in poverty, and more than five million live in "Third World conditions"—all within the world's richest economy.

These are especially worrying trends when you consider persistent relationships between social immobility, widening inequality, and political violence. Across data from more than one hundred countries, evidence suggests that the lower a country's social mobility, the more it experiences upheavals like riots, strikes, assassinations, revolutionary campaigns, and civil wars. When people feel stuck, that others are unfairly hogging the rewards, they get angry.

Not so long ago, the world was meant to be "flat"—a frictionless terrain of easy trade and rising prosperity. In fact, as the twenty-first century wears on, supply chain crunches and financial shocks remain indelible features of the economy. Those countries leaning into nationalism are, in part, experiencing a turning away from the bright twentieth-century promise that greater interconnectedness would accelerate the spread of wealth and democracy.

Onshoring, national security, resilient supply chains, self-sufficiency—today's language of trade is once again the language of borders, barriers, and tariffs. At the same time, food, energy, raw materials, and goods of all kinds have become more expensive. Essentially the entire postwar security and economic order is facing unprecedented strain.

Global challenges are reaching a critical threshold. Rampant inflation. Energy shortages. Stagnant incomes. A breakdown of trust. Waves of populism. None of the old visions from either left or right seem to offer convincing answers, yet better options seem in short supply. It would take a brave, or possibly delusional, person to argue that all is well, that there are not serious forces of populism, anger, and dysfunction raging across societies—all despite the highest living standards the world has ever known.

This makes containment far more complicated. Forming national and international consensus and establishing new norms around fast-moving technologies are already steep challenges. How can we hope to do this when our baseline mode seems to be instability?

TECHNOLOGY IS POLITICAL:
THE WAVE'S CHALLENGE TO STATES

Every previous wave of technology has had profound political implications. We should expect the same in the future. The last wave—the
arrival of mainframes, desktop PCs and desktop software, the internet,
and the smartphone—delivered immense benefits to society. It laid
down the new tools for the modern economy, bolstering growth,
transforming access to knowledge, to entertainment, and to one another. Amid the present hand-wringing about the negative effects of
social media, it's easy to overlook these myriad positives. Yet over the
last decade a growing consensus suggests these technologies did something else as well: creating the conditions to feed and amplify this underlying political polarization and institutional fragility.

It's hardly news that social media platforms can trigger gut emotional responses, the jolts of adrenaline so effectively delivered by perceived threats. Social media thrives on heightened emotions and, quite
often, outrage. A meta-analysis published in the journal *Nature* re-
viewed the results of nearly five hundred studies, concluding there is a
clear correlation between growing use of digital media and rising distrust in politics, populist movements, hate, and polarization. Correlation may not be causation, but this systematic review throws up "clear
evidence of serious threats to democracy" coming from new technologies.

Technology has already eroded the stable, sovereign borders of
nation-states, creating or supporting innately global flows of people,
information, ideas, know-how, commodities, finished goods, capital,
and wealth. It is, as we have seen, a significant component of geopolitical strategy. It touches on almost every aspect of people's lives. Even
before the coming wave hits, technology is a driver on the world stage,
a major factor in the deteriorating health of nation-states around the
world. Too fast in its development, too global, too protean and enticing
for any simple model of containment, strategically critical, relied upon
by billions, modern technology itself is a prime actor, a monumental
force nation-states struggle to manage. AI, synthetic biology, and the
rest are being introduced to dysfunctional societies *already* rocked back

and forth on technological waves of immense power. This is not a world ready for the coming wave. This is a world buckling under the existing strain.

I'VE OFTEN HEARD IT said that technology is "value neutral" and that its politics arise from its use. This is so reductive and simplistic that it's almost meaningless. Technology didn't straightforwardly "cause" or create the modern state (or indeed any political structure). But the potential it unleashes is not neutral in that story.

As the historian of technology Langdon Winner puts it, "Technology in its various manifestations is a significant part of the human world. Its structures, processes, and alterations enter into and become part of the structures, processes, and alterations of human consciousness, society, and politics." In other words, technology is political.

This fact is radically under-recognized not only by our leaders but even by those building the technology itself. At times this subtle but omnipresent politicization is nearly invisible. It shouldn't be. Social media is just the most recent reminder that technology and political organization cannot be divorced. States and technologies are intimately tied together. This has important ramifications for what's coming.

While technology doesn't simplistically push people in a predetermined direction, it's not naive techno-determinism to recognize its tendency to afford certain capabilities or see how it prompts some outcomes over others. In this, technology is one of the key determinants of history, but never alone and never in a mechanistic, inherently predictable way. It doesn't superficially cause given behaviors or outcomes, but what it produces does guide or circumscribe possibilities.

War, peace, commerce, political order, culture—these have always been fundamentally interlinked, and interlinked moreover with technology. Technologies are ideas, manifested in products and services that have profound and lasting consequences for people, social structures, the environment, and everything in between.

Modern technology and the state evolved symbiotically, in constant dialogue. Think of how technology facilitated the state's core working parts, helping construct the edifice of national identity and administration. Writing was invented as an administrative and accounting tool to keep track of debts, inheritances, laws, taxes, contracts, and records of ownership. The clock produced set times, first in limited spaces like monasteries but then in mechanical form across late medieval mercantile cities and eventually across nations, creating common, and ever larger, social units. The printing press helped standardize national languages from a chaos of dialects and thus helped produce a national "imagined community," the unitary people behind a nation-state. Supplanting more fluid oral traditions, the printed word fixed geography, knowledge, and history in place, promulgating set legal codes and ideologies. Radio and TV turbocharged this process, creating moments of national and even international commonality experienced simultaneously, like FDR's fireside chats or the World Cup.

Weapons, too, are technologies central to the power wielded by nation-states. Indeed, theorists of the state often suggest that war itself was foundational to its creation (in the words of the political scientist Charles Tilly, "War made the state and the state made war"), just as conflict has always been a spur to new technologies—from chariots and metal armor to radar and the advanced chips that guide precision munitions. Introduced to Europe in the thirteenth century, gunpowder broke the old pattern of defensive medieval castles. Fortified settlements were now sitting ducks for bombardment. By the Hundred Years' War between Britain and France, offensive capabilities gave the advantage to those who could afford to buy, build, maintain, move, and deploy capital-intensive cannons. Over the years, the state concentrated ever-increasing lethal power in its own hands, claiming a monopoly on the legitimate use of force.

Put simply, technology and political order are intimately connected. The introduction of new technologies has major political consequences. Just as the cannon and the printing press upended society, so we should expect the same from technologies like AI, robotics, and synthetic biology.

Pause for a moment and imagine a world where robots with the dexterity of human beings that can be "programmed" in plain English are available at the price of a microwave. Can you begin to think of all the uses to which such a valuable technology will be put? Or how widely such tools will be adopted? Who or rather what will be looking after your elderly mother at a care home? How will you order food at a restaurant, and who will bring it to your table? What does law enforcement look like in a hostage situation? Who will staff orchards at harvest time? How will military and paramilitary planners react when no humans need be sent into combat? What will the sports field be like when kids are training at football? What will your window cleaner look like? Who owns all this hardware and IP, who controls it, what safeguards are in place for if—when—it goes wrong?

Imagine all this, and it implies a very different political economy from today's.

THE MODERN, LIBERAL DEMOCRATIC industrialized nation-state has been the dominant global force since the early twentieth century, the clear "victor" of last century's great political clash. It came with defining functions now taken for granted. The provision of security. Great concentrations of legitimate power at the center, capable of utterly dominating within their jurisdictions, but also sensible checks and balances on, and separations between, all forms of power. Adequate welfare via redistribution and sound economic management. Stable frameworks of technological innovation and regulation, alongside a whole socioeconomic-legal architecture of globalization.

In the next few chapters we will see how the coming wave places all of this under great threat.

What emerges will, I think, tend in two directions with a spectrum of outcomes in between. On one trajectory, some liberal democratic states will continue to be eroded from within, becoming a kind of zombie government. Trappings of liberal democracy and the traditional nation-state remain, but functionally they are hollowed out, the core services increasingly threadbare, the polity unstable and fractious. Lurching on in the absence of anything else, they become ever more degraded and dysfunctional. On another, unthinking adoption of some aspects of the coming wave opens pathways to domineering state control, creating supercharged Leviathans whose power goes beyond even history's most extreme totalitarian governments. Authoritarian regimes may also tend toward zombie status, but equally they may double down, get boosted, become fully fledged techno-dictatorships. On either path, the delicate balance holding states together is tipped into chaos.

Both failing states and authoritarian regimes are disastrous outcomes, not just on their own terms, but also for governing technology; neither flailing bureaucracies, populist opportunists, nor all-powerful dictators are people you'd want to be fundamentally responsible for controlling powerful new technologies. Neither direction can or will contain the coming wave.

On either side, then, lies danger, given that managing the coming wave requires confident, agile, coherent states, accountable to the people, filled with expertise, balancing interests and incentives, capable of reacting fast and decisively with legislative action and, crucially, close international coordination. Leaders will need to take bold actions without precedent, trading off short-term gain for long-term benefit. Responding effectively to one of the most far-reaching and transformative events in history will require mature, stable, and most of all trusted governments to perform at their best. States that work really, really well. That is what it will take to ensure that the coming wave delivers the great benefits it promises. It's an incredibly tall order.

Cheap, omnipresent robots like those sketched above are, alongside a host of other transformative technologies we saw in part 2, utterly inevitable over a twenty-year horizon, and possibly much sooner. In this context we should expect profound changes to the economy, the nation-state, and everything that goes with them. The grand bargain is already in trouble. As the deluge begins, a series of new stressors will shake its foundations.

CHAPTER 10

FRAGILITY AMPLIFIERS

NATIONAL EMERGENCY 2.0:
UNCONTAINED ASYMMETRY IN ACTION

ON THE MORNING OF MAY 12, 2017, BRITAIN'S NATIONAL HEALTH Service (NHS) ground to a halt. Thousands of its facilities nationwide suddenly saw their IT systems freeze up. In hospitals, staff were locked out of crucial medical equipment like MRI scanners and unable to access patient records. Thousands of scheduled procedures, ranging from cancer appointments to elective surgeries, had to be canceled. Panicked care teams reverted to manual stopgaps, using paper notes and personal phones. The Royal London Hospital shuttered its emergency department, with patients left lying on gurneys outside the operating theaters.

The NHS had been hit by a ransomware attack. It was called Wanna-Cry, and its scale was immense. Ransomware works by compromising a system to encrypt and thus lock down access to key files and capabilities. Cyberattackers typically demand a ransom in exchange for liberating a captive system.

The NHS wasn't WannaCry's only target. Exploiting a vulnerability in older Microsoft systems, hackers had found a way to grind swaths of the digital world to a halt, including organizations like Deutsche Bahn, Telefónica, FedEx, Hitachi, even the Chinese Ministry of Public Security. WannaCry tricked some users into opening an email, which released a "worm" replicating and transporting itself to infect a quarter of a million computers across 150 countries in just one day. For a few hours after the attack much of the digital world teetered, held for ransom by a distant, faceless assailant. The ensuing damage cost up to $8 billion, but the implications were even graver. The WannaCry attack exposed just how vulnerable institutions whose operation we take for granted were to sophisticated cyberattacks.

In the end, the NHS—and the world—caught a lucky break. A twenty-two-year-old British hacker called Marcus Hutchins stumbled on a kill switch. Going through the malware's code, he saw an odd-looking domain name. Guessing this might be part of the worm's command and control structure, and seeing the domain was unregistered, Hutchins bought it for just $10.69, allowing him to control the virus while Microsoft pushed out updates closing the vulnerability.

Perhaps the most extraordinary thing about WannaCry is where it came from. WannaCry was built using technology created by the U.S. National Security Agency (NSA). An elite NSA unit called the Office of Tailored Access Operations had developed a cyberattack exploit called EternalBlue. In the words of one NSA staffer these were "the keys to the kingdom," tools designed to "undermine the security of a lot of major government and corporate networks both here and abroad."

How had this formidable technology, developed by one of the most technically sophisticated organizations on the planet, been obtained by a group of hackers? As Microsoft pointed out at the time, "An equivalent scenario with conventional weapons would be the U.S. military having some of its Tomahawk missiles stolen." Unlike Tomahawk missiles, the NSA's digital weapons could quietly slip onto a thumb drive. The hackers who stole the technology, a group known as the Shadow Brokers, put EternalBlue up for sale. From there it soon ended up in the hands of North Korean hackers, probably the state-sponsored Bureau 121 cyber unit. They then launched it on the world.

Despite speedy patches, the fallout from the EternalBlue leak wasn't over. In June 2017 a new version of the weapon emerged, this time specifically designed to target Ukrainian national infrastructure in an attack quickly attributed to Russian military intelligence. The NotPetya cyberattack almost brought the country to its knees. Radiation monitoring systems at Chernobyl lost power. ATMs stopped dispensing money. Mobile phones went silent. Ten percent of the country's computers were infected, and basic infrastructure from the electrical grid to the Ukrainian State Savings Bank went down. Major multinationals like the shipping giant Maersk were immobilized, collateral damage.

Here is a parable for technology in the twenty-first century. Software created by the security services of the world's most technologically sophisticated state is leaked or stolen. From there it finds its way into the hands of digital terrorists working for one of the world's most failed states and capricious nuclear powers. It is then weaponized, turned against the core fabric of the contemporary state: health services, transport and power infrastructures, essential businesses in global communications and logistics. In other words, thanks to a basic failure of containment, a global superpower became a victim of its own powerful and supposedly secure technology.

This is uncontained asymmetry in action.

LUCKILY, THE RANSOMWARE ATTACKS described above relied on conventional cyberweapons. Luckily, inasmuch as they did not rely on the features of the coming wave. Their power and potential were limited. The nation-state was scratched and bruised, but it wasn't fundamentally undermined. Yet it is a matter of when, not if, the next attack will occur, and next time we may not be so lucky.

It's tempting to argue cyberattacks are far less effective than we might have imagined, given the speed at which critical systems recovered from attacks like WannaCry. With the coming wave that assumption is a serious mistake. Such attacks demonstrate that there are those who would use cutting-edge technologies to degrade and disable key state functions. They show that core institutions of modern life are vulnerable. A lone individual and a private company (Microsoft) patched up the systemic weakness. This attack did not respect national boundaries. Government's role in handling the crisis was limited.

Now imagine if, instead of accidentally leaving open a loophole, the hackers behind WannaCry had designed the program to systematically learn about its own vulnerabilities and repeatedly patch them. Imagine if, as it attacked, the program evolved to exploit further weaknesses. Imagine that it then started moving through every hospital, every office, every home, constantly mutating, learning. It could hit life-support systems, military infrastructure, transport signaling, the energy grid, financial databases. As it spread, imagine the program learning to detect and stop further attempts to shut it down. A weapon like this is on the horizon if not already in development.

WannaCry and NotPetya are limited compared with the kinds of increasingly general-purpose learning agents that will make up the next generation of cyberweapons, which threaten to bring on national emergency 2.0. Today's cyberattacks are not the real threat; they are the canary in the coal mine of a new age of vulnerability and instability, degrading the nation-state's role as the sole arbiter of security.

Here is a specific, near-term application of next-wave technology fraying the state's fabric. In this chapter, we look at how this and other stressors chip away at the very edifice responsible for governing technology. These fragility amplifiers, system shocks, emergencies 2.0, will greatly exacerbate existing challenges, shaking the state's foundation, upsetting our already precarious social balance. This is, in part, a story of who can do what, a story of power and where it lies.

THE PLUMMETING COST OF POWER

Power is "the ability or capacity to do something or act in a particular way; . . . to direct or influence the behavior of others or the course of events." It's the mechanical or electrical energy that underwrites civilization. The bedrock and central principle of the state. Power in one form or another shapes everything. And it, too, is about to be transformed.

Technology is ultimately political because technology is a form of power. And perhaps the single overriding characteristic of the coming wave is that it will democratize access to power. As we saw in part 2, it will enable people to *do* things in the real world. I think of it like this: just as the costs of processing and broadcasting information plummeted in the consumer internet era, the cost of actually doing something, taking action, projecting power, will plummet with the next wave. Knowing is great, but doing is much more impactful.

Instead of just consuming content, anyone can *produce* expert-quality video, image, and text content. AI doesn't just help you find information for that best man speech; it will *write* the speech, too. And all on a scale unseen before. Robots won't just manufacture cars and organize warehouse floors; they'll be available to every garage tinkerer with a little time and imagination. The past wave enabled us to sequence, or read, DNA. The coming wave will make DNA synthesis universally available.

Wherever power is today, it will be amplified. Anyone with goals—that is, everyone—will have huge help in realizing them. Overhauling a business strategy, putting on social events for a local community, or capturing enemy territory all get easier. Building an airline or grounding a fleet are both more achievable. Whether it's commercial, religious, cultural, or military, democratic or authoritarian, every possible motivation you can think of can be dramatically enhanced by having cheaper power at your fingertips.

Today, no matter how wealthy you are, you simply cannot buy a more powerful smartphone than is available to billions of people. This phenomenal achievement of civilization is too often overlooked. In the next decade, access to ACIs will follow the same trend. Those same billions will soon have broadly equal access to the best lawyer, doctor, strategist, designer, coach, executive assistant, negotiator, and so on. Everyone will have a world-class team on their side and in their corner.

This will be the greatest, most rapid accelerant of wealth and prosperity in human history. It will also be one of the most chaotic. If everyone has access to more capability, that clearly also includes those who wish to cause harm. With technology evolving faster than defensive measures, bad actors, from Mexican drug cartels to North Korean hackers, are given a shot in the arm. Democratizing access necessarily means democratizing risk.

We are about to cross a critical threshold in the history of our species. This is what the nation-state will have to contend with over the next decade. In this chapter we run through some of the key examples of fragility amplification stemming from the coming wave. First let's look more closely at this near-term risk: how bad actors will be able to launch new offensive operations. Such attacks could be lethal, broadly accessible, and a chance for someone to strike at scale with impunity.

ROBOTS WITH GUNS:
THE PRIMACY OF OFFENSE

In November 2020, Mohsen Fakhrizadeh was the head scientist and linchpin of Iran's long effort to attain nuclear weapons. Patriotic, dedicated, highly experienced, he was a prime target for Iran's adversaries. Cognizant of the risks, he kept his whereabouts and movements cloaked in secrecy with help from Iran's security services.

Driving in a heavily guarded convoy down a dusty road to his country house near the Caspian Sea, Fakhrizadeh's motorcade suddenly screeched to a halt. The scientist's vehicle was hit by a barrage of bullets. Wounded, Fakhrizadeh stumbled out of his car, only to be killed by a second burst of machine-gun fire that tore through him. His bodyguards, members of Iran's Revolutionary Guard, scrambled to make sense of what was happening. Where was the shooter? A few moments later there was an explosion, and a nearby pickup truck erupted into flames.

The truck, however, was empty save for a gun. There were no assassins on the ground that day. In the words of a *New York Times* investigation, this was a "debut test of a high-tech, computerized sharpshooter kitted out with artificial intelligence and multiple-camera eyes, operated via satellite and capable of firing 600 rounds a minute." Mounted on a strategically parked but innocuous-looking pickup truck fitted with cameras, it was a kind of robot weapon assembled by Israeli agents. A human authorized the strike, but it was the AI that automatically adjusted the gun's aim. Just fifteen bullets were fired and one of the most high-profile and well-guarded people in Iran was killed in under a minute. The explosion was merely a failed attempt to hide the evidence.

Fakhrizadeh's assassination is a harbinger of what's to come. More sophisticated armed robots will further reduce barriers to violence. Videos of the latest generation of robots, with names like Atlas and BigDog, are easy to find on the internet. Here you'll see stocky, strange-looking humanoids and small doglike robots scamper over obstacle courses. They look curiously unbalanced yet never seem to fall. They navigate complex landscapes with an uncanny motion, their heavy-looking frames never toppling. They do backflips, jumps, spins, and tricks. Push them over, and they calmly, inexorably get up. And they're ready to do it again and again. It's spooky.

Now imagine robots equipped with facial recognition, DNA sequencing, and automatic weapons. Future robots may not take the form of scampering dogs. Miniaturized even further, they will be the size of a bird or a bee, armed with a small firearm or a vial of anthrax. They might soon be accessible to anyone who wants them. This is what bad actor empowerment looks like.

THE COST OF MILITARY-GRADE drones has fallen by three orders of magnitude over the last decade. By 2028, $26 billion a year will be spent on military drones, and at that point many are likely to be fully autonomous.

Live deployments of autonomous drones are becoming more plausible by the day. In May 2021, for example, an AI drone swarm in Gaza was used to find, identify, and attack Hamas militants. Start-ups like Anduril, Shield AI, and Rebellion Defense have raised hundreds of millions of dollars to build autonomous drone networks and other military applications of AI. Complementary technologies like 3-D printing and advanced mobile communications will reduce the cost of tactical drones to a few thousand dollars, putting them within reach of everyone from amateur enthusiasts to paramilitaries to lone psychopaths.

In addition to easier access, AI-enhanced weapons will improve themselves in real time. WannaCry's impact ended up being far more limited than it could have been. Once the software patch was applied, the immediate issue was resolved. AI transforms this kind of attack. AI cyberweapons will continuously probe networks, adapting themselves autonomously to find and exploit weaknesses. Existing computer worms replicate themselves using a fixed set of preprogrammed heuristics.

But what if you had a worm that improved itself using reinforcement learning, experimentally updating its code with each network interaction, each time finding more and more efficient ways to take advantage of cyber vulnerabilities? Just as systems like AlphaGo learn unexpected strategies from millions of self-played games, so too will

AI-enabled cyberattacks. However much you war-game every eventuality, there's inevitably going to be a tiny vulnerability discoverable by a persistent AI.

Everything from cars and planes to fridges and data centers relies on vast code bases. The coming AIs make it easier than ever to identify and exploit weaknesses. They could even find legal or financial means of damaging corporations or other institutions, hidden points of failure in banking regulation or technical safety protocols. As the cybersecurity expert Bruce Schneier has pointed out, AIs could digest the world's laws and regulations to find exploits, arbitraging legalities. Imagine a huge cache of documents from a company leaked. A legal AI might be able to parse this against multiple legal systems, figure out every possible infraction, and then hit that company with multiple crippling lawsuits around the world at the same time. AIs could develop automated trading strategies designed to destroy competitors' positions or create disinformation campaigns (more on this in the next section) engineering a run on a bank or a product boycott, enabling a competitor to swoop in and buy the company—or simply watch it collapse.

AI adept at exploiting not just financial, legal, or communications systems but also human psychology, our weaknesses and biases, is on the way. Researchers at Meta created a program called CICERO. It became an expert at playing the complex board game Diplomacy, a game in which planning long, complex strategies built around deception and backstabbing is integral. It shows how AIs could help us plan and collaborate, but also hints at how they could develop psychological tricks to gain trust and influence, reading and manipulating our emotions and behaviors with a frightening level of depth, a skill useful in, say, winning at Diplomacy or electioneering and building a political movement.

The space for possible attacks against key state functions grows even as the same premise that makes AI so powerful and exciting—its ability to learn and adapt—empowers bad actors.

FOR CENTURIES CUTTING-EDGE OFFENSIVE capabilities, like massed artillery, naval broadsides, tanks, aircraft carriers, or ICBMs, have initially been so costly that they remained the province of the nation-state. Now they are evolving so fast that they quickly proliferate into the hands of research labs, start-ups, and garage tinkerers. Just as social media's one-to-many broadcast effect means a single person can suddenly broadcast globally, so the capacity for far-reaching consequential action is becoming available to everyone.

This new dynamic—where bad actors are emboldened to go on the offensive—opens up new vectors of attack thanks to the interlinked, vulnerable nature of modern systems: not just a single hospital but an entire health system can be hit; not just a warehouse but an entire supply chain. With lethal autonomous weapons the costs, in both material and above all human terms, of going to war, of attacking, are lower than ever. At the same time, all this introduces greater levels of deniability and ambiguity, degrading the logic of deterrence. If no one can be sure who initiated an assault, or what exactly has happened, why not go ahead?

When non-state and bad actors are empowered in this way, one of the core propositions of the state is undermined: the semblance of a security umbrella for citizens is deeply damaged. Provisions of safety and security are fundamental underpinnings of the nation-state system, not nice-to-have add-ons. States broadly know how to respond to questions of law and order, or direct attacks from hostile countries. But this is far murkier, more amorphous and asymmetric, blurring the lines of territoriality and easy attribution.

How does a state maintain the confidence of its citizens, uphold that grand bargain, if it fails to offer the basic promise of security? How can it ensure that hospitals will keep running, schools stay open, lights remain—literally—switched on in this world? If the state can't protect you and your family, what's the point of compliance and belonging? If we feel that the fundamentals—the electricity running our houses, the transport systems getting us around, the energy networks keeping us warm, our personal everyday security—are falling to pieces and there is nothing either we or the government can do, a foundation of the system is chipped away. If the state began in new forms of war, perhaps it will end in the same way.

Throughout history technology has produced a delicate dance of offensive and defensive advantage, the pendulum swinging between the two but a balance roughly holding: for every new projectile or cyberweapon, a potent countermeasure has quickly arisen. Cannons may wear down a castle's walls, but they can also rip apart an invading army. Now powerful, asymmetric, omni-use technologies are certain to reach the hands of those who want to damage the state. While defensive operations will be strengthened in time, the nature of the four features favors offense: this proliferation of power is just too wide, fast, and open. An algorithm of world-changing significance can be stored on a laptop; soon it won't even require the kind of vast, regulatable infrastructure of the last wave and the internet. Unlike an arrow or even a hypersonic missile, AI and bioagents will evolve more cheaply, more rapidly, and more autonomously than any technology we've ever seen. Consequently, without a dramatic set of interventions to alter the current course, millions will have access to these capabilities in just a few years.

Maintaining a decisive, indefinite strategic advantage across such a broad spectrum of general-use technologies is simply not possible. Eventually, the balance might be restored, but not before a wave of immensely destabilizing force is unleashed. And as we've seen, the nature of the threat is far more widespread than blunt forms of physical assault. Information and communication together is its own escalating vector of risk, another emerging fragility amplifier requiring attention.

Welcome to the deepfake era.

THE MISINFORMATION MACHINE

In the 2020 local elections in India, the Bharatiya Janata Party Delhi president, Manoj Tiwari, was filmed making a campaign speech—in both English and a local Hindi dialect. Both looked and sounded convincingly real. In the video he goes on the attack, accusing the head of a rival party of having "cheated us." But the version in the local dialect was a deepfake, a new kind of AI-enabled synthetic media. Produced by a political communications firm, it exposed the candidate to new, hard-to-reach constituencies. Lacking awareness of the discourse around fake media, many assumed it was real. The company behind the deepfake argued it was a "positive" use of the technology, but to any sober observer this incident heralded a perilous new age in political communication. In another widely publicized incident, a clip of Nancy Pelosi was reedited to make her look ill and impaired and then proceeded to circulate widely on social media.

Ask yourself, what happens when anyone has the power to create and broadcast material with incredible levels of realism? These examples occurred *before* the means to generate near-perfect deepfakes—whether text, images, video, or audio—became as easy as writing a query into Google. As we saw in chapter 4, large language models now show astounding results at generating synthetic media. A world of deepfakes indistinguishable from conventional media is here. These fakes will be so good our rational minds will find it hard to accept they aren't real.

Deepfakes are spreading fast. If you want to watch a convincing fake of Tom Cruise preparing to wrestle an alligator, well, you can. More and more everyday people will be imitated as the required training data falls to just a handful of examples. It's already happening. A bank in Hong Kong transferred millions of dollars to fraudsters in 2021, after one of their clients was impersonated by a deepfake. Sounding identical to the real client, the fraudsters phoned the bank manager and explained how the company needed to move money for an acquisition. All the documents seemed to check out, the voice and character were flawlessly familiar, so the manager initiated the transfer.

Anyone motivated to sow instability now has an easier time of it. Say three days before an election the president is caught on camera using a racist slur. The campaign press office strenuously denies it, but everyone knows what they've seen. Outrage seethes around the country. Polls nose-dive. Swing states suddenly shift toward the opponent, who, against all expectations, wins. A new administration takes charge. But the video is a deepfake, one so sophisticated it evades even the best fake-detecting neural networks.

The threat here lies not so much with extreme cases as in subtle, nuanced, and highly plausible scenarios being exaggerated and distorted. It's not the president charging into a school screaming nonsensical rubbish while hurling grenades; it's the president resignedly saying he has no choice but to institute a set of emergency laws or reintroduce the draft. It's not Hollywood fireworks; it's the purported surveillance camera footage of a group of white policemen caught on tape beating a Black man to death.

Sermons from the radical preacher Anwar al-Awlaki inspired the Boston Marathon bombers, the attackers of *Charlie Hebdo* in Paris, and the shooter who killed forty-nine people at an Orlando nightclub. Yet al-Awlaki died in 2011, the first U.S. citizen killed by a U.S. drone strike, before any of these events. His radicalizing messages were, though, still available on YouTube until 2017. Suppose that using deepfakes new videos of al-Awlaki could be "unearthed," each commanding further targeted attacks with precision-honed rhetoric. Not everyone would buy it, but those who wanted to believe would find it utterly compelling.

Soon these videos will be fully and believably interactive. You are talking directly to him. He knows you and adapts to your dialect and style, plays on your history, your personal grievances, your bullying at school, your terrible, immoral Westernized parents. This is not disinformation as blanket carpet bombing; it's disinformation as surgical strike.

Phishing attacks against politicians or businesspeople, disinformation with the aim of major financial-market disruption or manipulation, media designed to poison key fault lines like sectarian or racial divides, even low-level scams—trust is damaged and fragility again amplified.

Eventually entire and rich synthetic histories of seemingly real-world events will be easy to generate. Individual citizens won't have time or the tools to verify a fraction of the content coming their way. Fakes will easily pass sophisticated checks, let alone a two-second smell test.

STATE-SPONSORED INFO ASSAULTS

In the 1980s, the Soviet Union funded disinformation campaigns suggesting that the AIDS virus was the result of a U.S. bioweapons program. Years later, some communities were still dealing with the mistrust and fallout. The campaigns, meanwhile, have not stopped. According to Facebook, Russian agents created no fewer than eighty thousand pieces of organic content that reached 126 million Americans on their platforms during the 2016 election.

AI-enhanced digital tools will exacerbate information operations like these, meddling in elections, exploiting social divisions, and creating elaborate astroturfing campaigns to sow chaos. Unfortunately, it's far from just Russia. More than seventy countries have been found running disinformation campaigns. China is quickly catching up with Russia; others from Turkey to Iran are developing their skills. (The CIA, too, is no stranger to info ops.)

Early in the COVID-19 pandemic a blizzard of disinformation had deadly consequences. A Carnegie Mellon study analyzed more than 200 million tweets discussing COVID-19 at the height of the first lockdown. Eighty-two percent of influential users advocating for "reopening America" were bots. This was a targeted "propaganda machine," most likely Russian, designed to intensify the worst public health crisis in a century.

Deepfakes automate these information assaults. Until now effective disinformation campaigns have been labor-intensive. While bots and fakes aren't difficult to make, most are of low quality, easily identifiable, and only moderately effective at actually changing targets' behavior.

High-quality synthetic media changes this equation. Not all nations currently have the funds to build huge disinformation programs, with dedicated offices and legions of trained staff, but that's less of a barrier when high-fidelity material can be generated at the click of a button. Much of the coming chaos will not be accidental. It will come as existing disinformation campaigns are turbocharged, expanded, and devolved out to a wide group of motivated actors.

The rise of synthetic media at scale and minimal cost amplifies both disinformation (malicious and intentionally misleading information) and misinformation (a wider and more unintentional pollution of the information space) at once. Cue an "Infocalypse," the point at which society can no longer manage a torrent of sketchy material, where the information ecosystem grounding knowledge, trust, and social cohesion, the glue holding society together, falls apart. In the words of a Brookings Institution report, ubiquitous, perfect synthetic media means "distorting democratic discourse; manipulating elections; eroding trust in institutions; weakening journalism; exacerbating social divisions; undermining public safety; and inflicting hard-to-repair damage on the reputation of prominent individuals, including elected officials and candidates for office."

Not all stressors and harms come from bad actors, however. Some come from the best of intentions. Amplification of fragility is accidental as well as deliberate.

LEAKY LABS AND
UNINTENDED INSTABILITY

In one of the world's most secure laboratories, a group of researchers were experimenting with a deadly pathogen. No one can be sure what happened next. Even with the benefit of hindsight, detail about the research is scant. What is certain is that, in a country famed for secrecy and government control, a strange new illness began appearing.

Soon it was found around the world, in the U.K., the United States, and beyond. Oddly, this didn't seem like an entirely natural strain of the disease. Certain features raised alarm in the scientific community and suggested that something at the lab had gone horribly wrong, that this wasn't a natural event. Soon the death toll started rising. That hyper-secure lab wasn't looking so secure after all.

If this sounds like a familiar story, it probably isn't the one you're thinking about. This was 1977 and an influenza epidemic known as the Russian flu. First discovered in China, it was detected in the Soviet Union soon after, spreading from there and reportedly killing up to 700,000 people. What was unusual about the H1N1 flu strain was how closely it resembled one circulating in the 1950s. The disease hit young people hardest, a possible sign they had a weaker immunity than those around a few decades earlier.

Theories abound over what happened. Had something escaped from the permafrost? Was it part of Russia's extensive and shadowy bioweapons program? To date, though, the best explanation is a lab leak. A version of the earlier virus likely somehow escaped during lab experiments with a vaccine. The epidemic was itself caused by well-meaning research intended to prevent epidemics.

Biological labs are subject to global standards that should stop accidents. The most secure are known as biosafety level 4 (BSL-4) labs. They represent the highest standards of containment for working with the most dangerous pathogenic materials. Facilities are completely sealed. Entry is by air lock. Everything going in and out gets thoroughly checked. Everyone wears a pressurized suit. Anyone leaving needs to shower. All materials are disposed of, subject to the strictest protocols. Sharp edges of any kind, capable of puncturing gloves or suits, are banned. Researchers at BSL-4 labs are quite rightly trained to create the most bio-secure environments humanity has ever seen.

And yet accidents and leaks still happen. The 1977 Russian flu is just one example. Just two years later anthrax spores were accidentally released from a secret Soviet bioweapons facility, producing a fifty-kilometer trail of disease that killed at least sixty-six people.

In 2007 a leaking pipe at the U.K.'s Pirbright Institute, which includes BSL-4 labs, caused an outbreak of foot-and-mouth disease costing £147 million. In 2021, a pharmaceutical company researcher near Philadelphia left smallpox vials in an unmarked, unsecured freezer. Luckily, they were found by someone cleaning the freezer. The person was lucky to be wearing a mask and gloves. Had it got out, the consequences would have been catastrophic. Before it was eradicated, smallpox killed an estimated 300 to 500 million people in the twentieth century alone, with a reproduction rate equivalent to more contagious strains of COVID-19, but with a mortality rate thirty times that of COVID.

SARS is supposed to be kept in BSL-3 conditions, but it has escaped from virology labs in Singapore, Taiwan, and China. Quite incredibly, it escaped four times from the same laboratory in Beijing. The errors were all too human and mundane. The Singapore case was down to a graduate student unaware of the presence of SARS. In Taiwan a research scientist mishandled biohazardous waste. In Beijing, the leaks were attributed to poor deactivation of the virus and handling in nonbiosecure labs. And all that's before you even mention Wuhan, home to the world's largest BSL-4 lab and a center for coronavirus research.

Even as the number of BSL-4 labs booms, only a quarter of them score highly on safety, according to the Global Health Security Index. Between 1975 and 2016, researchers cataloged at least seventy-one either deliberate or accidental exposures to highly infectious and toxic pathogens. Most were tiny accidents that even the most highly trained human is surely bound to make sometimes—a slip with a needle, a spilled vial, an experiment prepared with a small error. Our picture is almost certainly incomplete. Few researchers report accidents publicly or promptly. A survey of biosafety officers found that most never reported accidents beyond their institution. A U.S. risk assessment from 2014 estimated that over a decade the chance of "a major lab leak" across ten labs was 91 percent; the risk of a resulting pandemic, 27 percent.

Nothing *should* get out. Yet pathogens do, time and again. Despite being some of the toughest around, the protocols, technologies, and regulations for containment fail. A shaking pipette. A punctured piece of plastic sheeting. A drop of solution spilled on a shoe. These are tangible failures of containment. Accidental. Incidental. Occurring with a grim, inevitable regularity. In the age of synthetic life, though, it introduces the chance of accidents that could represent both an enormous stressor and something we'll return to later in part 3—catastrophe.

FEW AREAS OF BIOLOGY are as controversial as gain-of-function (GOF) research. Put simply, gain-of-function experiments deliberately engineer pathogens to be more lethal or infectious, or both. In nature, viruses usually trade off lethality for transmissibility. The more transmissible a virus, the less lethal it often is. But there is no absolute reason this must be so. One way of understanding how it might happen—that is, how viruses might become more lethal and transmissible at the same time—and how we might combat that is to, well, make it happen.

That's where gain-of-function research comes in. Researchers investigate disease incubation times, or how they evade vaccine resistance, or maybe how they can spread asymptomatically through a population. Work like this has been undertaken on diseases including Ebola, influenzas like H1N1, and measles.

Such research efforts are generally credible and well intentioned. Work with an avian flu in Holland and the United States around a decade ago is a good example. This disease had shockingly high mortality rates but luckily was very difficult to catch. Researchers wanted to understand how that picture might change, how this disease could morph into a more transmissible form, and used ferrets to see how this might occur. In other words they made a deadly disease in principle easier to catch.

It doesn't take a wild imagination, however, to envisage how such research could go wrong. Deliberately engineering or evolving viruses like this was, some felt, including myself, a bit like playing with the nuclear trigger.

Gain-of-function research is, suffice to say, controversial. For a time U.S. funding agencies imposed a moratorium on funding it. In a classic failure of containment, such work resumed in 2019. There is at least some indication that COVID-19 has been genetically altered and a growing body of (circumstantial) evidence, from the Wuhan Institute's track record to the molecular biology of the virus itself, suggesting a lab leak might have been the origin of the pandemic.

Both the FBI and the U.S. Department of Energy believe this to be the case, with the CIA undecided. Unlike in previous outbreaks, there is no smoking gun on zoonotic transmission. It's eminently plausible that biological research has already killed millions, brought society worldwide to a standstill, and cost trillions of dollars. In late 2022, an NIH study at Boston University combined the original, more deadly strain of COVID with the spike protein of the more transmissible omicron variant. Many felt the research shouldn't have gone ahead, but there it was, funded by public money.

This is not about bad actors weaponizing technology; this is about unintended consequences from good people who want to improve health outcomes. It's about what goes wrong when powerful tools proliferate, what mistakes get made, what "revenge effects" unfurl, what random, unforeseen mess results from technology's collision with reality. Off the drawing board, away from the theory, that central problem of uncontained technology holds even with the best of intentions.

GOF research is meant to keep people safe. Yet it inevitably occurs in a flawed world, where labs leak, where pandemics happen. Regardless of what did happen in Wuhan, it's still grimly plausible that such research on coronaviruses was taking place and leaked. The historical record of lab leaks is hard to overlook.

GAIN-OF-FUNCTION RESEARCH AND LAB leaks are just two particularly sharp examples of how the coming wave will introduce a plethora of revenge effects and inadvertent failure modes. If every half-competent lab or even random biohacker can embark on this research, tragedy cannot be indefinitely postponed. It was this kind of scenario that was outlined to me in that seminar I mentioned in chapter 1.

As the power and spread of any technology grows, so its failure modes escalate. If a plane crashes, it's a terrible tragedy. But if a whole fleet of planes crash, it's something altogether more frightening. To reiterate: these risks are not about malicious harm; they come from simply operating on the bleeding edge of the most capable technologies in history widely embedded throughout core societal systems. A lab leak is just one good example of unintended consequences, the heart of the containment problem, a coming-wave equivalent of reactor meltdowns or lost warheads. Accidents like this create another unpredictable stressor, another splintering crack in the system.

Yet stressors might also be less discrete events, less a robot attack, lab leak, or deepfake video, and more a slow and diffuse process undermining foundations. Consider that throughout history, tools and technologies have been designed to help us do more with less. Each individual instance counts for almost nothing. But what happens if the ultimate side effect of these compounding efficiencies is that humans aren't needed for much work at all?

THE AUTOMATION DEBATE

In the years since I co-founded DeepMind, no AI policy debate has been given more airtime than the future of work—to the point of oversaturation.

Here was the original thesis. In the past, new technologies put people out of work, producing what the economist John Maynard Keynes called "technological unemployment." In Keynes's view, this was a good thing, with increasing productivity freeing up time for further innovation and leisure. Examples of tech-related displacement are myriad. The introduction of power looms put old-fashioned weavers out of business; motorcars meant that carriage makers and horse stables were no longer needed; lightbulb factories did great as candlemakers went bust.

Broadly speaking, when technology damaged old jobs and industries, it also produced new ones. Over time these new jobs tended toward service industry roles and cognitive-based white-collar jobs. As factories closed in the Rust Belt, demand for lawyers, designers, and social media influencers boomed. So far at least, in economic terms, new technologies have not ultimately replaced labor; they have in the aggregate complemented it.

But what if new job-displacing systems scale the ladder of human cognitive ability itself, leaving nowhere new for labor to turn? If the coming wave really is as general and wide-ranging as it appears, how will humans compete? What if a large majority of white-collar tasks can be performed more efficiently by AI? In few areas will humans still be "better" than machines. I have long argued this is the more likely scenario. With the arrival of the latest generation of large language models, I am now more convinced than ever that this is how things will play out.

These tools will only temporarily augment human intelligence. They will make us smarter and more efficient for a time, and will unlock enormous amounts of economic growth, but they are fundamentally labor replacing. They will eventually do cognitive labor more efficiently and more cheaply than many people working in administration, data entry, customer service (including making and receiving phone calls), writing emails, drafting summaries, translating documents, creating content, copywriting, and so on. In the face of an abundance of ultra-low-cost equivalents, the days of this kind of "cognitive manual labor" are numbered.

We are only just now starting to see what impact this new wave is about to have. Early analysis of ChatGPT suggests it boosts the productivity of "mid-level college educated professionals" by 40 percent on many tasks. That in turn could affect hiring decisions: a McKinsey study estimated that more than half of all jobs could see many of their tasks automated by machines in the next seven years, while fifty-two million Americans work in roles with a "medium exposure to automation" by 2030.

The economists Daron Acemoglu and Pascual Restrepo estimate that robots cause the wages of local workers to fall. With each additional robot per thousand workers there is a decline in the employment-to-population ratio, and consequently a fall in wages. Today algorithms perform the vast bulk of equity trades and increasingly act across financial institutions, and yet, even as Wall Street booms, it sheds jobs as technology encroaches on more and more tasks.

Many remain unconvinced. Economists like David Autor argue that new technology consistently raises incomes, creating demand for new labor. Technology makes companies more productive, it generates more money, which then flows back into the economy. Put simply, demand is insatiable, and this demand, stoked by the wealth technology has generated, gives rise to new jobs requiring human labor. After all, skeptics say, ten years of deep learning success has not unleashed a jobs automation meltdown. Buying into that fear was, some argue, just a repeat of the old "lump of labor" fallacy, which erroneously claims there is only a set amount of work to go around. Instead, the future looks more like billions of people working in high-end jobs still barely conceived of.

I believe this rosy vision is implausible over the next couple of decades; automation is unequivocally another fragility amplifier. As we saw in chapter 4, AI's rate of improvement is well beyond exponential, and there appears no obvious ceiling in sight. Machines are rapidly imitating all kinds of human abilities, from vision to speech and language. Even without fundamental progress toward "deep understanding," new language models can read, synthesize, and generate eye-wateringly accurate and highly useful text. There are literally hundreds of roles where this single skill alone is the core requirement, and yet there is so much more to come from AI.

Yes, it's almost certain that many new job categories will be created.

Who would have thought that "influencer" would become a highly sought-after role? Or imagined that in 2023 people would be working as "prompt engineers"—nontechnical programmers of large language models who become adept at coaxing out specific responses? Demand for masseurs, cellists, and baseball pitchers won't go away. But my best guess is that new jobs won't come in the numbers or timescale to truly help. The number of people who can get a PhD in machine learning will remain tiny in comparison to the scale of layoffs. And, sure, new demand will create new work, but that doesn't mean it all gets done by human beings.

Labor markets also have immense friction in terms of skills, geography, and identity. Consider that in the last bout of deindustrialization the steelworker in Pittsburgh or the carmaker in Detroit could hardly just up sticks, retrain mid-career, and get a job as a derivatives trader in New York or a branding consultant in Seattle or a schoolteacher in Miami. If Silicon Valley or the City of London creates lots of new jobs, it doesn't help people on the other side of the country if they don't have the right skills or aren't able to relocate. If your sense of self is wedded to a particular kind of work, it's little consolation if you feel your new job demeans your dignity.

Working on a zero-hours contract in a distribution center doesn't provide the sense of pride or social solidarity that came from working for a booming Detroit auto manufacturer in the 1960s. The Private Sector Job Quality Index, a measure of how many jobs provide above-average income, has plunged since 1990; it suggests that well-paying jobs as a proportion of the total have already started to fall.

Countries like India and the Philippines have seen a huge boom from business process outsourcing, creating comparatively high-paying jobs in places like call centers. It's precisely this kind of work that will be targeted by automation. New jobs might be created in the long term, but for millions they won't come quick enough or in the right places.

At the same time, a jobs recession will crater tax receipts, damaging public services and calling into question welfare programs just as they are most needed. Even before jobs are decimated, governments will be stretched thin, struggling to meet all their commitments, finance themselves sustainably, and deliver services the public has come to expect. Moreover, all this disruption will happen globally, on multiple dimensions, affecting every rung of the development ladder from primarily agricultural economies to advanced service-based sectors. From Lagos to L.A., pathways to sustainable employment will be subject to immense, unpredictable, and fast-evolving dislocations.

Even those who don't foresee the most severe outcomes of automation still accept that it is on course to cause significant medium-term disruptions. Whichever side of the jobs debate you fall on, it's hard to deny that the ramifications will be hugely destabilizing for hundreds of millions who will, at the very least, need to re-skill and transition to new types of work. Optimistic scenarios still involve troubling political ramifications from broken government finances to underemployed, insecure, and angry populations.

It augurs trouble. Another stressor in a stressed world.

LABOR MARKET DISRUPTIONS ARE, like social media, fragility amplifiers. They damage and undermine the nation-state. The first signs of this are coming into view, but like social media late in the first decade of the twenty-first century, it's not quite clear what the exact shape and extent of the implications will be. In any case, just because the consequences aren't yet evident doesn't mean they can be wished away.

The stressors outlined in this chapter (which are by no means exhaustive)—new forms of attack and vulnerability, the industrialization of misinformation, lethal autonomous weapons, accidents like lab leaks, and the consequences of automation—are all familiar to people in tech, policy, and security circles. Yet they are too often viewed in isolation. What gets lost in the analysis is that all these new pressures on our institutions stem from the same underlying general-purpose revolution. How they will arrive together, simultaneous stressors intersecting, buttressing, and boosting one another. The full amplification of fragility is missed because it often appears as if these impacts were happening incrementally and in convenient silos. They are not. They stem from a single coherent and interrelated phenomenon manifesting itself in different ways. The reality is much more enmeshed, entwined, emergent, and chaotic than any sequential presentation can convey. Fragility, amplified. The nation-state, weakened.

It has weathered bouts of instability before. What's different here is that a general-purpose revolution is not limited to specific niches, given problems, neatly demarcated sectors. It is, by definition, everywhere. The falling costs of power, of doing, aren't just about rogue bad actors or nimble start-ups, cloistered and limited applications.

Instead, power is redistributed and reinforced across the entire sum and span of society. The fully omni-use nature of the coming wave means it is found at every level, in every sector, every business, or sub-culture, or group, or bureaucracy, in every corner of our world. It produces trillions of dollars in new economic value while also destroying certain existing sources of wealth. Some individuals are greatly enabled; others stand to lose everything. Militarily it empowers some nation-states and militias alike. This is not, then, confined to amplifying specific points of fragility; it is, in the slightly longer term, about a transformation of the very ground on which society is built. And in this great redistribution of power, the state, already fragile and growing more so, is shaken to its core, its grand bargain left tattered and precarious.

THE FUTURE
OF NATIONS

THE STIRRUP

AT FIRST BLUSH, STIRRUPS MAY NOT SEEM ALL THAT REVOLUTIONARY.
They are, after all, fairly rudimentary triangles of metal attached to
leather straps and a horse's saddle. Look a bit closer, and another picture emerges.

Before the stirrup, a cavalry's battlefield impact was surprisingly
limited. Well-organized defensive shield walls could generally beat
back a horse-led charge. Because riders weren't fixed to their horses,
they were vulnerable. Soldiers armed with long spears and large
shields, standing in tightly drilled lines, could dismount even the heavi-
est cavalry. As a result, the primary function of your horse was in transporting you to the battlefield.

The stirrup revolutionized all that. It fixed the spear and rider to the
charging animal, making them a single unit. The full force of the spear
was now the combined power of the horse and the knight. Hitting a
shield no longer meant you fell off; it meant you smashed the shield
and the person holding it. Suddenly, galloping at full speed, lances out,
riders fixed, a heavy cavalry charge was an overwhelming shock tactic.
It could break even the staunchest of infantry lines.

This tiny innovation tipped the balance of power in favor of offense. Soon after the stirrup was introduced into Europe, Charles
Martel, leader of the Franks, saw its potential. Using it to devastating
effect, he defeated and expelled the Saracens from France. But the introduction of these heavy cavalry units required immense supporting

changes in Frankish society. Horses were hungry and expensive. Heavy cavalry required long years of training. In response, Martel and his heirs expropriated church lands and used them to raise a warrior elite. Their newfound wealth let them maintain horses, freed them to train, tied them into the kingdom, and, later, gave them funds to purchase armor. In return for their new wealth and status that elite promised to keep arms and fight for the king. Another grand bargain was struck.

Over time this improvised pact grew into an elaborate system of feudalism, with networks of obligations to liege lords and an immense stratum of bonded serfs. This was a world of estates and titles, jousting tournaments and apprenticeships, blacksmiths and artisans, armor and castles, a self-conscious culture of heraldic imagery and romantic stories of knightly courage. It became the dominant political form of the entire medieval period.

The stirrup was an apparently simple innovation. But with it came a social revolution changing hundreds of millions of lives. A system of politics, economics, war, and culture that structured European life for nearly a thousand years rested, in part, on those small metallic triangles. The story of stirrups and feudalism highlights an important truth: new technologies help create new centers of power with new social infrastructures both enabling them and supporting them. In the last chapter we saw how this process today adds to a series of immediate challenges facing the nation-state. But over the longer term, the implications of power's plummeting costs are tectonic, techno-political earthquakes shaking the ground upon which the state is built.

While small changes in technology can fundamentally alter the balance of power, trying to predict exactly how, decades into the future, is incredibly difficult. Exponential technologies amplify everyone and everything. And that creates seemingly contradictory trends. Power is both concentrated and dispersed. Incumbents are both strengthened and weakened. Nation-states are both more fragile and at greater risk of slipping into abuses of unchecked power.

Recall that growing access to power means *everyone's* power will be amplified. In the coming decades, historical patterns will play out once again, new centers will form, new infrastructures develop, new forms of governance and social organization emerge. At the same time, existing loci of power will be amplified in unpredictable ways. Sometimes, when one reads about technology, there is a heady sense that it will sweep away all that has come before, that no older businesses or institutions will survive the whirlwind. I don't think that's true; some will be swept away, but many will be augmented. Television can broadcast the revolution, but it can also help erase it. Technologies can reinforce social structures, hierarchies, and regimes of control as well as upend them.

In the resulting turbulence, without a major shift in focus, many open democratic states face a steady decay of their institutional foundations, a withering of legitimacy and authority. This is a circular dynamic of technology spreading and power shifting, which undermines the foundations, dents the capacity to rein it in, and so leads to further spread. At the same time, authoritarian states are given a potent new arsenal of repression.

The nation-state will be subject to massive centrifugal and centripetal forces, centralization and fragmentation. It's a fast track to chaos, calling into question who makes decisions and how; how those decisions are executed, by whom, when, and where, pressurizing those delicate balances and accommodations toward the breaking point. This recipe for turbulence will create epic new concentrations and dispersals of power, splintering the state from above and below. It will ultimately cast doubt on the viability of some nations altogether.

This ungovernable "post-sovereign" world, in the words of the political scientist Wendy Brown, will go far beyond a sense of near-term fragility; it will be instead a long-term macro-trend toward deep instability grinding away over decades. The first result will be massive new concentrations of power and wealth that reorder society.

CONCENTRATIONS:
THE COMPOUNDING RETURNS ON INTELLIGENCE

From the Mongols to the Mughals, for more than a thousand years the most powerful force in Asia was a traditional empire. By 1800 that had changed. It was rather a private company, owned by a relatively small number of shareholders, run by a handful of dusty accountants and administrators operating out of a building just five windows wide in a city thousands of miles away.

At the turn of the nineteenth century, the British East India Company controlled huge swaths of the Indian subcontinent. It ruled more land and people than existed in all of Europe, collecting taxes and setting laws. It commanded a well-drilled standing army of 200,000 men, twice as large as Britain's own army at home, and operated the world's largest mercantile fleet. Its collective firepower was greater than that of any state in Asia. Its global trading relationships were fundamental in everything from the foundation of Hong Kong to the Boston Tea Party. Its customs, duties, and dividends were critical to the British economy; no less than half of Britain's foreign trade at the time ran through the company.

This was clearly no ordinary corporation. In truth it *was* a kind of empire. It's difficult to conceive of a company like this in modern terms. We are not quite heading for a neocolonial East India Company 2.0. But I do think we have to confront the sheer scale and influence that some boardrooms have not just over the subtle nudges and choice architectures that shape culture and politics today but, more importantly, over where this could lead in decades to come. They are empires of a sort, and with the coming wave their scale, influence, and capability are set to radically expand.

PEOPLE OFTEN LIKE TO measure progress in AI by comparing it with how well an individual human can perform a certain task. Researchers talk about achieving superhuman performance in language translation, or on real-world tasks like driving. But what this misses is that the most powerful forces in the world are actually *groups* of individuals coordinating to achieve shared goals. Organizations too are a kind of intelligence. Companies, militaries, bureaucracies, even markets— these are artificial intelligences, aggregating and processing huge amounts of data, organizing themselves around specific goals, building mechanisms to get better and better at achieving those goals. Indeed, machine intelligence resembles a massive bureaucracy far more than it does a human mind. When we talk about something like AI having an enormous impact on the world, it's worth bearing in mind just how far-reaching these old-fashioned AIs are.

What happens when many, perhaps the majority, of the tasks required to operate a corporation, or a government department, can be run more efficiently by machines? Who will benefit first from these dynamics, and what will they likely do with this new power?

We are already in an era where megacorporations have trillion-dollar valuations and more assets, in every sense, than entire countries. Take Apple. It has produced one of the most beautiful, influential, and widely used products in the history of our species. The iPhone is genius. With its product used by more than 1.2 billion people worldwide, the company has deservedly collected rich rewards for its success: in 2022, Apple was valued at more than all the companies listed on the U.K.'s FTSE 100 stock exchange *combined*. With close to $200 billion of cash and investments in the bank and a captive audience largely locked into its ecosystem, Apple seems well placed to take advantage of this new wave.

Similarly, a vast span of services, from very different sectors, across huge parts of the planet, have been collapsed into a single corporation, Google: mapping and location, reviews and business listings, advertising, video streaming, office tools, calendars, email, photo storage, videoconferencing, and so on. Big tech companies provide tools for everything from organizing a birthday to running multimillion-dollar businesses. The only equivalent organizations, touching so deeply into the lives of so many, are national governments. Call it "Googlization": a range of services provided for free or at low cost leading to single entities functionally enabling massive sections of the economy and human experience.

To get a sense of these concentrations, consider that the combined revenues of companies in *Fortune*'s Global 500 are already at 44 percent of world GDP. Their total profits are larger than all but the top six countries' annual GDPs. Companies already control the largest clusters of AI processors, the best models, the most advanced quantum computers, and the overwhelming majority of robotics capacity and IP. Unlike with rockets, satellites, and the internet, the frontier of this wave is found in corporations, not in government organizations or academic labs. Accelerate this process with the next generation of technology, and a future of corporate concentration doesn't seem so extraordinary.

There is already a pronounced and accelerating "superstar" effect, where leading players take ever more outsized shares of the pie. The world's top fifty cities have the lion's share of wealth and corporate power (45 percent of big company HQs; 21 percent of world GDP) despite having only 8 percent of the world's population. The top 10 percent of global firms take 80 percent of the total profits. Expect the coming wave to feed into this picture, producing ever-richer and more successful superstars—whether regions, business sectors, companies, or research groups.

I think we'll see a group of private corporations grow beyond the size and reach of many nation-states. Consider the outsized influence of a sprawling corporate empire like the Samsung Group in South Korea. Founded as a noodle shop almost a century ago, it became a major conglomerate after the Korean War. As Korean growth accelerated in the 1960s and 1970s, Samsung was at the heart of it, not only a diversified manufacturing powerhouse but a major player in banking and insurance. The Korean economic miracle was a Samsung-powered miracle. By this point Samsung was the leading chaebol, the name given to a small group of massive firms dominating the country.

Smartphones, semiconductors, and TVs are Samsung specialties. But so too are life insurance, ferry operators, and theme parks. Careers at Samsung are enormously prized. Samsung Group revenue represents up to 20 percent of the Korean economy. For Koreans today, Samsung is almost like a parallel government, a constant presence throughout people's lives. Given the dense network of interests and ongoing corporate and governmental scandals, the balance of power between the state and the corporation is precarious and fuzzy.

Samsung and Korea are outliers but perhaps not for much longer. Given the range of concentrated capabilities, things typically the province of governments today, like education and defense, perhaps even currency or law enforcement, could be provided by this new generation of companies. Already, for example, eBay and PayPal's dispute resolution system handles around sixty million disagreements a year, three times as many as the entire U.S. legal system. Ninety percent of these disputes are settled using technology alone. There's more to come.

TECHNOLOGY HAS ALREADY CREATED modern empires, of a sort. The coming wave rapidly accelerates this trend, putting immense power and riches into the hands of those who create and control it. New, private interests will step into spaces vacated by overstretched and strained governments. This process won't, like the East India Company, come enforced at the barrel of a musket, but it will, exactly like the East India Company, create private companies with the scale, reach, and power of governments. Those companies with the cash, expertise, and distribution to take advantage of the coming wave, to greatly augment their intelligence and simultaneously extend their reach, will see colossal gains.

In the last wave, things dematerialized; goods became services. You don't buy software or music on CDs anymore; it's streamed. You just expect antivirus and security software as a by-product of using Google or Apple. Products break, get obsolete. Services less so. They are seamless and easy to use. For their part, companies are eager for you to subscribe to their software ecosystems; regular payments are alluring. All the big tech platforms either are mainly service businesses or have very large service businesses. Apple has the App Store, despite primarily selling devices, and Amazon, while operating as the world's biggest retailer of physical goods, also provides e-commerce services to merchants and TV streaming to individuals, and hosts a good chunk of the internet on its cloud offering, Amazon Web Services.

Everywhere you look, technology accelerates this dematerialization, reducing complexity for the end consumer by providing continuous consumption services rather than traditional buy-once products. Whether it's services like Uber, DoorDash, and Airbnb, or open publishing platforms like Instagram and TikTok, the drift of megabusinesses is toward not participating in the market but being the market, not making the product but operating the service. The question now becomes, what else could be made into a service, collapsed into the existing suite of another mega-business?

In a few decades, I predict most physical products will look like services. Zero marginal cost production and distribution will make it possible. The migration to the cloud will become all-encompassing, and the trend will be spurred by the ascendancy of low-code and no-code software, the rise of bio-manufacturing, and the boom in 3-D printing. When you combine all the facets of the coming wave, from the design, management, and logistical capabilities of AI to the modeling of chemical reactions enabled by quantum computing to the fine-grained assembly capabilities of robotics, you get a wholesale revolution in the nature of production.

Foods, drugs, home products, indeed almost anything might be 3-D printed, or bio-produced, or made using atomically precise manufacturing close to or at the site of use, governed by sophisticated AIs fluidly working with customers using natural language. You simply buy the execution code and let an AI or robot do the task or create the product. Yes, this glosses over a hideous mass of material complexity, and yes, it's a long way off. But squint into the distance, and this scenario is clearly plausible. Even if you don't buy the whole argument here, it seems impossible that these forces will not create major changes and new concentrations of value throughout the global economic supply chain.

Meeting demand for cheap and seamless services usually requires scale (massive up-front investment in chips, people, security, innovation), which rewards and accelerates centralization. In this scenario there will be just a few mega-players whose scale and power will begin to rival traditional states. What's more, owners of the best systems may be able to establish an immense competitive advantage. Those huge centralized coming-wave firms I just mentioned? They likely end up bigger, richer, and more entrenched than businesses in the past.

The more that systems successfully generalize across sector after sector, the more that power and wealth concentrates with their owners. Those with the resources to invent or adopt new technologies fastest—those that can pass my updated Turing test, for example—will enjoy rapidly compounding returns. Their systems have more data and "real-world deployment experience" and so work better, generalize faster, and lock in the advantage, sucking in the best talent to build them. An unbridgeable "intelligence gap" becomes plausible. If one organization gets far enough ahead, it might become a revenue generator and ultimately a power center without parallel. If that process extends to something like full AGI or quantum supremacy, it could make things very difficult for new entrants or indeed governments.

Whatever the end point, we are heading to a place where unprecedented powers and abilities are out there, in the hands of already powerful actors who'll no doubt use them to amplify their reach and further their own agenda.

Such concentrations will enable vast, automated megacorporations to transfer value away from human capital—work—and toward raw capital. Put all the inequalities resulting from concentration together, and it adds up to another great acceleration and structural deepening of an existing fracture. Little wonder there is talk of neo- or techno-feudalism—a direct challenge to the social order, this time built on something beyond even stirrups.

In sum, returns on intelligence will compound exponentially. A select few artificial intelligences that we used to call organizations will massively benefit from a new concentration of ability—probably the greatest such concentration yet seen. Re-creating the essence of what's made our species so successful into tools that can be reused and reapplied over and over, in myriad different settings, is a mighty prize, which corporations and bureaucracies of all kinds will pursue, and wield. How these entities are governed, how they will rub against, capture, and reengineer the state, is an open question. That they will challenge it seems certain.

But the consequences of greater concentrations of power don't end with corporations.

SURVEILLANCE: ROCKET FUEL FOR AUTHORITARIANISM

When compared with superstar corporations, governments appear slow, bloated, and out of touch. It's tempting to dismiss them as headed for the trash can of history. However, another inevitable reaction of nation-states will be to use the tools of the coming wave to tighten their grip on power, taking full advantage to entrench their dominance.

In the twentieth century, totalitarian regimes wanted planned economies, obedient populations, and controlled information ecosystems. They wanted complete hegemony. Every aspect of life was managed. Five-year plans dictated everything from the number and content of films to bushels of wheat expected from a given field. High modernist planners hoped to create pristine cities of stark order and flow. An ever-watchful and ruthless security apparatus kept it all ticking over. Power concentrated in the hands of a single supreme leader, capable of surveying the entire picture and acting decisively. Think Soviet collectivization, Stalin's five-year plans, Mao's China, East Germany's Stasi. This is government as dystopian nightmare.

And so far at least, it has always gone disastrously wrong. Despite the best efforts of revolutionaries and bureaucrats alike, society could not be bent into shape; it was never fully "legible" to the state, but a messy, ungovernable reality that would not conform with the purist dreams of the center. Humanity is too multifarious, too impulsive to be boxed in like this. In the past, the tools available to totalitarian governments simply weren't equal to the task. So those governments failed; they failed to improve quality of life, or eventually they collapsed or reformed. Extreme concentration wasn't just highly undesirable; it was practically impossible.

The coming wave presents the disturbing possibility that this may no longer be true. Instead, it could initiate an injection of centralized power and control that will morph state functions into repressive distortions of their original purpose. Rocket fuel for authoritarians and for great power competition alike. The ability to capture and harness data at an extraordinary scale and precision; to create territory-spanning systems of surveillance and control, reacting in real time; to put, in other words, history's most powerful set of technologies under the command of a single body, would rewrite the limits of state power so comprehensively that it would produce a new kind of entity altogether.

———

YOUR SMART SPEAKER WAKES you up. Immediately you turn to your phone and check your emails. Your smart watch tells you you've had a normal night's sleep and your heart rate is average for the morning. Already a distant organization knows, in theory, what time you are awake, how you are feeling, and what you are looking at. You leave the house and head to the office, your phone tracking your movements, logging the keystrokes on your text messages and the podcast you listen to. On the way, and throughout the day, you are captured on CCTV hundreds of times. After all, this city has at least one camera for every ten people, maybe many more than that. When you swipe in at the office, the system notes your time of entry. Software installed on your computer monitors productivity down to eye movements.

On the way home you stop to buy dinner. The supermarket's loyalty scheme tracks your purchases. After eating, you binge-stream another TV series; your viewing habits are duly noted. Every glance, every hurried message, every half thought registered in an open browser or fleeting search, every step through bustling city streets, every heartbeat and bad night's sleep, every purchase made or backed out of—it is all captured, watched, tabulated. And this is only a tiny slice of the possible data harvested every day, not just at work or on the phone, but at the doctor's office or in the gym. Almost every detail of life is logged, somewhere, by those with the sophistication to process and act on the data they collect. This is not some far-off dystopia. I'm describing daily reality for millions in a city like London.

The only step left is bringing these disparate databases together into a single, integrated system: a perfect twenty-first-century surveillance apparatus. The preeminent example is, of course, China. That's hardly news, but what's become clear is how advanced and ambitious the party's program already is, let alone where it might end up in twenty or thirty years.

Compared with the West, Chinese research into AI concentrates on areas of surveillance like object tracking, scene understanding, and voice or action recognition. Surveillance technologies are ubiquitous, increasingly granular in their ability to home in on every aspect of citizens' lives. They combine visual recognition of faces, gaits, and license plates with data collection—including bio-data—on a mass scale. Centralized services like WeChat bundle everything from private messaging to shopping and banking in one easily traceable place. Drive the highways of China, and you'll notice hundreds of Automatic Number Plate Recognition cameras tracking vehicles. (These exist in most large urban areas in the Western world, too.) During COVID quarantines, robot dogs and drones carried speakers blasting messages warning people to stay inside.

Facial recognition software builds on the advances in computer vision we saw in part 2, identifying individual faces with exquisite accuracy. When I open my phone, it starts automatically upon "seeing" my face: a small but slick convenience, but with obvious and profound implications. Although the system was initially developed by corporate and academic researchers in the United States, nowhere embraced or perfected the technology more than China.

Chairman Mao had said "the people have sharp eyes" when watching their neighbors for infractions against communist orthodoxy. By 2015 this was the inspiration for a massive "Sharp Eyes" facial recognition program that ultimately aspired to roll such surveillance out across no less than 100 percent of public space. A team of leading researchers from the Chinese University of Hong Kong went on to found Sense-Time, one of the world's largest facial recognition companies, built on a database of more than two billion faces. China is now the leader in facial recognition technologies, with giant companies like Megvii and CloudWalk vying with SenseTime for market share. Chinese police even have sunglasses with built-in facial recognition technology capable of tracking suspects in crowds.

Around half the world's billion CCTV cameras are in China. Many have built-in facial recognition and are carefully positioned to gather maximal information, often in quasi-private spaces: residential buildings, hotels, even karaoke lounges. A *New York Times* investigation found the police in Fujian Province alone estimated they held a database of 2.5 billion facial images. They were candid about its purpose: "controlling and managing people." Authorities are also looking to suck in audio data—police in the city of Zhongshan wanted cameras that could record audio within a three-hundred-foot radius—and close monitoring and storage of bio-data became routine in the COVID era.

The Ministry of Public Security is clear on the next priority: stitch these scattered databases and services into a coherent whole, from license plates to DNA, WeChat accounts to credit cards. This AI-enabled system could spot emerging threats to the CCP like dissenters and protests in real time, allowing for a seamless, crushing government response to anything it perceived as undesirable. Nowhere does this come together with more horrifying potential than in the Xinjiang Autonomous Region.

This rugged and remote part of northwest China has seen the systematic and technologically empowered repression and ethnic cleansing of its native Uighur people. All these systems of monitoring and control are brought together here. Cities are placed under blankets of camera surveillance with facial recognition and AI tracking. Checkpoints and "reeducation" camps govern movements and freedoms. A system of social credit scores based on numerous surveilled databases keeps tabs on the population. Authorities have built an iris-scan database that has the capacity to hold up to thirty million samples—more than the region's population.

Societies of overweening surveillance and control are already here, and now all of this is set to escalate enormously into a next-level concentration of power at the center. Yet it would be a mistake to write this off as just a Chinese or authoritarian problem. For a start, this tech is being exported wholesale to places like Venezuela and Zimbabwe, Ecuador and Ethiopia. Even to the United States. In 2019, the U.S. government banned federal agencies and their contractors from buying telecommunications and surveillance equipment from a number of Chinese providers including Huawei, ZTE, and Hikvision. Yet, just a year later, three federal agencies were found to have bought such equipment from prohibited vendors. More than one hundred U.S. towns have even acquired technology developed for use on the Uighurs in Xinjiang. A textbook failure of containment.

Western firms and governments are also in the vanguard of building and deploying this tech. Invoking London above was no accident: it competes with cities like Shenzhen for most surveilled in the world. It's no secret that governments monitor and control their own populations, but these tendencies extend deep into Western firms, too. In smart warehouses every micromovement of every worker is tracked down to body temperature and loo breaks. Companies like Vigilant Solutions aggregate movement data based on license plate tracking, then sell it to jurisdictions like state or municipal governments. Even your take-out pizza is being watched: Domino's uses AI-powered cameras to check its pies. Just as much as anyone in China, those in the West leave a vast data exhaust every day of their lives. And just as in China, it is harvested, processed, operationalized, and sold.

BEFORE THE COMING WAVE the notion of a global "high-tech panopticon" was the stuff of dystopian novels, Yevgeny Zamyatin's *We* or George Orwell's *1984*. The panopticon is becoming possible. Billions of devices and trillions of data points could be operated and monitored at once, in real time, used not just for surveillance but for prediction. Not only will it foresee social outcomes with precision and granularity, but it might also subtly or overtly steer or coerce them, from grand macroprocesses like election results down to individual consumer behaviors.

This raises the prospect of totalitarianism to a new plane. It won't happen everywhere, and not all at once. But if AI, biotech, quantum, robotics, and the rest of it are centralized in the hands of a repressive state, the resulting entity would be palpably different from any yet seen. In the next chapter we will return to this possibility. However, before then comes another trend. One completely, and paradoxically, at odds with centralization.

FRAGMENTATIONS: POWER TO THE PEOPLE

Hear the word "Hezbollah" and for most people it doesn't suggest parliaments, schools, and hospitals. This is, after all, a militant organization born of the long tragedy of Lebanon's civil war, with a track record of violence, officially classed as terrorist by the U.S. government and often acting as a proxy for Iranian interests. But there's a lot more happening here, and it hints at an alternative direction for power and the state.

In its Lebanese home territory, Hezbollah operates as a Shiite "state within a state." There's the sizable and notorious military wing. It may be the best-armed non-state actor in the world, with, in the words of one analyst, "a larger arsenal of artillery than most nations." It has drones, tanks, long-range rockets, and many thousands of foot soldiers who've fought alongside the Assad regime in the Syrian civil war and regularly engaged Israel.

Perhaps to the surprise of some, Hezbollah is also a major mainstream political force, a conventional party in the ongoing psychodrama that is the Lebanese government. It is in many ways just another part of the political system, building alliances, drafting laws, and working with the conventional instruments of state. Its members sit on local municipal councils and in parliament and hold ministerial cabinet positions. Across the large swaths of Lebanese territory it controls, Hezbollah operates schools, hospitals, health-care centers, infrastructure, water projects, and microcredit-lending initiatives. Indeed, some of these programs even have the support of Sunnis and Christians. Whole districts are essentially run by Hezbollah in the manner of a state. It also conducts various commercial activities, of both a legal and a more criminal nature, including smuggling oil.

So what is Hezbollah? State or non-state? Extremist group or conventional territory-based power? It is instead a strange "hybrid" entity functioning both within and outside state institutions. A state, and yet not a state, capable of cherry-picking responsibilities and activities to the benefit of its own interests, often with dire consequences for the wider country and region. There aren't too many organizations like Hezbollah, which evolved amid unique regional tensions.

The coming wave, however, could make a range of small, state-like entities a lot more plausible. Contrary to centralization, it might actually spur a kind of "Hezbollahization," a splintered, tribalized world where everyone has access to the latest technologies, where everyone can support themselves on their own terms, where it is far more possible for anyone to maintain living standards without the great superstructures of nation-state organization.

Consider that a combination of AI, cheap robotics, and advanced biotech coupled with clean energy sources might, for the first time in modernity, make living "off-grid" nearly equivalent to being plugged-in. Recall that over just the last decade the cost of solar photovoltaics has fallen by more than 82 percent and will plunge further, putting energy self-sufficiency for smaller communes within reach. As electrification of infrastructure and alternatives to fossil fuels percolate, more of the world could become self-sufficient—but now equipped with an infrastructure of AI, bio, robotics, and so on, capable of generating information and manufacturing locally.

Fields like education and medicine currently rely on huge social and financial infrastructures. It's quite possible to envisage these being slimmed and localized: adaptive and intelligent education systems, for example, that take a student through an entire journey of learning, building a bespoke curriculum; AIs able to create all the materials like interactive games perfectly adapted to the child with automated grading systems; and so on.

You might have no collective security umbrella, as in a nation-state system, but hire different forms of physical and cyber protection on an ad hoc basis. AI hackers and autonomous drones will be available to private security groups as well. We saw earlier how offensive capacity is being spread to anyone who wants it; the converse is that the same distribution will, in time, happen to defense. When anyone has access to the bleeding edge, it's not just nation-states that can mount formidable physical and virtual defenses.

In short, key parts of modern society and social organization that today rely on scale and centralization could be radically devolved by capabilities unlocked with the coming wave. Mass rebellion, secessionism, and state formation of any kind look very different in this world. Redistributing real power means communities of all kinds can live as they wish, whether they are ISIS, FARC, Anonymous, secessionists from Biafra to Catalonia, or a major corporation building luxury theme parks on a remote island in the Pacific.

SOME ASPECTS OF THE coming wave point toward further centralization of power. The biggest AI models will cost hundreds of millions of dollars to train, and consequently few will have ownership. But paradoxically a countertrend will play out in parallel. AI breakthroughs already make their way into open-source code repositories within days of being published in open-access journals, making topflight models easy for anyone to access, experiment with, build, and modify in turn. Models down to the weights are published, leaked, and stolen.

Companies like Stability AI and Hugging Face accelerate distributed, decentralized forms of AI. Techniques like CRISPR make biological experimentation easier, meaning biohackers in their garages can tinker at the absolute frontier of science. Ultimately, sharing or copying DNA or the code of a large language model is trivial. Openness is the default, imitations are endemic, cost curves relentlessly go down, and barriers to access crumble. Exponential capabilities are given to anyone who wants them.

This heralds a colossal redistribution of power *away* from existing centers. Imagine a future where small groups—whether in failing states like Lebanon or in off-grid nomad camps in New Mexico—provide AI-empowered services like credit unions, schools, and health care, services at the heart of the community often reliant on scale or the state. Where the chance to set the terms of society at a micro level becomes irresistible: come to our boutique school and avoid critical race theory forever, or boycott the evil financial system and use our DeFi product. Where any grouping of any kind—ideological, religious, cultural, racial—can self-organize a viable society. Think about setting up your own school. Or hospital or army. It's such a complex, vast, and difficult project, even the thought of it is tiring. Just gathering the resources, getting necessary permissions and equipment, is a lifelong endeavor. Now consider having an array of assistants who, when asked to create a school, a hospital, or an army, can make it happen in a realistic time frame.

ACI and synthetic biology empower Extinction Rebellion as much as the Dow Jones megacorp; the microstate with a charismatic leader as much as a lumbering giant. While some advantages of size may be augmented, they may also be nullified. Ask yourself what happens to already fraying states if every sect, separatist movement, charitable foundation, and social network, every zealot and xenophobe, every populist conspiracy theory, political party, or even mafia, drug cartel, or terrorist group has their shot at state building. The disenfranchised will simply re-enfranchise themselves—on their own terms.

Fragmentations could occur all over. What if companies themselves start down a journey of becoming states? Or cities decide to break away and gain more autonomy? What if people spend more time, money, and emotional energy in virtual worlds than the real? What happens to traditional hierarchies when tools of awesome power and expertise are as available to street children as to billionaires? It's already a remarkable fact that corporate titans spend most of their lives working on software, like Gmail or Excel, accessible to most people on the planet. Extend that, radically, with the democratization of empowerment, when everyone on the planet has unfettered access to the most powerful technologies ever built.

AS PEOPLE INCREASINGLY TAKE power into their own hands, I expect inequality's newest frontier to lie in biology. A fragmented world is one where some jurisdictions are far more permissive about human experimentation than others, where pockets of advanced bio-capabilities and self-modification produce divergent outcomes at the level of DNA, which in turn produce divergent outcomes at the levels of states and microstates. There could then be something like a biohacking personal enhancement arms race. A country desperate for investment or advantage might see potential in becoming an anything-goes biohacker paradise. What does the social contract look like if a select group of "post-humans" engineer themselves to some unreachable intellectual or physical plane? How would this intersect with the dynamic of fragmenting politics, some enclaves trying to leave the whole behind?

All of this is still firmly in the realm of speculation. But we are entering a new era where the previously unthinkable is now a distinct possibility. Being blinkered about what's happening is, in my view, more dangerous than being overly speculative.

Governance works by consent; it is a collective fiction resting on the belief of everyone concerned. In this scenario the sovereign state is pressured to the breaking point. The old social contract gets ripped to pieces. Institutions are bypassed, undermined, superseded. Taxation, law enforcement, compliance with norms: all under threat. In this scenario rapid fragmentation of power could accelerate a kind of "turbo-balkanization" that gives nimble and newly capable actors unprecedented freedom to operate. An unbundling of the great consolidations of authority and service embodied by the state begins.

Something more like the pre-nation-state world emerges in this scenario, neo-medieval, smaller, more local, and constitutionally diverse, a complex, unstable patchwork of polities. Only this time with hugely powerful technology. When northern Italy was a patchwork of small city-states, it gave us the Renaissance, yet was also a field of constant internecine war and feuding. Renaissance is great; unceasing war with tomorrow's military technology, not so much.

For many people working in or adjacent to technology, these kinds of radical outcomes are not just unwelcome by-products; they're the goal itself. Hyper-libertarian technologists like the PayPal founder and venture capitalist Peter Thiel celebrate a vision of the state withering away, seeing this as liberation for an overmighty species of business leaders or "sovereign individuals," as they call themselves. A bonfire of public services, institutions, and norms is cheered on with an explicit vision where technology might "create the space for new modes of dissent and new ways to form communities not bounded by historical nation-states."

The techno-libertarian movement takes Ronald Reagan's 1981 dictum "Government is the problem" to its logical extreme, seeing government's many flaws but not its immense benefits, believing that its regulatory and tax functions are destructive rate limiters with few upsides—for them at least. I find it deeply depressing that some of the most powerful and privileged take such a narrow and destructive view, but it adds a further impetus to fragmentation.

This is a world where billionaires and latter-day prophets can build and run microstates; where non-state actors from corporations to communes to algorithms begin to overshadow the state from above but also from below. Think again of the stirrup and the profound downstream effects of a single, simple invention. And then think of the scale of invention in the coming wave. Coupled with the existing pressures and fragility, sweeping change on the order of my speculation above doesn't seem so far-out. What would be stranger is no radical change at all.

THE COMING WAVE
OF CONTRADICTIONS

If centralization and decentralization sound as if they are in direct contradiction, that's with good reason: they are. Understanding the future means handling multiple conflicting trajectories at once. The coming wave launches immense centralizing and decentralizing riptides *at the same time*. Both will be in play at once. Every individual, every business, every church, every nonprofit, every nation, will eventually have its own AI and ultimately its own bio and robotics capability. From a single individual on their sofa to the world's largest organizations, each AI will aim to achieve the goals of its owner. Herein lies the key to understanding the coming wave of contradictions, a wave full of collisions.

Each new formulation of power will offer a different vision of delivering public goods, or propose a different way to make products or a different set of religious beliefs to evangelize. AI systems already make critical decisions with overt political implications: who receives a loan, a job, a place at college, parole; who gets seen by a senior physician. Within the decade AIs will decide how public money gets spent, where military forces are assigned, or what students should learn. This will occur in both centralizing and decentralizing ways. An AI might, for example, operate as one massive, state-spanning system, a single general-purpose utility governing hundreds of millions. Equally we will also have vastly capable systems, available at low cost, open-source, highly adapted, catering to a village.

Multiple ownership structures will exist in tandem: technology democratized in open-source collectives, the products of today's corporate leaders or insurgent blitz-scaling start-ups, and government held, whether through nationalization or in-house nurturing. All will coexist and coevolve, and everywhere they will alter, magnify, produce, and disrupt flows and networks of power.

Where and how the forces play out will vary dramatically according to existing social and political factors. This should not be an oversimplified picture, and there will be numerous points of resistance and adaptation not obvious in advance. Some sectors or regions will go one way, some the other, some will see powerful contortions of both. Some hierarchies and social structures will be reinforced, others overturned; some places may become more equal or authoritarian, others much less so. In all cases, the additional stress and volatility, the unpredictable amplification of power, the wrenching disruption of radical new centers of capability, will further stress the foundation of the liberal democratic nation-state system.

And if this picture sounds too strange, paradoxical, and impossible, consider this. The coming wave will only deepen and recapitulate the exact same contradictory dynamics of the last wave. The internet does precisely this: centralizes in a few key hubs while also empowering billions of people. It creates behemoths and yet gives everyone the opportunity to join in. Social media created a few giants and a million tribes. Everyone can build a website, but there's only one Google. Everyone can sell their own niche products, but there's only one Amazon. And on and on. The disruption of the internet era is largely explained by this tension, this potent, combustible brew of empowerment and control.

Now, with the coming wave, forces like these will expand beyond the internet and the digital sphere. Apply them to any given area of life. Yes, this recipe for wrenching change is one we've seen before. But if the internet seemed big, this is bigger. Massively omni-use general-purpose technologies will change both society and what it means to be human. This might sound hyperbolic. But within the next decade, we must anticipate radical flux, new concentrations and dispersals of information, wealth, and above all power.

So, where does it leave technology and, much more important, where does it leave us? What happens if the state can no longer control, in a balanced fashion, the coming wave? So far in part 3, we've discussed the already precarious condition of the modern nation-state and previewed new threats arriving with the coming wave. We've seen how a crushing set of stressors and a colossal redistribution of power will converge to take the one force capable of managing the wave—the state—to a point of crisis.

That moment is almost here. Brought about by the inexorable rise of technology and the end of nations, this crisis will take the form of a huge, existential-level bind, a set of brutal choices and trade-offs that represents the most important dilemma of the twenty-first century.

Leaving us with no good options would be technology's ultimate failure. Yet this is precisely where we are headed.

CHAPTER 12

THE DILEMMA

CATASTROPHE:
THE ULTIMATE FAILURE

T HE HISTORY OF HUMANITY IS, IN PART, A HISTORY OF CATASTROPHE. Pandemics feature widely. Two killed up to 30 percent of the world population: the sixth-century Plague of Justinian and the fourteenth-century Black Death. England's population was seven million in 1300, but by 1450, crushed by waves of the plague, it was down to just two million.

Catastrophes are also, of course, man-made. World War I killed around 1 percent of the global population; World War II, 3 percent. Or take the violence unleashed by Genghis Khan and the Mongol army across China and central Asia in the thirteenth century, which took the lives of up to 10 percent of the world's population. With the advent of the atomic bomb, humanity now possesses enough lethal force to kill everyone on the planet several times over. Catastrophic events that once took place over years and decades could happen in minutes, at the push of a button.

With the coming wave, we are poised to take yet another such leap, expanding both the upper bound of risk and the number of avenues available to those seeking to unleash catastrophic force. In this chapter, we go beyond fragility and threats to the functioning of the state and envisage what happens—sooner or later—if containment is not possible.

The overwhelming majority of these technologies will be used for good. Although I have focused on their risks, it's important to keep in mind they will improve countless lives on a daily basis. In this chapter we are looking at extreme edge cases almost no one wants to see, least of all those working with these tools. However, just because they will be a vanishing minority of use cases doesn't mean we can ignore them. We've seen that bad actors can do serious damage, igniting mass instability. Now imagine when any half-competent lab or hacker could synthesize complex strands of DNA. How long before disaster strikes?

Eventually, as some of history's most powerful technologies percolate everywhere, those edge cases become more likely. Eventually, something will go wrong—at scales and speeds commensurate with the capabilities unleashed. The upshot of the coming wave's four features is that, absent strong methods of containment operating at every level, catastrophic outcomes like an engineered pandemic are more possible than ever.

That is unacceptable. And yet here's the dilemma: the most secure solutions for containment are equally unacceptable, leading humanity down an authoritarian and dystopian pathway.

On the one hand, societies could turn toward the kind of tech-enabled total surveillance we saw in the last chapter, a gut response enforcing hard mechanisms against wayward or uncontrolled technology. Security—at the price of freedom. Or humanity might step away from the technological frontier altogether. Although unlikely, it's no answer. The only entity in principle capable of navigating this existential bind is the same system of nation-states currently falling apart, dragged down by the very forces it needs to contain.

Over time, then, the implications of these technologies will push humanity to navigate a path between the poles of catastrophe and dystopia. This is the essential dilemma of our age.

The promise of technology is that it improves lives, the benefits far outweighing the costs and downsides. This set of wicked choices means that promise has been savagely inverted.

Doom-mongering makes people—myself included—glassy-eyed. At this point, you may be feeling wary or skeptical. Talking of catastrophic effects often invites ridicule: accusations of catastrophism, indulgent negativity, shrill alarmism, navel-gazing on remote and rarefied risks when plenty of clear and present dangers scream for attention. Like breathless techno-optimism, breathless techno-catastrophism is easy to dismiss as a twisted, misguided form of hype unsupported by the historical record.

But just because a warning has dramatic implications isn't good grounds to automatically reject it. The pessimism-averse complacency greeting the prospect of disaster is itself a recipe for disaster. It feels plausible, rational in its own terms, "smart" to dismiss warnings as the overblown chatter of a few weirdos, but this attitude prepares the way for its own failure.

No doubt, technological risk takes us into uncertain territory. Nonetheless, all the trends point to a profusion of risk. This speculation is grounded in constantly compounding scientific and technological improvements. Those who dismiss catastrophe are, I believe, discounting the objective facts before us. After all, we are not talking here about the proliferation of motorbikes or washing machines.

VARIETIES OF CATASTROPHE

To see what catastrophic harms we should prepare for, simply extrapolate the bad actor attacks we saw in chapter 10. Here are just a few plausible scenarios.

Terrorists mount automatic weapons equipped with facial recognition to an autonomous drone swarm hundreds or thousands strong, each capable of quickly rebalancing from the weapon's recoil, firing short bursts, and moving on. These drones are unleashed on a major downtown with instructions to kill a specific profile. In busy rush hour these would operate with terrifying efficiency, following an optimized route around the city. In minutes there would be an attack at far greater scale than, say, the 2008 Mumbai attacks, which saw armed terrorists roaming through city landmarks like the central train station.

A mass murderer decides to hit a huge political rally with drones, spraying devices, and a bespoke pathogen. Soon attendees become sick, then their families. The speaker, a much-loved and much-loathed political lightning rod, is one of the first victims. In a febrile partisan atmosphere an assault like this ignites violent reprisals around the country and the chaos cascades.

Using only natural language instruction, a hostile conspiracist in America disseminates masses of surgically constructed and divisive disinformation. Numerous attempts are made, most of which fail to gain traction. One eventually catches on: a police murder in Chicago. It's completely fake, but the trouble on the streets, the widespread revulsion, is real. The attackers now have a playbook. By the time the video is verified as a fraud, violent riots with multiple casualties roil around the country, the fires continually stoked by new gusts of disinformation.

Or imagine all that happening at the same time. Or not just at one event or in one city, but in hundreds of places. With tools like this it doesn't take too much to realize that bad actor empowerment opens the door to catastrophe. Today's AI systems try hard not to tell you how to poison the water supply or build an undetectable bomb. They are not yet capable of defining or pursuing goals on their own. However, as we have seen, both more widely diffused and less safe versions of today's cutting-edge and more powerful models are coming, fast.

Of all the catastrophic risks from the coming wave, AI has received the most coverage. But there are plenty more. Once militaries are fully automated, the barriers to entry for conflict will be far lower. A war might be sparked accidentally for reasons that forever remain unclear, AIs detecting some pattern of behavior or threat and then reacting, instantaneously, with overwhelming force. Suffice to say, the nature of that war could be alien, escalate quickly, and be unsurpassed in destructive consequences.

We've already come across engineered pandemics and the perils of accidental releases, and glimpsed what happens when millions of self-improvement enthusiasts can experiment with the genetic code of life. An extreme bio-risk event of a less obvious kind, targeting a given portion of the population, say, or sabotaging an ecosystem, cannot be discounted. Imagine activists wanting to stop the cocaine trade inventing a new bug that targets only coca plants as a way to replace aerial fumigation. Or if militant vegans decided to disrupt the entire meat supply chain, with dire anticipated and unanticipated consequences. Either might spiral out of control.

We know what a lab leak might look like in the context of amplifying fragility, but if it was not quickly brought under control, it would rank with previous plagues. To put this in context, the omicron variant of COVID infected a quarter of Americans within a hundred days of first being identified. What if we had a pandemic that had, say, a 20 percent mortality rate, but with that kind of transmissibility? Or what if it was a kind of respiratory HIV that would lie incubating for years with no acute symptoms? A novel human transmissible virus with a reproduction rate of, say, 4 (far below chicken pox or measles) and a case fatality rate of 50 percent (far below Ebola or bird flu) could, even accounting for lockdown-style measures, cause more than a billion deaths in a matter of months. What if multiple such pathogens were released at once? This goes far beyond fragility amplification; it would be an unfathomable calamity.

BEYOND HOLLYWOOD CLICHÉS, a subculture of academic researchers has pushed an extreme narrative of how AI could instigate an existential disaster. Think an all-powerful machine somehow destroying the world for its own mysterious ends: not some malignant AI wreaking intentional destruction like in the movies, but a full-scale AGI blindly optimizing for an opaque goal, oblivious to human concerns.

The canonical thought experiment is that if you set up a sufficiently powerful AI to make paper clips but don't specify the goal carefully enough, it may eventually turn the world and maybe even the contents of the entire cosmos into paper clips. Start following chains of logic like this and myriad sequences of unnerving events unspool. AI safety researchers worry (correctly) that should something like an AGI be created, humanity would no longer control its own destiny. For the first time, we would be toppled as the dominant species in the known universe. However clever the designers, however robust the safety mechanisms, accounting for all eventualities, guaranteeing safety, is impossible. Even if it was fully aligned with human interests, a sufficiently powerful AI could potentially overwrite its programming, discarding safety and alignment features apparently built in.

Following this line of thinking, I often hear people say something along the lines of "AGI is the greatest risk humanity faces today! It's going to end the world!" But when pressed on what this actually looks like, how this actually comes about, they become evasive, the answers woolly, the exact danger nebulous. AI, they say, might run away with all the computational resources and turn the whole world into a giant computer. As AI gets more and more powerful, the most extreme scenarios will require serious consideration and mitigation. However, well before we get there, much could go wrong.

Over the next ten years, AI will be the greatest force amplifier in history. This is why it could enable a redistribution of power on a historic scale. The greatest accelerant of human progress imaginable, it will also enable harms—from wars and accidents to random terror groups, authoritarian governments, overreaching corporations, plain theft, and willful sabotage. Think about an ACI capable of easily passing the Modern Turing Test, but turned toward catastrophic ends. Advanced AIs and synthetic biology will not only be available to groups finding new sources of energy or life-changing drugs; they will also be available to the next Ted Kaczynski.

AI is both valuable and dangerous precisely because it's an extension of our best and worst selves. And as a technology premised on learning, it can keep adapting, probing, producing novel strategies and ideas potentially far removed from anything before considered, even by other AIs. Ask it to suggest ways of knocking out the freshwater supply, or crashing the stock market, or triggering a nuclear war, or designing the ultimate virus, and it will. Soon. Even more than I worry about speculative paper-clip maximizers or some strange, malevolent demon, I worry about what existing forces this tool will amplify in the next ten years.

Imagine scenarios where AIs control energy grids, media programming, power stations, planes, or trading accounts for major financial houses. When robots are ubiquitous, and militaries stuffed with lethal autonomous weapons—warehouses full of technology that can commit autonomous mass murder at the literal push of a button—what might a hack, developed by another AI, look like? Or consider even more basic modes of failure, not attacks, but plain errors. What if AIs make mistakes in fundamental infrastructures, or a widely used medical system starts malfunctioning? It's not hard to see how numerous, capable, quasi-autonomous agents on the loose, even those chasing well-intentioned but ill-formed goals, might sow havoc. We don't yet know the implications of AI for fields as diverse as agriculture, chemistry, surgery, and finance. That's part of the problem; we don't know what failure modes are being introduced and how deep they could extend.

There is no instruction manual on how to build the technologies in the coming wave safely. We cannot build systems of escalating power and danger to experiment with ahead of time. We cannot know how quickly an AI might self-improve, or what would happen after a lab accident with some not yet invented piece of biotech. We cannot tell what results from a human consciousness plugged directly into a computer, or what an AI-enabled cyberweapon means for critical infrastructure, or how a gene drive will play out in the wild. Once fast-evolving, self-assembling automatons or new biological agents are released, out in the wild, there's no rewinding the clock. After a certain point, even curiosity and tinkering might be dangerous. Even if you believe the chance of catastrophe is low, that we are operating blind should give you pause.

Nor is building safe and contained technology in itself sufficient. Solving the question of AI alignment doesn't mean doing so once; it means doing it *every time* a sufficiently powerful AI is built, wherever and whenever that happens. You don't just need to solve the question of lab leaks in one lab; you need to solve it in every lab, in every country, forever, even while those same countries are under serious political strain. Once technology reaches a critical capability, it isn't enough for early pioneers to just build it safely, as challenging as that undoubtedly is. Rather, true safety requires maintaining those standards across every single instance: a mammoth expectation given how fast and widely these are already diffusing.

This is what happens when anyone is free to invent or use tools that affect us all. And we aren't just talking about access to a printing press or a steam engine, as extraordinary as they were. We are talking about outputs with a fundamentally new character: new compounds, new life, new species.

If the wave is uncontained, it's only a matter of time. Allow for the possibility of accident, error, malicious use, evolution beyond human control, unpredictable consequences of all kinds. At some stage, in some form, something, somewhere, will fail. And this won't be a Bhopal or even a Chernobyl; it will unfold on a worldwide scale. This will be the legacy of technologies produced, for the most part, with the best of intentions.

However, not everyone shares those intentions.

CULTS, LUNATICS, AND SUICIDAL STATES

Most of the time the risks arising from things like gain-of-function research are a result of sanctioned and benign efforts. They are, in other words, supersized revenge effects, unintended consequences of a desire to do good. Unfortunately, some organizations are founded with precisely the opposite motivation.

Founded in the 1980s, Aum Shinrikyo (Supreme Truth) was a Japanese doomsday cult. The group originated in a yoga studio under the leadership of a man who called himself Shoko Asahara. Building a membership among the disaffected, they radicalized as their numbers swelled, becoming convinced that the apocalypse was nigh, that they alone would survive, and that they should hasten it. Asahara grew the cult to somewhere between forty thousand and sixty thousand members, coaxing a loyal group of lieutenants all the way to using biological and chemical weapons. At Aum Shinrikyo's peak popularity it is estimated to have held more than $1 billion in assets and counted dozens of well-trained scientists as members. Despite a fascination with bizarre, sci-fi weapons like earthquake-generating machines, plasma guns, and mirrors to deflect the sun's rays, they were a deadly serious and highly sophisticated group.

Aum built dummy companies and infiltrated university labs to procure material, purchased land in Australia with the intent of prospecting for uranium to build nuclear weapons, and embarked on a huge biological and chemical weapons program in the hilly countryside outside Tokyo. The group experimented with phosgene, hydrogen cyanide, soman, and other nerve agents. They planned to engineer and release an enhanced version of anthrax, recruiting a graduate-level virologist to help. Members obtained the neurotoxin *C. botulinum* and sprayed it on Narita International Airport, the National Diet Building, the Imperial Palace, the headquarters of another religious group, and two U.S. naval bases. Luckily, they made a mistake in its manufacture and no harm ensued.

It didn't last. In 1994, Aum Shinrikyo sprayed the nerve agent sarin from a truck, killing eight and wounding two hundred. A year later they struck the Tokyo subway, releasing more sarin, killing thirteen and injuring some six thousand people. The subway attack, which involved depositing sarin-filled bags around the metro system, was more harmful partly because of the enclosed spaces. Thankfully neither attack used a particularly effective delivery mechanism. But in the end it was only luck that stopped a more catastrophic event.

Aum Shinrikyo combined an unusual degree of organization with a frightening level of ambition. They wanted to initiate World War III and a global collapse by murdering at shocking scale and began building an infrastructure to do so. On the one hand, it's reassuring how rare organizations like Aum Shinrikyo are. Of the many terrorist incidents and other non-state-perpetrated mass killings since the 1990s, most have been carried out by disturbed loners or groups with specific political or ideological agendas.

But on the other hand, this reassurance has limits. Procuring weapons of great power was previously a huge barrier to entry, helping keep catastrophe at bay. The sickening nihilism of the school shooter is bounded by the weapons they can access. The Unabomber had only homemade devices. Building and disseminating biological and chemical weapons were huge challenges for Aum Shinrikyo. As a small, fanatical coterie operating in an atmosphere of paranoid secrecy, with only limited expertise and access to materials, they made mistakes.

As the coming wave matures, however, the tools of destruction will, as we've seen, be democratized and commoditized. They will have greater capability and adaptability, potentially operating in ways beyond human control or understanding, evolving and upgrading at speed, some of history's greatest offensive powers available widely.

Those who would use new technologies like Aum are fortunately rare. Yet even one Aum Shinrikyo every fifty years is now one too many to avert an incident orders of magnitude worse than the subway attack. Cults, lunatics, suicidal states on their last legs, all have motive and now means. As a report on the implications of Aum Shinrikyo succinctly puts it, "We are playing Russian roulette."

A new phase of history is here. With zombie governments failing to contain technology, the next Aum Shinrikyo, the next industrial accident, the next mad dictator's war, the next tiny lab leak, will have an impact that is difficult to contemplate.

IT'S TEMPTING TO DISMISS all these dark risk scenarios as the distant daydreams of people who grew up reading too much science fiction, those biased toward catastrophism. Tempting, but a mistake. Regardless of where we are with BSL-4 protocols or regulatory proposals or technical publications on the AI alignment problem, those incentives grind away, the technologies keep developing and diffusing. This is not the stuff of speculative novels and Netflix series. This is real, being worked on right this second in offices and labs around the world.

So serious are the risks, however, that they necessitate consideration of all the options. Containment is about the ability to control technology. Further back, that means the ability to control the people and societies behind it. As catastrophic impacts unfurl or their possibility becomes unignorable, the terms of debate will change. Calls for not just control but crackdowns will grow. The potential for unprecedented levels of vigilance will become ever more appealing. Perhaps it might be possible to spot and then stop emergent threats? Wouldn't that be for the best—the right thing to do?

It's my best guess this will be the reaction of governments and populations around the world. When the unitary power of the nation-state is threatened, when containment appears increasingly difficult, when lives are on the line, the inevitable reaction will be a tightening of the grip on power.

The question is, at what cost?

THE DYSTOPIAN TURN

Stopping catastrophe is an obvious imperative. The greater the catas-trophe, the greater the stakes, the greater the need for countermea-sures. If the threat of disaster becomes too acute, then governments will likely conclude that the only way of stopping it is tightly control-ling every aspect of technology, ensuring that nothing slips through a security cordon, that no rogue AI or engineered virus can ever escape, get built, or even be researched.

Technology has penetrated our civilization so deeply that watching technology means watching everything. Every lab, fab, and factory, every server, every new piece of code, every string of DNA synthe-sized, every business and university, from every biohacker in a shack in the woods to every vast and anonymous data center. To counter calam-ity in the face of the unprecedented dynamics of the coming wave means an unprecedented response. It means not just watching every-thing but reserving the capacity to stop it and control it whenever and wherever necessary.

Some will inevitably say this: centralize power to an extreme de-gree, build the panopticon, and tightly orchestrate every aspect of life to ensure that no pandemic or rogue AI ever happens. Steadily, many nations will convince themselves that the only way of truly ensuring this is to install the kind of blanket surveillance we saw in the last chap-ter: total control, backed by hard power. The door to dystopia is cracked open. Indeed, in the face of catastrophe, for some dystopia may feel like a relief.

Suggestions like this remain fringe, especially in the West. How-ever, it seems to me only a matter of time before they grow. The wave provides both motive and means for dystopia, a self-reinforcing "AI-tocracy" of steadily increasing data collection and coercion. If you doubt the appetite for surveillance and control, think about how society-wide closures, inconceivable even a few weeks earlier, suddenly became an inescapable reality during the COVID pandemic. Compli-ance, at least at the start, was near universal in the face of distressed governments' pleas to "do your part." Public tolerance for potent mea-sures in the name of safety appears high.

A cataclysm would galvanize calls for an extreme surveillance apparatus to stop future such events. If or when something goes wrong with technology, how long before the crackdown starts? How could anyone plausibly argue against it in the face of a disaster? How long before the surveillance dystopia puts down roots, one creeping tendril at a time, and grows? As smaller-scale technology failures mount, calls for control increase. As control increases, checks and balances get whittled down, the ground shifts and makes way for further interventions, and a steady downward spiral to techno-dystopia begins.

Trading off liberty and security is an ancient dilemma. It was there in the foundational account of the Leviathan state from Thomas Hobbes. It has never gone away. To be sure, this is often a complex and multidimensional relationship, but the coming wave raises the stakes to a new pitch. What level of societal control is appropriate to stopping an engineered pandemic? What level of interference in *other* countries is appropriate toward the same end? The consequences for liberty, sovereignty, and privacy have never been so potentially painful.

A repressive surveillance society of transparency and fine-tuned control is, I believe, simply another failure, another way in which the capacities of the coming wave will lead not to human flourishing but to its opposite. Every coercive, biased, and grossly unfair application will stand to be greatly amplified. Hard-won rights and freedoms rolled back. National self-determination, for many nations, at best compromised. Not fragility this time, but outright oppression amplified. If the answer to catastrophe is dystopia like this, then that is no kind of answer at all.

WITH THE ARCHITECTURE OF monitoring and coercion being built in China and elsewhere, the first steps have arguably been taken. The threat of cataclysm and the promise of safety will enable many more. Every wave of technology has introduced the high possibility of systemic disruptions to the social order. But they haven't, until now, introduced wide and systemic risks of globalized disaster. That is what has changed. That is what could prompt a dystopian response.

If zombielike states will sleepwalk into catastrophe, their openness and growing chaos a petri dish for uncontained technology, authoritarian states are already gladly charging into just this techno-dystopia, setting the stage, technologically if not morally, for massive invasions of privacy and curtailments of liberty. And on the continuum between the two there is also a chance of the worst of all worlds: scattered but repressive surveillance and control apparatuses that still don't add up to a watertight system.

Catastrophe *and* dystopia.

The philosopher of technology Lewis Mumford talked about the "megamachine," where social systems combine with technologies to form "a uniform, all-enveloping structure" that is "controlled for the benefit of depersonalized collective organizations." In the name of security, humanity could unleash the megamachine to, literally, stop other megamachines from coming into being. The coming wave then might paradoxically create the very tools needed to contain itself. Yet in doing so, it would open up a failure mode where self-determination, freedom, and privacy are erased, where systems of machine surveillance and control metastasize into society-strangling forms of domination.

To those who might say this repressive picture is where we are now, I'd say it's nothing compared with what the future might hold. Nor is this the only possible dystopian pathway. There are many others, but this one is directly correlated with both the political challenges of the wave and its catastrophic potential. It is not just a vague thought experiment. Faced with this, we must ask these questions: Even though the drivers behind it seem so great and immovable, should humanity get off the train? Should we reject continual technological development altogether? Might it be time, however improbable, to have a moratorium on technology itself?

STAGNATION:
A DIFFERENT KIND OF CATASTROPHE

Looking at our vast cities, the sturdy civic buildings built of steel and stone, the great chains of roads and rails stitching them all together, the immense landscaping and engineering works that manage their environments, there's a tempting sense of permanence exuded by our society. Despite the weightlessness of the digital world, there's a solidness and a profusion to the material world around us. It shapes our everyday expectations.

We go to the supermarket and expect it to be stuffed with fresh fruits and vegetables. We expect it to be kept cool in the summer, warm in the winter. Even despite constant turbulence, we assume that the supply chains and affordances of the twenty-first century are as robust as an old town hall. All the most historically extreme parts of our existence appear utterly banal, and so for the most part we carry on our lives as if they can go on indefinitely. Most of those around us, up to and including our leaders, do the same.

And yet, nothing lasts forever. Throughout history societal collapses are legion: from ancient Mesopotamia to Rome, the Maya to Easter Island, again and again it's not just that civilizations don't last; it's that unsustainability appears baked in. Civilizations that collapse are not the exception; they are the rule. A survey of sixty civilizations suggests they last about four hundred years on average before falling apart. Without new technologies, they hit hard limits to development—in available energy, in food, in social complexity—that bring them crashing down.

Nothing has changed except this: for hundreds of years constant technological development has seemingly enabled societies to escape the iron trap of history. But it would be wrong to think that this dynamic has come to an end. Twenty-first-century civilization is a long way from the Maya, naturally, but the pressures of a huge and hungry superstructure, a large population, the hard limits of energy and civilizational capacity have not magically gone away; they've just been kept at bay.

Suppose there was a world where those incentives could be stopped. Might it be time for a moratorium on technological development altogether? Absolutely not.

MODERN CIVILIZATION WRITES CHECKS only continual technological development can cash. Our entire edifice is premised on the idea of long-term economic growth. And long-term economic growth is ultimately premised on the introduction and diffusion of new technologies. Whether it's the expectation of consuming more for less or getting ever more public service without paying more tax, or the idea that we can unsustainably degrade the environment while life keeps getting better indefinitely, the bargain—arguably the grand bargain itself—needs technology.

The development of new technologies is, as we've seen, a critical part of meeting our planet's grand challenges. Without new technologies, these challenges will simply not be met. Costs of the status quo in human and material exploitation cannot be set aside. Our present suite of technologies is in many ways remarkable, but there is little sign that it can be sustainably rolled out to support more than eight billion people at levels those in developed countries take for granted. Unpalatable as it is to some, it's worth repeating: solving problems like climate change, or maintaining rising living and health-care standards, or improving education and opportunity is not going to happen without delivering new technologies as part of the package.

Pausing technological development, assuming it was possible, would in one sense lead to safety. It would for a start limit the introduction of new catastrophic risks. But it wouldn't mean successfully avoiding dystopia. Instead, as the unsustainability of twenty-first-century societies began to tell, it would simply deliver another form of dystopia. Without new technologies, sooner or later everything stagnates, and possibly collapses altogether.

Over the next century, the global population will start falling, in some countries precipitously. As the ratio of workers to retirees shifts and the labor force dwindles, economies will simply not be able to function at their present levels. In other words, without new technologies it will be impossible to maintain living standards.

This is a global problem. Countries including Japan, Germany, Italy, Russia, and South Korea are even now approaching a crisis of working-age population. More surprising perhaps is that by the 2050s countries like India, Indonesia, Mexico, and Turkey will be in a similar position. China is a major part of the story of technology in the coming decades, but by the century's end the Shanghai Academy of Social Sciences predicts the country could have only 600 million people, a staggering reversal of nearly a century's population increases. China's total fertility rate is one of the lowest in the world, matched only by neighbors like South Korea and Taiwan. Truth is, China is completely unsustainable without new technology.

This is not only about numbers but about expertise, tax base, and investment levels; retirees will be pulling money out of the system, not investing it for the long term. All of this means that "the governing models of the post–World War II era do not simply go broke, they become societal suicide pacts." Demographic trends take decades to shift. Generational cohorts do not change size. This slow, inexorable decline is already locked in, a looming iceberg we can do nothing to avoid— except find ways of replacing those workers.

Stress on our resources, too, is a certainty. Recall that sourcing materials for cleantech, let alone anything else, is incredibly complex and vulnerable. Demand for lithium, cobalt, and graphite is set to rise 500 percent by 2030. Currently batteries are the best hope for a clean economy, and yet there is barely enough storage capacity to get most places through minutes or even seconds of energy consumption. To replace fast-diminishing stocks or remedy supply chain failure across a whole plethora of materials, we need options. That means new technological and scientific breakthroughs in areas like materials science.

Given the population and resource constraints, just standing still would probably require a global two- to threefold productivity improvement, and standing still is not acceptable for the world's vast majority, among whom, for example, child mortality is twelve times higher than in developed countries. Of course, any continuation at even current levels doesn't just herald demographic and resource stress; it bolts on climate emergency.

Make no mistake: standstill in itself spells disaster.

This wouldn't be just a matter of some labor shortages in restaurants and expensive batteries. It would mean the unraveling of every precarious aspect of modern life, with numerous unpredictable downstream effects, intersecting with a host of already unmanageable problems. I think it's easy to discount how much of our way of life is underwritten by constant technological improvements. Those historical precedents—the norm, remember, for every prior civilization—are screaming loud and clear. Standstill means a meager future of at best decline but probably an implosion that could spiral alarmingly. Some might argue this forms a third pole, a great trilemma. For me that doesn't quite hold. First, this is by far the least likely option at this stage. And second, if it does happen, it simply restates the dilemma in a new form. A moratorium on technology is not a way out; it's an invitation to another kind of dystopia, another kind of catastrophe.

Even if it were possible, the idea of stopping the coming wave isn't a comforting thought. Maintaining, let alone improving, standards of living needs technology. Forestalling a collapse needs technology. The costs of saying no are existential. And yet every path from here brings grave risks and downsides.

This is the great dilemma.

WHERE NEXT?

From the start of the nuclear and digital age, this dilemma has been growing clearer. In 1955, toward the end of his life, the mathematician John von Neumann wrote an essay called "Can We Survive Technology?" Foreshadowing the argument here, he believed that global society was "in a rapidly maturing crisis—a crisis attributable to the fact that the environment in which technological progress must occur has become both undersized and underorganized." At the end of the essay, von Neumann puts survival as only "a possibility," as well he might in the shadow of the mushroom cloud his own computer had made a reality. "For progress there is no cure," he writes. "Any attempt to find automatically safe channels for the present explosive variety of progress must lead to frustration."

I am not alone in wanting to build technology that can reap many of the benefits while closing down the risks. Some will ridicule that ambition as just another form of Silicon Valley hubris, but I'm still convinced that technology remains a primary driver for making improvements to our world and our lives. For all its harms, downsides, and unintended consequences, technology's contribution to date has been overwhelmingly net positive. After all, even technology's harshest critics are generally happy to use a kettle, take an aspirin, watch TV, and ride on the subway. For every gun there is a dose of lifesaving penicillin; for every scrap of misinformation, a truth is quickly uncovered.

And yet somehow, from von Neumann and his peers on, I and many others are anxious about the long-term trajectory. My profound worry is that technology is demonstrating the real possibility to sharply move net negative, that we don't have answers to arrest this shift, and that we're locked in with no way out.

None of us can be sure how exactly all this unfolds. Within the broad parameters of the dilemma are an immense and unknowable range of specific outcomes. I am, however, confident that the coming decades will see complex, painful trade-offs between prosperity, surveillance, and the threat of catastrophe growing ever more acute. Even a system of states in the best possible health would struggle.

We are facing the ultimate challenge for *Homo technologicus*.

If this book feels contradictory in its attitude toward technology, part positive and part foreboding, that's because such a contradictory view is the most honest assessment of where we are. Our great-grandparents would be astonished at the abundance of our world. But they would also be astonished at its fragility and perils. With the coming wave, we face a real threat, a cascade of potentially disastrous consequences—yes, even an existential risk to the species. Technology is the best and worst of us. There isn't a neat one-sided approach that does it justice. The only coherent approach to technology is to see both sides at the same time.

Over the last decade or so this dilemma has become even more pronounced, the task of tackling it more urgent. Look at the world and it seems that containment is not possible. Follow the consequences and something else becomes equally stark: for everyone's sake, containment *must* be possible.

PART IV

THROUGH THE WAVE

CHAPTER 13

CONTAINMENT MUST BE POSSIBLE

THE PRICE OF SCATTERED INSIGHTS

I ONCE INTENDED TO WRITE A BOOK WITH A ROSIER PICTURE ABOUT the future of technology and the future in general. Although the world is far wiser and warier about "tech" these days, there's still a huge amount to be positive about. But during the COVID-19 pandemic I had time to stop and reflect. I allowed myself to reconnect with a truth that I have been, if not denying, then downplaying for too long. Exponential change is coming. It is inevitable. That fact needs to be addressed.

If you accept even a small part of this book's central argument, the real question is what to actually *do* about it. Once we've acknowledged this reality, what will really make a difference? Faced with a dilemma like the one I've outlined in the first three parts of this book, what might containment, even in theory, look like?

In recent years I've had countless conversations about this question. I've discussed it with the top AI researchers, with CEOs, with old friends, with policy makers in Washington, Beijing, and Brussels, with scientists and lawyers, with students in high schools, and with random people who'll listen to me at the pub. Everyone immediately reaches for easy answers, and almost without exception everyone has the same prescription: regulation.

Here it seems is the answer, the way out of the dilemma, the key to containment, savior of the nation-state, and of civilization as we know it. Deft regulation, balancing the need to make progress alongside sensible safety constraints, on national and supranational levels, spanning everything from tech giants and militaries to small university research groups and start-ups, tied up in a comprehensive, enforceable framework. *We've done it before,* so the argument goes; *look at cars, planes, and medicines. Isn't this how we manage and contain the coming wave?*

If only it were that simple. Saying "Regulation!" in the face of awesome technological change is the easy part. It's also the classic pessimism-averse answer. It's a simple way to shrug off the problem. On paper regulation looks enticing, even obvious and straightforward; suggesting it lets people sound smart, concerned, and even relieved. The unspoken implication being that it's solvable, but it's someone else's problem. Look deeper, though, and the fissures become evident.

In part 4 we'll explore the many ways society can begin to face the dilemma, to shake off pessimism aversion and really grapple with the containment problem, to seek answers in a world where solving it must be possible. Before we do that, however, it's vital to acknowledge a central truth: regulation alone is not enough. Convening a White House roundtable and delivering earnest speeches are easy; enacting effective legislation is a different proposition. As we've seen, governments face multiple crises independent of the coming wave—declining trust, entrenched inequality, polarized politics, to name a few. They're overstretched, their workforces under-skilled and unprepared for the kinds of complex and fast-moving challenges that lie ahead.

While garage amateurs gain access to more powerful tools and tech companies spend billions on R&D, most politicians are trapped in a twenty-four-hour news cycle of sound bites and photo ops. When a government has devolved to the point of simply lurching from crisis to crisis, it has little breathing room for tackling tectonic forces requiring deep domain expertise and careful judgment on uncertain timescales. It's easier to ignore these issues in favor of low-hanging fruit more likely to win votes in the next election.

Even technologists and researchers in areas like AI struggle with the pace of change. What chance, then, do regulators have, with fewer resources? How do they account for an age of hyper-evolution, for the pace and unpredictability of the coming wave?

Technology evolves week by week. Drafting and passing legislation takes years. Consider the arrival of a new product on the market like Ring doorbells. Ring put a camera on your front door and connected it to your phone. The product was adopted so quickly and is now so widespread that it has fundamentally changed the nature of what needs regulating; suddenly your average suburban street went from relatively private space to surveilled and recorded. By the time the regulation conversation caught up, Ring had already created an extensive network of cameras, amassing data and images from the front doors of people around the world. Twenty years on from the dawn of social media, there's no consistent approach to the emergence of a powerful new platform (and besides, is privacy, polarization, monopoly, foreign ownership, or mental health the core problem—or all of the above?). The coming wave will worsen this dynamic.

Discussions of technology sprawl across social media, blogs and newsletters, academic journals, countless conferences and seminars and workshops, their threads distant and increasingly lost in the noise. Everyone has a view, but it doesn't add up to a coherent program. Talking about the ethics of machine learning systems is a world away from, say, the technical safety of synthetic bio. These discussions happen in isolated, echoey silos. They rarely break out.

Yet I believe they are aspects of what amounts to the same phenomenon; they all aim to address different aspects of the same wave. It's not enough to have dozens of separate conversations about algorithmic bias or bio-risk or drone warfare or the economic impact of robotics or the privacy implications of quantum computing. It completely underplays how interrelated both causes and effects are. We need an approach that unifies these disparate conversations, encapsulating all those different dimensions of risk, a general-purpose concept for this general-purpose revolution.

The price of scattered insights is failure, and we know what that looks like. Right now, scattered insights are all we've got: hundreds of distinct programs across distant parts of the technosphere, chipping away at well-meaning but ad hoc efforts without an overarching plan or direction. At the highest level we need a clear and simple goal, a banner imperative integrating all the different efforts around technology into a coherent package. Not just tweaking this or that element, not just in this or that company or research group or even country, but everywhere, across all the fronts and risk zones and geographies at once. Whether it's facing an emergent AGI or a strange but useful new lifeform, the goal has to be unified: containment.

The central problem for humanity in the twenty-first century is how we can nurture sufficient legitimate political power and wisdom, adequate technical mastery, and robust norms to constrain technologies to ensure they continue to do far more good than harm. How, in other words, we can contain the seemingly uncontainable.

From the history of *Homo technologicus* to the reality of an era when technology pervades every aspect of life, the odds are stacked against us in making this a reality. But, it doesn't mean we shouldn't try.

Most organizations, however, not just governments, are ill-suited to the complex challenges on the way. As we've seen, even wealthy nations can struggle in the face of an unfolding crisis. Going into 2020, the Global Health Security Index ranked the United States number one in the world and the U.K. not far behind in terms of pandemic readiness. Yet a catalog of disastrous decisions delivered mortality rates and financial costs materially worse than in peer countries like Canada and Germany. Despite what looked like excellent expertise, institutional depth, planning, and resources, even those best prepared on paper were sideswiped.

Governments should, on the face of it, be better primed for managing novel risks and technologies than ever before. National budgets for such things are generally at record levels. Truth is, though, novel threats are just exceptionally difficult for any government to navigate. That's not a flaw with the idea of government; it's an assessment of the scale of the challenge before us. When they are faced with something like an ACI that can pass my version of the Modern Turing Test, the response of even the most thoughtful, farsighted bureaucracies will resemble the response to COVID. Governments fight the last war, the last pandemic, regulate the last wave. Regulators regulate for things they can anticipate.

This, meanwhile, is an age of surprises.

REGULATION IS NOT ENOUGH

Despite the headwinds, efforts to regulate frontier technologies *are* necessary and growing. The most ambitious legislation is probably the EU's AI Act, first proposed in 2021. As of this writing in 2023, the act is going through the lengthy process of becoming European law. If it is enacted, AI research and deployment will be categorized on a risk-based scale. Technologies with "unacceptable risk" of causing direct harm will be prohibited. Where AI affects fundamental human rights or critical systems like basic infrastructure, public transport, health, or welfare, it will get classed as "high risk," subjected to greater levels of oversight and accountability. High-risk AI must be "transparent, secure, subject to human control and properly documented."

Yet the act, although one of the world's most advanced, ambitious, and farsighted regulatory attempts to date, also demonstrates the inherent problems with regulation. It has been attacked from all sides, for going too far and not going far enough. Some argue it's too focused on nascent, future-facing risks, trying to regulate something that doesn't even exist; others that it's not farsighted enough. Some believe it lets big tech companies off the hook, that they were instrumental in its drafting and watered down its provisions. Others think it overreaches and will chill research and innovation in the EU, hurting jobs and tax revenues.

Most regulation walks a tightrope of competing interests. But in few areas other than frontier technology must it tackle something so widely diffused, so critical to the economy, and yet so fast evolving. All the noise and confusion makes clear how hard and complex any form of regulation is, especially amid accelerating change, and how, because of that, it will almost certainly leave gaps, falling short of effective containment.

Regulating not just hyper-evolutionary but omni-use general-purpose technologies is incredibly challenging. Consider how motorized transport is regulated. There isn't a single regulator, or even just a few laws. Instead, we have regulations around traffic, roads, parking, seatbelts, emissions, driver training, and so on. This comes not just from national legislatures but also from local governments, highway agencies, transport ministries issuing guidance, licensing bodies, offices of environmental standards. It relies not just on lawmakers but on police forces, traffic wardens, car companies, mechanics, city planners, and insurers.

Complex regulations refined over decades made roads and vehicles incrementally safer and more ordered, enabling their growth and spread. And yet 1.35 million people a year still die in traffic accidents. Regulation may lessen the negative effects, but it can't erase bad outcomes like crashes, pollution, or sprawl. We have decided that this is an acceptable human cost, given the benefits. That "we" is crucial. Regulation doesn't just rely on the passing of a new law. It is also about norms, structures of ownership, unwritten codes of compliance and honesty, arbitration procedures, contract enforcement, oversight mechanisms. All of this needs to be integrated and the public needs to buy in.

This takes time—time we don't have. With the coming wave we don't have half a century for numerous bodies to figure out what to do, for the right values and best practices to emerge. Advanced regulation needs to get it right, and quickly. Nor is it clear how all this will be managed over such a broad spectrum of unprecedented technologies. When you regulate synthetic biology, are you regulating food, medicine, industrial tools, academic research, or all of them at once? Which bodies are responsible for what? How does it all fit together? Which actors are liable for which parts of the supply chain? The pitfalls of even one serious accident are extreme, and yet even deciding which agency would be responsible is a minefield.

ABOVE THE CUT AND thrust of legislative debate, nations are also caught in a contradiction. On the one hand, they are in a strategic competition to accelerate the development of technologies like AI and synthetic biology. Every nation wants to be, and be seen, at the technological frontier. It's a measure of national pride, of national security, and an existential imperative. On the other hand, they're desperate to regulate and manage these technologies—to contain them, not least for fear they will threaten the nation-state as the ultimate seat of power. The scary thing is that this assumes a best-case scenario of strong, reasonably competent, cohesive (liberal democratic) nation-states capable of working coherently as units internally and coordinating well internationally.

For containment to be possible, rules need to work well in places as diverse as the Netherlands and Nicaragua, New Zealand and Nigeria. Where someone slows down, others will rush forward. Every country already brings its distinct legal and cultural customs to the development of technology. The EU heavily restricts genetically modified organisms in the food supply. Yet in the United States genetically modified organisms are a routine part of agribusiness. China, on the face of it, is a regulatory leader of sorts. The government has issued multiple edicts on AI ethics, seeking to impose wide-ranging restrictions. It proactively banned various cryptocurrencies and DeFi initiatives, and limits the time children under eighteen can spend on games and social apps to ninety minutes a day during the week, three hours on the weekend. Draft regulation of recommendation algorithms and LLMs in China far exceeds anything we've yet seen in the West.

China is slamming on the brakes in some areas while also—as we've seen—charging ahead in others. Its regulation is matched by an unparalleled deployment of technology as a tool of authoritarian government power. Speak to Western defense and policy insiders and they're adamant that although China talks a good game on AI ethics and limitations, when it comes to national security, there are no meaningful barriers. In effect, Chinese AI policy has two tracks: a regulated civilian path and a freewheeling military-industrial one.

Unless regulation can address the deep-seated nature of the incentives outlined in part 2, it won't be enough to contain technology. It doesn't stop motivated bad actors or accidents. It doesn't cut to the heart of an open and unpredictable research system. It doesn't provide alternatives given the immense financial rewards on offer. And above all, it doesn't mitigate strategic necessity. It doesn't describe how countries might coordinate on an enticing, hard-to-define transnational phenomenon, building a delicate critical mass of alliances, especially in a context where international treaties all too often fail. There is an unbridgeable gulf between the desire to rein in the coming wave and the desire to shape and own it, between the need for protections against technologies and the need for protections against others. Advantage and control point in opposing directions.

The reality is that containment is not something that a government, or even a group of governments, can do alone. It requires innovation and boldness in partnering between the public and the private sectors and a completely new set of incentives for all parties. Regulations like the EU AI Act do at least hint at a world where containment is on the map, one where leading governments take the risks of proliferation seriously, demonstrating new levels of commitment and willingness to make serious sacrifices.

Regulation is not enough, but at least it's a start. Bold steps. A real understanding of the stakes involved in the coming wave. In a world where containment seems like it's not possible, all of this gestures toward a future where it might be.

CONTAINMENT REVISITED: A NEW GRAND BARGAIN

Does any entity have the power to prevent mass proliferation while capturing the immense power and benefits arising from the coming wave? To stop bad actors acquiring a technology, or shape the spread of nascent ideas around it? As autonomy increases, can anyone or anything really hope to have meaningful control at the macro level? Containment means answering yes to questions like these. In theory, contained technology gets us out of the dilemma. It means at once harnessing and controlling the wave, a vital tool for building sustainable and flourishing societies, while checking it in ways that avoid serious catastrophe, but not so invasively as to invite dystopia. It means writing a new kind of grand bargain.

Earlier in the book I described containment as a foundation for controlling and governing technology, spanning technical, cultural, and regulatory aspects. At root, I believe this means having the power to drastically curtail or outright stop technology's negative impacts, from the local and small scale up to the planetary and existential. Encompassing hard enforcement against misuse of proliferated technologies, it also steers the development, direction, and governance of nascent technologies. Contained technology is technology whose modes of failure are known, managed, and mitigated, a situation where the means to shape and govern technology escalate in parallel with its capabilities.

It's tempting to think of containment in an obvious, literal sense, a kind of magic box in which a given technology can be sealed away. At the outer limit—in the case of rogue malware or pathogens—such drastic steps might be needed. Generally, though, consider containment more as a set of guardrails, a way to keep humanity in the driver's seat when a technology risks causing more harm than good. Picture those guardrails operating at different levels and with different modes of implementation. In the next chapter we'll consider what they might look like at a more granular level, from AI alignment research to lab design, international treaties to best practice protocols. For now, the key point is that those guardrails need to be strong enough that, in theory, they could stop a runaway catastrophe.

Containment will need to respond to the nature of a technology, and channel it in directions that are easier to control. Recall the four features of the coming wave: asymmetry, hyper-evolution, omni-use, and autonomy. Each feature must be viewed through the lens of containability. Before outlining a strategy it's worth asking the following kinds of questions to prompt promising avenues:

- *Is the technology omni-use and general-purpose or specific?* A nuclear weapon is a highly specific technology with one purpose, whereas a computer is inherently multi-use. The more potential use cases, the more difficult to contain. Rather than general systems, then, those that are more narrowly scoped and domain specific should be encouraged.
- *Is the tech moving away from atoms toward bits?* The more dematerialized a technology, the more it is subject to hard-to-control hyper-evolutionary effects. Areas like materials design or drug development are going to rapidly accelerate, making the pace of progress harder to track.
- *Are price and complexity coming down, and if so how fast?* The price of fighter jets has not come down in the way the

price of transistors or consumer hardware has. A threat originating in basic computing is of a wider nature than that of fighter jets, despite the latter's obvious destructive potential.

- *Are there viable alternatives ready to go?* CFCs could be banned partly because there are cheaper and safer alternatives for refrigeration. What alternatives are available? The more that safe alternatives are available, the easier it is to phase out use.
- *Does the technology enable asymmetric impact?* Think of a drone swarm against the conventional military or a tiny computer or biological virus damaging vital social systems. The risk of certain technologies to surprise and exploit vulnerabilities is greater.
- *Does it have autonomous characteristics?* Is there scope for self-learning, or operation without oversight? Think gene drives, viruses, malware, and of course robotics. The more a technology by design requires human intervention, the less chance there is of losing control.
- *Does it confer outsized geopolitical strategic advantage?* Chemical weapons, for example, have limited advantages and lots of downsides, whereas getting ahead in AI or bio has enormous upsides, both economic and military. Saying no is consequently harder.
- *Does it favor offense or defense?* In World War II the development of missiles like the V-2 helped offensive operations. But a technology like radar bolstered defense. Orienting development toward defense over offense tends toward containment.
- *Are there resource or engineering constraints on its invention, development, and deployment?* Silicon chips require specialized and highly concentrated materials, machines, and knowledge. The talent available for a synthetic biology start-up is, in global terms, still quite small. Both help containment in the near term.

Where additional friction keeps things in the tangible world of atoms, for example, or makes things expensive, or if safer alternatives are easily available, there is more chance of containment because it is easier to slow the technologies down, limit access, or drop them altogether. Specific technologies are easier to regulate than omni-use technologies, but regulating omni-use is more important. Likewise, the more potential for offensive actions or autonomy, the greater the requirement for containment. If you can keep price and ease of access out of reach for many, proliferation becomes more difficult. Ask questions like these, and a holistic vision of containment begins to emerge.

BEFORE THE FLOOD

I've worked on this issue for the best part of fifteen years. Over that time I have felt the sheer force of what's described in this book, of those incentives, and of the urgent need for answers even as the contours of the dilemma became ever clearer. And yet even I have been taken aback at what technology has made possible in a few short years. I've struggled with these ideas, watching as the pace of development keeps picking up.

The reality is, we have often not controlled or contained technologies in the past. And if we want to do so now, it would take something dramatically new, an all-encompassing program of safety, ethics, regulation, and control that doesn't even really have a name and doesn't seem possible in the first place.

The dilemma should be a pressing call to action. But over the years it's become obvious that most people find this a lot to take in. I absolutely get it. It barely seems real on first encounter. In all those many discussions about AI and regulation, I've been struck by how hard it is, compared with a host of existing or looming challenges, to convey exactly why the risks in this book need to be taken seriously, why they aren't just nearly irrelevant tail risks or the province of science fiction.

One challenge in even beginning to have this conversation is that technology, in the popular imagination, has become associated with a narrow band of often superfluous applications. "Technology" now mostly means social media platforms and wearable gadgets to measure our steps and heart rate. It's easy to forget that technology includes the irrigation systems essential to feeding the planet and newborn life-support machines. Technology isn't just a way to store your selfies; it represents access to the world's accumulated culture and wisdom. Technology is not a niche; it is a hyper-object dominating human existence.

A useful comparison here is climate change. It too deals with risks that are often diffuse, uncertain, temporally distant, happening elsewhere, lacking the salience, adrenaline, and immediacy of an ambush on the savanna—the kind of risk we are well primed to respond to. Psychologically, none of this feels present. Our prehistoric brains are generally hopeless at dealing with amorphous threats like these.

However, over the last decade or so, the challenge of climate change has come into better focus. Although the world still spews out increasing amounts of CO_2, scientists everywhere can measure CO_2 parts per million (ppm) in the atmosphere. As recently as the 1970s, global atmospheric carbon was around the low 300s ppm. In 2022 it was at 420 ppm. Whether in Beijing, Berlin, or Burundi, whether an oil major or a family farm, everyone can see, objectively, what is happening to the climate. Data brings clarity.

Pessimism aversion is much harder when the effects are so nakedly quantifiable. Like climate change, technological risk can only be addressed at planetary scale, but there is no equivalent clarity. There's no handy metric of risk, no objective unit of threat shared in national capitals, boardrooms, and public sentiment, no parts per million for measuring what technology might do or where it is. There's no commonly agreed on or obvious standard we can check year by year. No consensus among scientists and technologists on the cutting edge. No popular movement behind stopping it, no graphic images of melting icebergs and stranded polar bears or flooded villages to raise awareness. Obscure research published on arXiv, in cult Substack blogs, or in dry think tank white papers hardly cuts it here.

How do we find common ground amid competing agendas? China and the United States don't share a vision of restricting development of AI; Meta wouldn't share the view that social media is part of the problem; AI researchers and virologists believe their work is a critical part not of causing catastrophe but of understanding and averting it. "Technology" is not, on the face of it, a problem in the same sense as a heating planet.

And yet it might be.

The first step is recognition. We need to calmly acknowledge that the wave is coming and the dilemma is, absent a jarring change in course, unavoidable. Either we can grapple with the vast array of good and bad outcomes ignited by our continued openness and heedless chase, or we can confront the dystopian and authoritarian risks arising from our attempts to limit proliferation of powerful technologies, risks moreover inherent in concentrated ownership of those same technologies.

Pick your poison. Ultimately, this balance has to be struck in consultation with everyone. The more it's on the public's radar, the better. If this book prompts criticisms, arguments, proposals, and counterproposals, the more the better.

There will be no single, magic fix from a roomful of smart people in a bunker somewhere. Quite the opposite. Current elites are so invested in their pessimism aversion that they are afraid to be honest about the dangers we face. They're happy to opine and debate in private, less so to come out and talk about it. They are used to a world of control and order: the control of a CEO over a company, of a central banker over interest rates, of a bureaucrat over military procurement, or of a town planner over which potholes to fix. Their levers of control are imperfect, sure, but they are known, tried, and tested and they generally work. Not so here.

This is a unique moment. The coming wave *really is* coming, but it hasn't washed over us yet. While unstoppable incentives are locked in, the wave's final form, the precise contours of the dilemma, are still to be decided. Let's not waste decades waiting to find out. Let's get started on managing it today.

In the next chapter, I outline ten areas of focus. This is not a complete map, not remotely a set of final answers, but necessary groundwork. My intent is to seed ideas in the hopes of taking the crucial first steps *toward* containment. What unifies these ideas is that they are all about marginal gains, the slow and constant aggregation of small efforts to produce a greater probability of good outcomes. They are about creating a different context for how technology is built and deployed: finding ways of buying time, slowing down, giving space for more work on the answers, bringing attention, building alliances, furthering technical work.

Containment of the coming wave is, I believe, not possible in our *current* world. What these steps might do, however, is change the underlying conditions. Nudge forward the status quo so containment has a chance. We should do all this with the knowledge that it might fail but that it is our best shot at building a world where containment—and human flourishing—are possible.

There are no guarantees here, no rabbits pulled out of hats. Anyone hoping for a quick fix, a smart answer, is going to be disappointed. Approaching the dilemma, we are left in the same all-too-human position as always: giving it everything and hoping it works out. Here's how I think it might—just might—come together.

CHAPTER 14

TEN STEPS TOWARD CONTAINMENT

T HINK OF THE TEN IDEAS PRESENTED HERE AS CONCENTRIC CIRCLES. We start small and direct, close to the technology, focusing on specific mechanisms for imposing constraints by design. From there each idea gets progressively broader, ascending a ladder of interventions further away from the hard technical specifics, the raw code and materials, and moving up and out toward the nontechnical but no less important actions, the kinds that add up to new business incentives, reformed government, international treaties, a healthier technological culture, and a popular global movement.

It's the way all these layers of the onion build that makes them powerful; each alone is insufficient. Each necessitates very different kinds of interventions, with different skills, competencies, and people; each is generally its own vast and specialized subfield. Collectively, I believe, they could add up to something that works.

Let's start at the beginning, with the technology itself.

1. SAFETY: AN APOLLO PROGRAM FOR TECHNICAL SAFETY

A few years ago, many large language models had a problem. They were, to put it bluntly, racist. Users could quite easily find ways of making them regurgitate racist material, or hold racist opinions they had gleaned in scanning the vast corpus of texts on which they'd been trained. Toxic bias was, it seemed, ingrained in human writing and then amplified by AI. This led many to conclude the whole setup was ethically broken, morally nonviable; there was no way LLMs could be controlled well enough to be released to the public given the obvious harms.

But then LLMs, as we have seen, took off. In 2023 it's now clear that, compared with the early systems, it is extremely difficult to goad something like ChatGPT into racist comments. Is it a solved problem? Absolutely not. There are still multiple examples of biased, even overtly racist, LLMs, as well as serious problems with everything from inaccurate information to gaslighting. But for those of us who have worked in the field from the beginning, the exponential progress at eliminating bad outputs has been incredible, undeniable. It's easy to overlook quite how far and fast we've come.

A key driver behind this progress is called reinforcement learning from human feedback. To fix their bias-prone LLMs, researchers set up cunningly constructed multi-turn conversations with the model, prompting it to say obnoxious, harmful, or offensive things, seeing where and how it goes wrong. Flagging these missteps, researchers then reintegrate these human insights into the model, eventually teaching it a more desirable worldview, in a way not wholly dissimilar from how we try to teach children not to say inappropriate things at the dinner table. As engineers became more aware of their systems' inherent ethical problems, they became more open to finding technical innovations to help address them.

Addressing the racism and bias in LLMs is an example of how careful and responsible deployment is necessary to advance the safety of these models. Contact with reality helps developers learn, correct, and improve their safety.

While it's wrong to say technical fixes alone can solve the social and ethical problems engendered by AI, it does show how they will be a part of it. Technical safety, up close, in the code, in the lab, is the first item on any containment agenda.

HEAR THE WORD "CONTAINMENT" and, assuming you're not an international relations scholar, chances are you think of the physical sense of keeping something in. To be sure, physically containing technology is important. We've seen, for example, how even BSL-4 labs can leak.

What kind of environment might make that fully impossible? What does a BSL-7 or -*n* look like?

Although I argued in the last chapter that containment shouldn't be reduced to a kind of magic box, it doesn't mean we don't want to figure out ways of building one as part of it. The ultimate control is hard physical control, of servers, microbes, drones, robots, and algorithms. "Boxing" an AI is the original and basic form of technological containment. This would involve no internet connections, limited human contact, a small, constricted external interface. It would, literally, contain it in physical boxes with a definite location. A system like this—called an air gap—could, in theory, stop an AI from engaging with the wider world or somehow "escaping."

Physical segregation is just one aspect of transforming technical safety architecture to meet the challenge of the next wave. Taking the best of what's out there is a start. Nuclear power, for instance, gets a bad rep thanks to well-known disasters like Chernobyl and Fukushima. But it's actually remarkably safe. The International Atomic Energy Agency has published more than a hundred safety reports tackling specific technical standards for given situations, from the classification of radioactive waste to preparedness in cases of emergency. Bodies like the Institute of Electrical and Electronics Engineers maintain more than two thousand technical safety standards on technologies ranging from autonomous robot development to machine learning. Biotech and pharma have operated under safety standards far beyond those of most software businesses for decades. It's worth remembering just how safe years of effort have made many existing technologies—and building on it.

Frontier AI safety research is still an undeveloped, nascent field focusing on keeping ever more autonomous systems from superseding our ability to understand or control them. I see these questions around control or value alignment as subsets of the wider containment problem. While billions are plowed into robotics, biotech, and AI, comparatively tiny amounts get spent on a technical safety framework equal to keeping them functionally contained. The main monitor of bioweapons, for example, the Biological Weapons Convention, has a budget of just $1.4 million and only four full-time employees—fewer than the average McDonald's.

The number of AI safety researchers is still minuscule: up from around a hundred at top labs worldwide in 2021 to three or four hundred in 2022. Given there are around thirty to forty thousand AI researchers today (and a similar number of people capable of piecing together DNA), it's shockingly small. Even a tenfold hiring spree—unlikely given talent bottlenecks—wouldn't address the scale of the challenge. Compared with the magnitude of what could go wrong, safety and ethics research on AI is marginal. Only a handful of institutions, owing to the challenges of resources, take technical safety issues seriously. And yet safety decisions made today will alter the future course of technology and humanity.

There's a clear must-do here: encourage, incentivize, and directly fund much more work in this area. It's time for an Apollo program on AI safety and biosafety. Hundreds of thousands should be working on it. Concretely, a good proposal for legislation would be to require that a fixed portion—say, a minimum of 20 percent—of frontier corporate research and development budgets should be directed toward safety efforts, with an obligation to publish material findings to a government working group so that progress can be tracked and shared. The original Apollo missions were expensive and onerous, but they showed the right immense level of ambition, and their can-do attitude in the face of daunting odds catalyzed the development of technologies from semiconductors and software to quartz clocks and solar panels. This could do something similar for safety.

Although numbers are currently small, I know from experience that a groundswell of interest is emerging around these questions. Students and other young people I meet are buzzing about issues like AI alignment and pandemic preparedness. Talk to them and it's clear the intellectual challenge appeals, but they're also drawn to the moral imperative. They want to help, and feel a duty to do better. I'm confident that if the jobs and research programs are there, the talent will follow.

For the technical safety experts of tomorrow, there are plenty of promising directions to explore. Pandemic preparedness could, for example, be greatly enhanced by using low-wavelength lightbulbs that kill viruses. Giving off light with a wavelength between 200 and

230 nanometers, close to the ultraviolet spectrum, they can kill viruses while not penetrating the outer layer of the skin: a powerful weapon against pandemics and the spread of disease more widely. And if the COVID-19 pandemic taught us one thing, it's the value of an integrated, accelerated approach across research, rollout, and regulation for novel vaccines.

In AI, technical safety also means sandboxes and secure simulations to create provably secure air gaps so that advanced AIs can be rigorously tested before they are given access to the real world. It means much more work on uncertainty, a major focus right now—that is, how does an AI communicate when it might be wrong? One of the issues with LLMs is that they still suffer from *the hallucination problem,* whereby they often confidently claim wildly wrong information as accurate. This is doubly dangerous given they often *are right,* to an expert level. As a user, it's all too easy to be lulled into a false sense of security and assume anything coming out of the system is true.

At Inflection, for example, we are finding ways to encourage our AI called Pi—for personal intelligence—to be cautious and uncertain by default, and to encourage users to remain critical. We're designing Pi to express self-doubt, solicit feedback frequently and constructively, and quickly give way assuming the human, not the machine, is right. We and others are also working on an important track of research that aims to fact-check a statement by an AI using third-party knowledge bases we know to be credible. Here it's about making sure AI outputs provide citations, sources, and interrogable evidence that a user can further investigate when a dubious claim arises.

Explanation is another huge technical safety frontier. Recall that at present no one can explain why, precisely, a model produces the outputs it does. Devising ways for models to comprehensively explain their decisions or open them to scrutiny has become a critical technical puzzle for safety researchers. It's still early days for this research, but there are some promising signs that AI models might be able to provide justifications for their outputs, if not yet causal reasoning for them, although it is still unclear how reliable these will be.

There's also great work being done in using simplified architectures to explore more complex ones, even on automating the process of alignment research itself: building AIs to help us contain AI. Researchers are working on a generation of "critic AIs" that can monitor and give feedback on other AI outputs with the goal of improving them at speeds and scales that humans cannot match—speeds and scales that we see in the coming wave. Managing powerful tools itself requires powerful tools.

The computer scientist Stuart Russell proposes using the kind of built-in systematic doubt we are exploring at Inflection to create what he calls "provably beneficial AI." Rather than give an AI a set of fixed external objectives contained in what's known as a written constitution, he recommends that systems gingerly infer our preferences and ends. They should carefully watch and learn. In theory, this should leave more room for doubt within systems and avoid perverse outcomes.

Many key challenges remain: How can you build secure values into a powerful AI system potentially capable of overriding its own instructions? How might AIs infer these values from humans? Another ongoing question is how to crack the problem of "corrigibility," ensuring that it is always possible to access and correct systems. If you think all of this sounds like fairly fundamental must-have safety features of advanced AI, you'd be right. Progress here needs to keep up.

We should also build robust technical constraints into the development and production process. Think of how all modern photocopiers and printers are built with technology preventing you from copying or printing money, with some even shutting down if you try. For example, resource caps on the amount of training compute used to create models could place limits on the rate of progress (across that dimension at least). Performance might be throttled so that a model can run only on certain tightly controlled hardware. AI systems could be built with cryptographic protections ensuring model weights—the most valuable IP in the system—can be copied only a limited number of times or only in certain circumstances.

The highest-level challenge, whether in synthetic biology, robotics, or AI, is building a bulletproof off switch, a means of closing down any technology threatening to run out of control. It's raw common sense to always ensure there is an off switch in any autonomous or powerful system. How to do this with technologies that are as distributed, pro-tean, and far-reaching as in the coming wave—technologies whose pre-cise form isn't yet clear, technologies that in some cases might actively resist—is an open question. It's a huge challenge. Do I think it's possi-ble? Yes—but no one should downplay for a second the scale of how hard it will be.

Too much safety work is incremental, focused on narrow impact as-sessments, small technical issues, or fixing problems that flare up post-launch rather than working on foundational issues ahead of time. Instead, we should identify problems early and then invest more time and resources in the fundamentals. Think big. Create common stan-dards. Safety features should not be afterthoughts but inherent design properties of all these new technologies, the ground state of everything that comes next. Despite the fierce challenges, I'm genuinely excited by the range and ingenuity of ideas here. Let's give them the intellectual oxygen and material support to succeed, recognizing that while engi-neering is never the whole answer, it's a fundamental part of it.

2. AUDITS: KNOWLEDGE IS POWER; POWER IS CONTROL

Audits sound boring. Necessary, maybe—but deadly dull. But they are critical to containment. Creating secure physical and virtual containers—the kind of work we just saw—is foundational. But alone, it's insufficient. Actually having meaningful oversight and enforceable rules and reviewing technical implementations are vital. Technical safety advances and regulation will struggle to be effective if you can't verify that they are working as intended. How can you be sure what's really happening and check that you're in control? It's an immense technical and social challenge.

Trust comes from transparency. We absolutely need to be able to verify, at every level, the safety, integrity, or uncompromised nature of a system. That in turn is about access rights and audit capacity, about adversarially testing systems, having teams of white hat hackers or even AIs probing weaknesses, flaws, and biases. It's about building technology in an entirely different way, with tools and techniques that don't exist yet.

External scrutiny is essential. Right now there's no global, formal, or routine effort to test deployed systems. There's no early warning apparatus for technological risks and no uniform or rigorous way of knowing if they abide by regulations or even adhere to commonly agreed benchmarks. There are neither the institutions nor the standardized assessments nor the tools necessary. As a starting point, then, having companies and researchers working at the cutting edge, where there is a real risk of harm, proactively collaborating with trusted experts in government-led audits of their work, is basic common sense. If any such body existed, I would happily cooperate with it at Inflection.

A few years ago I co-founded a cross-industry and civil society organization called the Partnership on AI to help with this kind of work. We launched it with the support of all the major technology companies, including DeepMind, Google, Facebook, Apple, Microsoft, IBM, and OpenAI, along with scores of expert civil society groups, including the ACLU, the EFF, Oxfam, UNDP, and twenty others. Shortly after, it kick-started an AI Incidents Database, designed for confidentially reporting on safety events to share lessons with other developers. It has now collected more than twelve hundred reports. With more than a hundred partners from nonprofit, academic, and media groups, the partnership offers critical, neutral windows for interdisciplinary discussion and collaboration. There's scope for more organizations like this, and programs of audit within them.

Another interesting example is "red teaming"—that is, proactively hunting for flaws in AI models or software systems. This means attacking your systems in controlled ways to probe for weaknesses and other failure modes. Those thrown up today are likely to be magnified in the future, and so understanding them allows for safeguards to be built in as systems grow more powerful. The more this is done publicly and collectively, the better, enabling all developers to learn from one another. Again, it's high time that all big tech companies proactively collaborate here, quickly sharing insights about novel risks, just like the cybersecurity industry has long shared knowledge of new zero-day attacks.

It's also time to create government-funded red teams that would rigorously attack and stress test every system, ensuring that insights discovered along the way are shared widely across the industry. Eventually, this work could be scaled and automated, with publicly mandated AI systems designed specifically to audit and spot problems in others, while also allowing themselves to be audited.

Systems implemented to keep track of new technologies need to recognize anomalies, unforeseen jumps in capability, hidden failure modes. They must spot Trojan attacks that look legitimate but conceal unwelcome surprises. To do this, they will have to monitor a huge range of metrics without falling into the ever-tempting trap of the panopticon. Keeping close tabs on significant data sets that are used to train models, particularly open-source data sets, bibliometrics from research, and publicly available harmful incidents, would be a fruitful and noninvasive place to start. APIs that let others use foundational AI services should not be blindly open, but rather come with "know your customer" checks, as with, say, portions of the banking industry.

On the technical side, there's scope for targeted oversight mechanisms, what some researchers have called "scalable supervision" of "systems that potentially outperform us on most skills relevant to the task at hand." This proposal is about mathematically verifying the nonharmful nature of algorithms, requiring strict proofs from the model that mean actions or outputs are demonstrably constrained. Essentially, guaranteed records of activity and limits around capabilities are built in. Verifying and validating a model's behavior in this way can potentially provide an objective, formal means for guiding and tracking a system.

Another promising example of a new oversight mechanism is SecureDNA, a not-for-profit program started by a group of scientists and security specialists. At present only a fraction of synthesized DNA is screened for potentially dangerous elements, but a global effort like the SecureDNA program to plug every synthesizer—benchtop at home or large and remote—into a centralized, secure, and encrypted system that can scan for pathogenic sequences is a great start. If people are printing potentially harmful sequences, they're flagged. Cloud based, free, cryptographically secure, it updates in real time.

Screening all DNA synthesis would be a major bio-risk reduction exercise and would not, in my view, unduly curb civil liberties. This wouldn't stop a black market in the long term, but building noncompliant synthesizers or hacking an existing system introduces a nontrivial hurdle. Pre-vetting DNA synthesis or data inputs to AI models would front-load audits before systems were deployed, reducing risk.

Right now approaches to surveillance of the emergence of new technologies, or their misuse by hostile states and other actors, differ across the globe. It's an uneven picture: a mix of often opaque open-source information, academic research, and, in some cases, clandestine surveillance. It's a legal and political minefield, where the thresholds for intrusion are very mixed and, at worst, deliberately obscured. We can do better. Transparency cannot be optional. There has to be a well-defined, legal route to checking any new technology under the hood, in the code, in the lab, in the factory, or out in the wild.

Most of this should be carried out voluntarily, in collaboration with the technology producers. Where it can't be done that way, legislation must enforce cooperation. And if that does not work, there could be consideration of alternative approaches, such as the development of technical safeguards—including in some cases encrypted back doors—to provide a verifiable entry system controlled by the judiciary or an equivalent publicly sanctioned independent body.

Where a case was made to access any public or private system by law enforcement or regulators, this would be decided based on the merits of the case. Likewise, cryptographic ledgers that record any copying or sharing of a model, system, or knowledge would help track its proliferation and use. Melding social and technological containment mechanisms like this is critical. The details need new research and public debate. We will need to find a new, secure, and difficult-to-abuse balance between surveillance and safety that works for the coming wave.

Laws and treaties and brilliant technical solutions are all very well. But they still need aligning and checking, and doing so without resorting to draconian means of control. Building technologies like these initiatives is far from boring; it's one of the twenty-first century's most galvanizing technical and social challenges. Getting both technical safety features and audit measures in place is vital, but it takes something we don't have. Time.

3. CHOKE POINTS: BUY TIME

Xi Jinping was worried. "We rely on imports for some critical devices, components, and raw materials," the Chinese president told a group of the country's scientists in September 2020. Ominously, the "key and core technologies" he believed so vital to China's future and geopolitical security were "controlled by others." Indeed, China spends more on importing chips than it does on oil. Not much publicly rattles the Chinese leadership, but having pinned its long-term strategy on dominance of the coming wave, it was admitting an acute vulnerability.

Some years earlier a government-run newspaper had used a more graphic image to describe the same problem: Chinese technology was, it said, limited by a series of "choke points." If someone was to pressure those choke points, well, the implication was clear.

Xi's fears came to pass on October 7, 2022. America declared war on China, attacking one of those choke points. This didn't involve missiles shooting over the Taiwan Strait. There wasn't a naval blockade of the South China Sea or marines storming the Fujian coastline. It came instead from an unlikely source: the Commerce Department. The shots fired were export controls on advanced semiconductors, the chips that underwrite computing and so artificial intelligence.

The new export controls have made it illegal for U.S. companies to sell high-performance computing chips to China and for any company to share the tools to manufacture these chips, or provide the know-how to repair existing chips. The most advanced semiconductors (generally involving processes under fourteen nanometers, that is, fourteen-billionths of a meter, distances representing as few as twenty atoms)—including IP, manufacturing equipment, parts, design, software, services—for use in areas like artificial intelligence and supercomputing are now subject to stringent licensing. Leading American chip companies like NVIDIA and AMD can no longer supply Chinese customers with the means and know-how to produce the world's most advanced chips. U.S. citizens working on semiconductors with Chinese companies are faced with a choice: keep their jobs and lose American citizenship, or immediately quit.

It was a bolt from the blue, designed to annihilate China's grip on

the single most important building block of twenty-first-century technology. This isn't just an arcane trade dispute. This declaration was an
almighty Klaxon in Zhongnanhai, the Chinese leadership compound,
coming just as the Communist Party Congress effectively installed Xi
as ruler for life. One technology executive, speaking anonymously, outlined the move's scope: "They are not just targeting military applications, they are trying to block the development of China's technology
power by any means."

In the short to medium term, the consensus is that this is going to
hurt. The challenges of building this infrastructure are immense, especially in the sophisticated machines and techniques that produce the
world's most advanced chips, an area in which China lags. In the long
term, though, that probably won't stop it. Instead, it is pushing a difficult and hugely expensive but still plausible path toward domestic
semiconductor capacity. If it takes hundreds of billions of dollars (and
it will), they'll spend it.

Chinese companies are already finding ways to bypass the controls,
using networks of shell and front companies and cloud computing services in third-party countries. NVIDIA, the American manufacturer of
the world's most advanced AI chips, recently retroactively tweaked its
most advanced chips to evade the sanctions. Nonetheless, it shows us
something vital: there is at least one undeniable lever. The wave can be
slowed, at least for some period of time and in some areas.

Buying time in an era of hyper-evolution is invaluable. Time to develop further containment strategies. Time to build in additional safety
measures. Time to test that off switch. Time to build improved defensive technologies. Time to shore up the nation-state, regulate better, or
even just get that bill passed. Time to knit together international alliances.

Right now technology is driven by the power of incentives rather
than the pace of containment. Export controls like the United States'
semiconductor gambit have all kinds of uncertain implications for
great power competition, arms races, and the future, but almost everyone agrees on one thing: this will slow down at least some technological development in China, and by extension the world.

Recent history suggests that for all its global proliferation, technology rests on a few critical R&D and commercialization hubs: choke points. Consider these points of remarkable concentration: Xerox and Apple for interfaces, say, or DARPA and MIT, or Genentech, Monsanto, Stanford, and UCSF for genetic engineering. It's remarkable how this legacy is only slowly disappearing.

In AI, the lion's share of the most advanced GPUs essential to the latest models are designed by one company, the American firm NVIDIA. Most of its chips are manufactured by one company, TSMC, in Taiwan, the most advanced in just a single building, the world's most sophisticated and expensive factory. TSMC's machinery to make these chips comes from a single supplier, the Dutch firm ASML, by far Europe's most valuable and important tech company. ASML's machines, which use a technique known as extreme ultraviolet lithography and produce chips at levels of astonishing atomic precision, are among the most complex manufactured goods in history. These three companies have a choke hold on cutting-edge chips, a technology so physically constrained that one estimate argues they cost up to $10 billion per kilogram.

Chips aren't the only choke point. Industrial-scale cloud computing, too, is dominated by six major companies. For now, AGI is realistically pursued by a handful of well-resourced groups, most notably DeepMind and OpenAI. Global data traffic travels through a limited number of fiber-optic cables bunched in key pinch points (off the coast of southwest England or Singapore, for example). A crunch on the rare earth elements cobalt, niobium, and tungsten could topple entire industries. Some 80 percent of the high-quality quartz essential to things like photovoltaic panels and silicon chips comes from a single mine in North Carolina. DNA synthesizers and quantum computers are not commonplace consumer goods. Skills, too, are a choke point: the number of people working on all the frontier technologies discussed in this book is probably no more than 150,000.

So, as negative impacts become clear, we must use these choke points to create sensible rate-limiting factors, checks on the speed of development, to better ensure that good sense is implemented as fast as the science evolves. In practice, then, choke holds should apply not just to China; they could be widely applied to regulate the pace of development or rollout. Export controls are then not just a geostrategic play but a live experiment, a possible map for how technology can be contained but not strangled altogether. Eventually, all these technologies will be widely diffused. Before then, the next five or so years are absolutely critical, a tight window when certain pressure points can still slow technology down. While the option is there, let's take it and buy time.

4. MAKERS: CRITICS SHOULD BUILD IT

The fact that technology's incentives are unstoppable does not mean that those building it bear no responsibility for their creations. On the contrary, they, we, I, do; the responsibility is crystal clear. No one is compelled to experiment with genetic modification or build large language models. Technology's inevitable spread and development are not a get-out-of-jail-free card, a license to build what you want and see what happens. They are rather a hammering reminder of the need to get things right and the awful consequences of not doing so.

More than anyone else, those working on technology need to be actively working to solve the problems described in this book. The burden of proof and the burden of solutions rest on them, on us. People often ask me, given all this, why work in AI and build AI companies and tools? Aside from the huge positive contribution they can make, my answer is that I don't just want to talk about and debate containment. I want to proactively help make it happen, on the front foot, ahead of where the technology is going. Containment needs technologists utterly focused on making it a reality.

Technology's critics also have a vital role here. Standing on the sidelines and shouting, getting angry on Twitter, and writing long and obscure articles outlining the problems are all very well. But such actions won't stop the coming wave, and in truth they won't change it significantly either. When I first began working professionally, the outside view of technology was almost wholly benign, rapturous even. These were cool, friendly companies building a shiny future. That has changed. Yet as the voices of critique have grown much louder, it's notable how few and far between their successes are.

In their own way, tech's critics fall into a form of the pessimism-aversion trap that is hardwired into techno/political/business elites. Many who ridicule overly optimistic technologists stick to writing theoretical oversight frameworks or op-eds calling for regulation. If you believe technology is important and powerful, and you follow the implications of these critiques, such responses are clearly inadequate. Even the critics duck the true reality in front of them. Indeed, at times shrill criticism just becomes part of the same hype cycle as technology itself.

Credible critics must be practitioners. Building the right technology, having the practical means to change its course, not just observing and commenting, but actively showing the way, making the change, effecting the necessary actions at source, means critics need to be involved. They cannot stand shouting from the sidelines. This is in no way an argument against critics, quite the opposite. It's a recognition that technology deeply *needs* critics—at every level but especially on the front lines, building and making, grappling with the tangible everyday reality of creation. If you're reading this and are critical, then there's a clear response: get involved.

I fully acknowledge this doesn't make for an easy life. There's no comfortable place here. It's impossible not to recognize some of the paradoxes. It means people like me have to face the prospect that alongside trying to build positive tools and forestall bad outcomes, we may inadvertently accelerate the very things we're trying to avoid, just like gain-of-function researchers with their viral experiments. Technologies I develop may well cause some harm. I will personally continue to make mistakes, despite my best efforts to learn and improve. I've wrestled with this point for years—hang back or get involved? The closer you are to a technology's beating heart, the more you can affect outcomes, steer it in more positive directions, and block harmful applications. But this means also being part of what makes it a reality—for all the good and for all the harm it may do.

I don't have all the answers. I constantly question my choices. But the only other option is to relinquish the task of building altogether. Technologists cannot be distant, disconnected architects of the future, listening only to themselves. Without critics on the outside and within, the dilemma hurtles toward us inexorably. With them, there's a better shot of building technology that does not further damage the nation-state, is less prone to catastrophic failures, does not help increase the chances of authoritarian dystopias. Ten years ago, the tech industry was also monocultural, in every sense of the word. That's started to change, and there's now more intellectual diversity than ever before, including more critical, ethical, humanistic voices in the development process itself.

When I co-founded DeepMind, building safety and ethics concerns into the core fabric of a tech company felt novel. Simply using the word "ethics" in this context got me universally strange looks; today in contrast it's sadly in danger of being another overused buzzword. Nevertheless, it has led to real change, opening up meaningful opportunities for discussion and contestation. Promisingly, research on ethical AI has ballooned—a fivefold increase in publications since 2014. On the industry side this growth is even faster; ethical AI research with industry affiliations is up 70 percent year on year. Once, it would have been strange to find moral philosophers, political scientists, and cultural anthropologists working in tech, now less so. Major shortfalls in bringing nontechnical perspectives and diverse voices into the discussion are still all too commonplace, however: contained technology is a project requiring all kinds of disciplines and perspectives. Proactively hiring to that effect is a must.

In a world of entrenched incentives and failing regulation, technology needs critics not just on the outside but at its beating heart.

5. BUSINESSES: PROFIT + PURPOSE

Profit drives the coming wave. There's no pathway to safety that doesn't recognize and grapple with this fact. When it comes to exponential technologies like AI and synthetic biology, we must find new accountable and inclusive commercial models that incentivize safety and profit alike. It should be possible to create companies better adapted to containing technology by default. I and others have long been experimenting with this challenge, but to date results have been mixed.

Corporations traditionally have a single, unequivocal goal: share-holder returns. For the most part, that means the unimpeded development of new technologies. While this has been a powerful engine of progress in history, it's poorly suited to containment of the coming wave. I believe that figuring out ways to reconcile profit and social purpose in hybrid organizational structures is the best way to navigate the challenges that lie ahead, but making it work in practice is incredibly hard.

From the beginning of DeepMind, it was important to me that we factored in governance models equal to our end goal. When we were acquired by Google in 2014, I designed an "ethics and safety board" to oversee our technologies, and we made this a condition of the acquisition. Even back then we realized that if we were to be successful in achieving our mission of building true AGI, it would unleash a force far beyond what could reasonably be expected to be owned and controlled by a single corporation. We wanted to ensure that Google understood this and put in place a commitment to broaden our governance beyond us technologists. Ultimately, I wanted to create a global, multi-stakeholder forum for deciding what would happen with AGI when or if it was achieved, a kind of democratic world institute for AI. The more powerful a technology, it seemed to me, the more important it was to have multiple perspectives controlling and gaining access to it.

After our acquisition by Google, my co-founders and I spent years trying to build an ethics charter into the legal fabric of the company, endlessly arguing about how much of this charter could be public, how much of DeepMind's work could be further subject to independent oversight and scrutiny. Our goal in these discussions was always to ensure that unprecedented technology was matched by unprecedented governance. Our proposal was to spin DeepMind out as a new form of "global interest company," with a fully independent board of trustees separate from and in addition to the board of directors tasked with operationally running the company. Membership, decision-making, and even some of the board's reasoning would be more public. Transparency, accountability, ethics—these would be not just corporate PR but foundational, legally binding, and built into everything the company did. We felt this would let us work in an open way, proactively learning how companies could be resilient and modern long-term stewards of exponential technologies.

We established a plausible way profits from AI could be reinvested in an ethical and social mission. The spun-out company would be "limited by guarantee," without shareholders but with an obligation to provide Alphabet, the main funder, with an exclusive technology license. As part of its social and scientific mission DeepMind would use a large portion of its profits to work on public service technologies that might only be valuable years down the line: things like carbon capture and storage, ocean cleaning, plastic-eating robots, or nuclear fusion. The deal was that we'd be able to make some of our major breakthroughs open-source, much like an academic lab. IP core to Google's search business would stay with Google, but the rest would be available for us to advance DeepMind's social mission, working on new drugs, better health care, climate change, and so on. It would mean investors could be rewarded, but also ensured that social purpose was in the company's legal DNA.

In hindsight it was just too much for Google at the time. Lawyers were retained, years of intense negotiations took place, but there didn't seem to be a way to square the circle. In the end we couldn't find an answer that would satisfy everyone. DeepMind continued as a normal unit within Google with no formal legal independence, operating just as a separate brand. It was a foundational lesson for me: shareholder capitalism works because it is simple and clear, and governance models too have a tendency to default to the simple and clear. In the shareholder model, lines of accountability and performance tracking are quantified and very transparent. It may be possible to design more modern structures in theory, but operating them in practice is another story.

During my time at Google, I continued working on experimental efforts to create innovative governance structures. I drafted Google's AI Principles and was part of the team that launched the AI ethics advisory council, made up of eminent independent legal, technology, and ethics experts. The goal of both was to take the first steps toward establishing a charter around how Google handles cutting-edge technologies like AI and quantum computing. Our ambition was to invite a diverse group of external stakeholders to gain privileged access to the technical frontier, give feedback, and provide much-needed external perspectives from those far away from the excitement and optimism of building new technologies.

However, the council fell apart days after it was announced. Some employees at Google objected to the appointment of Kay Coles James, the president of the Heritage Foundation, a Washington-based conservative think tank. She had been appointed alongside a range of figures from the left and the center, but a campaign was quickly launched inside Google to get her removed. Forming a coalition with Twitter employees, the activists pointed out that she had made a number of anti-trans and anti-LGBTQ remarks over the years, including most recently arguing, "If they can change the definition of women to include men, they can erase efforts to empower women economically, socially, and politically." While I personally disagreed with her remarks and political positions, I defended our choice to ask her to join the board, arguing that the full range of values and perspectives deserved to be heard. After all, Google is a global company with global users, some of whom might share this view.

Many Google employees and external activists disagreed and within days of the announcement published an open letter demanding James's removal from the council. Staffers and others were actively lobbying university campuses to remove academic funding from other board members who refused to step down, arguing that their ongoing participation could only be understood as condoning transphobia. In the end three members resigned, and the effort was scrapped entirely in less than a week. The political atmosphere was, unfortunately, too much both for public figures and for a public company.

Once again, my attempts to rethink the corporate mandate failed, even as they spurred conversation and helped put some difficult discussions on the table, both at Alphabet and in wider policy, academic, and industry circles. What teams and what research are funded, how products are tested, what internal controls and reviews are in place, how much outside scrutiny is appropriate, what stakeholders need to be included—senior leaders at Alphabet and elsewhere started having these conversations on a regular basis.

Across tech companies the kinds of AI safety discussions that felt fringe a decade ago are now becoming routine. The need to balance profits with a positive contribution and cutting-edge safety is accepted in principle by all the major U.S. tech groups. Despite the awesome scale of the rewards on offer, entrepreneurs, execs, and employees alike should keep pushing and exploring corporate forms that can better accommodate the challenge of containment.

Encouraging experiments are underway. Facebook created its independent Oversight Board—staffed with ex-judges, campaigners, and expert academics to advise on governing the platform. It has come in for criticism from all quarters and clearly doesn't "solve" the problem alone. But it's important to begin by praising the effort, and encouraging Facebook and others to keep experimenting. Another example is the growing movement of public benefit corporations and B Corps, which are still for-profit companies but have a social mission inscribed into their legally defined goals. Technology companies that have strong containment mechanisms and goals written in as a fiduciary duty are a next step. There's a good chance of positive change here, given the growth of these alternative corporate structures (more than ten thousand companies now use the B Corp structure). While economic goals do not always align well with contained technology, innovative corporate forms make it more likely. This is the kind of experimentation that's needed.

Containment needs a new generation of corporations. It needs founders and those working in tech to contribute positively to society. It also needs something altogether more difficult. It needs politics.

6. GOVERNMENTS: SURVIVE, REFORM, REGULATE

Technological problems require technological solutions, as we've seen, but alone they are never sufficient. We also need the state to flourish. Every effort to buttress liberal democratic states and steel them against the stressors must be supported. Nation-states still control many fundamental elements of civilization: law, the money supply, taxation, the military, and so on. That helps with the task ahead, where they will need to create and maintain resilient social systems, welfare nets, security architectures, and governance mechanisms capable of surviving severe stress. But they also need to know, in detail, what is happening: right now they're operating blind in a hurricane.

The physicist Richard Feynman famously said, "What I cannot create, I do not understand." Today this couldn't be more true of governments and technology. I think the government needs to get way more involved, back to building real technology, setting standards, and nurturing in-house capability. It needs to compete for talent and hardware in the open market. There's no two ways about it: this is expensive and will come with wasteful mistakes. But proactive governments will exert far greater control than if they just commission services and live off outsourced expertise and tech owned and operated elsewhere.

Accountability is enabled by deep understanding. Ownership gives control. Both require governments to get their hands dirty. Although today companies have taken the lead, much of the most speculative fundamental research is still funded by governments. U.S. federal government expenditure on R&D is at an all-time-low share of the total— just 20 percent—but still amounts to a not inconsiderable $179 billion per year.

This is good news. Investing in science and technology education and research and supporting domestic tech businesses create a positive feedback loop where governments have a direct stake in state-of-the-art technology, poised to capitalize on benefits and stamp down harms. Put simply, as an equal partner in the creation of the coming wave, governments stand a better chance of steering it toward the overall public interest. Having *much* more in-house technical expertise, even at considerable cost, is money well spent. Governments should not rely on management consultants, contractors, or other third-party suppliers. Full-time, well-respected staffers who are properly compensated, competitively with the private sector, should be a core part of the solution. Instead, private sector salaries can be ten times their public sector equivalents in national critical roles: it's unsustainable.

Their first task should be to better monitor and understand developments in technology. Countries need to understand in detail, for example, what data their populations supply, how and where it is used, and what it means; administrations should have a strong sense of the latest research, where the frontier is, where it's going, how their country can maximize upsides. Above all they need to log all the ways technology causes harm—tabulate every lab leak, every cyberattack, every language model bias, every privacy breach—in a publicly transparent way so everyone can learn from failures and improve.

This information then needs to be used effectively by the state, responding in real time to emerging problems. Bodies close to executive power, like the White House's Office of Science and Technology Policy, are growing more influential. More is still needed: in the twenty-first century it doesn't make sense to have cabinet positions addressing matters like the economy, education, security, and defense without a similarly empowered and democratically accountable position in technology. The secretary or minister for emerging technology is still a governmental rarity. It shouldn't be; every country should have one in the era of the coming wave.

Regulation alone doesn't get us to containment, but any discussion that doesn't involve regulation is doomed. Regulation should focus on those incentives, better aligning individuals, states, companies, and the public as a whole with safety and security while building in the possibility of a hard brake. Certain use cases, like AI for electioneering, should be prohibited by law as part of the package.

Legislatures are beginning to act. In 2015 there was virtually no legislation around AI. But no fewer than seventy-two bills with the phrase "artificial intelligence" have been passed worldwide since 2019. The OECD AI Policy Observatory counts no fewer than eight hundred AI policies from sixty countries in its database. The EU's AI Act is bedeviled with problems, sure, but there is much to be praised in its provisions, and it represents the right focus and ambition.

In 2022 the White House released a blueprint for an AI Bill of Rights with five core principles "to help guide the design, development, and deployment of artificial intelligence and other automated systems so that they protect the rights of the American public." Citizens should, it says, be protected from unsafe and ineffective systems and algorithmic bias. No one should be forced to subject themselves to AI. Everyone has the right to say no. Efforts like this should be widely supported and quickly implemented.

However, policy makers' imaginations will need to match the scope of technology. Government needs to go further. For understandable reasons, we don't let any business build or operate nuclear reactors in any way they see fit. In practice, the state is intimately involved in—and closely watching, licensing, and governing—every aspect of their existence. Over time this will and should become more true of technology in general. Today anyone can build AI. Anyone can set up a lab. We should instead move to a more licensed environment. This would produce a clearer set of responsibilities and harder mechanisms for revoking access and remedying harms around advanced technologies. The most sophisticated AI systems or synthesizers or quantum computers should be produced only by responsible certified developers. As part of their license, they would need to subscribe to clear, binding security and safety standards, following rules, running risk assessments, keeping records, closely monitoring live deployments. Just as you cannot simply launch a rocket into space without FAA approval, so tomorrow you shouldn't simply be able to release a state-of-the-art AI.

Different licensing regimes could apply according to model size or capability: the bigger and more capable the model, the more stringent the licensing requirements. The more general a model, the more likely it is to pose a serious threat. This means that AI labs working on the most fundamental capabilities will require special attention. Moreover, this creates scope for more granular licensing if need be to home in on the specifics of development: training runs of models, chip clusters above a given size, certain kinds of organisms.

Taxation also needs to be completely overhauled to fund security and welfare as we undergo the largest transition of value creation—from labor to capital—in history. If technology creates losers, they need material compensation. Today U.S. labor is taxed at an average rate of 25 percent, equipment and software at just 5 percent. The system is designed to let capital frictionlessly reproduce itself in the name of creating flourishing businesses. In the future, taxation needs to switch emphasis toward capital, not only funding a redistribution toward those adversely affected, but creating a slower and fairer transition in the process. Fiscal policy is an important valve in controlling this transition, a means of exercising control over those choke points and building state resilience at the same time.

This should include a greater tax on older forms of capital like land, property, company shares, and other high-value, less liquid assets, as well as a new tax on automation and autonomous systems. This is sometimes called a "tax on robots"; MIT economists have argued that even a moderate tax of just 1 to 4 percent of their value could have a big impact. A carefully calibrated shift in the tax burden away from labor would incentivize continued hiring and cushion disruptions in house-hold life. Tax credits topping up the lowest incomes could be an im-mediate buffer in the face of stagnating or even collapsing incomes. At the same time, a massive re-skilling program and education effort should prepare vulnerable populations, raise awareness of risks, and increase opportunities for engagement with the capabilities of the wave. A universal basic income (UBI)—that is, an income paid by the state for every citizen irrespective of circumstances—has often been floated as the answer to the economic disruptions of the coming wave. In the future, there will likely be a place for UBI-like initiatives; how-ever, before one even gets to that, there are plenty of good ideas.

In an era of hyper-scaling corporate AIs, we should start to think of capital taxes like this applying to the largest corporations themselves, not just the assets or profits in question. Moreover, mechanisms must be found for cross-border taxation of those giant businesses, ensuring they pay their fair share in maintaining functioning societies. Experi-ments are encouraged here: a fixed portion of company value, for ex-ample, paid as a public dividend would keep value transferring back to the population in an age of extreme concentration. At the limit there is a core question about who owns the capital of the coming wave; a genuine AGI cannot be privately owned in the same manner as, say, a building or a fleet of trucks. When it comes to technology that could radically extend human life span or capabilities, there clearly has to be a big debate from the get-go about its distribution.

Who is able to design, develop, and deploy technologies like this is ultimately a matter for governments to decide. Their levers, institu-tions, and domains of expertise will all have to evolve as rapidly as technology, a generational challenge for everyone involved. An age of contained technology is, then, an age of extensively and intelligently regulated technology; no ifs or buts. But of course, regulation in one country has an inevitable flaw. No national government can do this alone.

7. ALLIANCES: TIME FOR TREATIES

Laser weapons sound like science fiction. Unfortunately, they're not. As laser technology developed, it was clear they could cause blindness. Weaponized, this could incapacitate adversary forces or, indeed, any-one targeted. An exciting new civilian technology was again opening up the prospect of horrible modes of attack (although not to date in the manner of *Star Wars*). No one wants armies or gangs roaming around with blinding lasers.

Luckily, it didn't happen. Use of blinding laser weapons was out-lawed under the 1995 Protocol on Blinding Laser Weapons, an update to the Convention on Certain Conventional Weapons that prohibited the use of "laser weapons specifically designed, as their sole combat function or as one of their combat functions, to cause permanent blindness to unenhanced vision." A hundred and twenty-six countries signed up. Laser weapons are, as a result, neither a major part of mili-tary hardware nor common weapons on the streets.

Sure, blinding lasers are not the kinds of omni-use technologies we're talking about in this book. But they are evidence that it can be done; a strong ban can work. Delicate alliances and international coop-eration can be pulled off, and they can change history.

Consider these examples, some of which we discussed earlier: the Treaty on the Non-proliferation of Nuclear Weapons; the Montreal Protocol outlawing CFCs; the invention, trialing, and rollout of a polio vaccine across a Cold War divide; the Biological Weapons Convention, a disarmament treaty effectively banning biological weapons; bans on cluster munitions, land mines, genetic editing of human beings, and eugenics policies; the Paris Agreement, aiming to limit carbon emis-sions and the worst impacts of climate change; the global effort to eradicate smallpox; phasing out lead in gasoline; and putting an end to asbestos.

Countries no more like giving up power than companies like missing out on profit, and yet these are precedents to learn from, shards of hope in a landscape riven with resurgent techno-competition. Each had specific conditions and challenges that both helped it come about and hindered perfect compliance. But each, crucially, is a precious example of the world's nations uniting and compromising to face a major challenge, offering hints and frameworks for tackling the coming wave. If a government wanted to ban synthetic biology or AI applications, could it? No, clearly not in anything but a partial, fragile sense. But a powerful, motivated alliance? Maybe.

Faced with the abyss, geopolitics can change fast. In the teeth of World War II, peace must have felt like a dream. As the Allies wearily fought on, few on the ground could have imagined that just a few years later their governments would pump billions into rebuilding their enemies. That, despite horrific and genocidal war crimes, Germany and Japan would soon become critical parts of a stable worldwide alliance. In hindsight it seems dizzying. Just a few short years separate the bullets, bitterness, and beaches of Normandy and Iwo Jima from a rock-solid military and commercial partnership, a deep friendship that lasts to this day, and the biggest foreign aid program ever attempted.

At the height of the Cold War high-level contacts were maintained in spite of severe tensions. In the event of something like a rogue AGI or major biohazard being released, this kind of high-level coordination will be critical, yet as the new Cold War takes shape, divides are growing. Catastrophic threats are innately global and should be a matter of international consensus. Rules that stop at national borders are obviously insufficient. While every country has a stake in advancing these technologies, they also have a good cause to curtail their worst consequences. So what do the nonproliferation treaty, the Montreal Protocol, the Paris Agreement look like for the coming wave?

Nuclear weapons are an exception partly but not only because they are so difficult to build: the long, patient hours of discussion, the decades of painstaking treaty negotiations at the UN, the international collaboration even at times of extreme tension, it all matters when it comes to keeping them in check. There are both moral and strategic components to nuclear containment. Reaching and enforcing such agreements has never been easy, doubly so in an era of great power competition. Diplomats hence play an underrated role in containing technology. A golden age of techno-diplomacy needs to emerge from the era of arms races. Many I've spoken with in the diplomatic community are acutely aware of this.

Alliances, however, can also work at the level of technologists or subnational bodies, collectively deciding what to fund, what to turn away from. A good example here comes from germ-line gene editing. A study of 106 countries found that regulation of germ-line gene editing is patchy. Most countries have some kind of regulation or policy guidelines, but there are considerable divergences and gaps. It doesn't add up to a global framework on a technology with global scope. More effective to date is the international collaboration of scientists on the front line. In the aftermath of the first gene editing of human beings, a letter signed by luminaries like Eric Lander, Emmanuelle Charpentier, and Feng Zhang called for "a global moratorium on all clinical uses of human germline editing—that is, changing heritable DNA (in sperm, eggs or embryos) to make genetically modified children" and "an international framework in which nations, while retaining the right to make their own decisions, voluntarily commit to not approve any use of clinical germline editing unless certain conditions are met."

They're not calling for a permanent ban, they're not banning germline editing for research purposes, and they're not saying every nation should follow the same path. But they are asking that practitioners take time to harmonize and make the right decisions. Enough people at the leading edge can still make a difference, allowing room for a pause, helping to create space and a foundation for nations and international bodies to come together and find a way through.

Earlier in the chapter I discussed the frictions between the United States and China. Despite their differences there are still obvious places for collaboration between these vying powers. Synthetic biology is a better starting point than AI here, thanks to lower existing competition and the obvious mutually assured destruction of novel biothreats. The SecureDNA project is a good example, laying out a path for governing synthetic biology similarly to how chemical weapons have been curtailed. If China and the United States could create, say, a shared bio-risk observatory, encompassing everything from advanced R&D to deployed commercial applications, it would be a precious area of collaboration to build on.

China and the United States also share an interest in restraining the long tail of bad actors. Given that an Aum Shinrikyo could come from anywhere, both countries will be keen to restrain the uncontrolled spread of the world's most powerful technologies. Currently China and the United States are in a struggle to set technological standards. But a shared approach is a clear win-win; splintered standards make things harder for everyone. Another point of commonality might be maintaining cryptographic systems in the face of advances in quantum computing or machine learning that could undermine them. Each could pave the way for wider compromise. As the century wears on, the lesson of the Cold War will have to be relearned: there is no path to technological safety without working with your adversaries.

Beyond encouraging bilateral initiatives, the obvious thing at this stage is to propose creating some new kind of global institution devoted to technology. I've heard it said many, many times: What does a World Bank for biotech or a UN for AI look like? Could a secure international collaboration be the way to approach an issue as daunting and complex as AGI? Who is the ultimate arbiter, the lender of last resort as it were, the body that when asked "Who contains technology?" can put its hand up?

We need our generation's equivalent of the nuclear treaty to shape a common worldwide approach—in this case not curbing proliferation altogether but setting limits and building frameworks for management and mitigation that, like the wave, cross borders. This would put clear limits on what work is undertaken, mediate among national licensing efforts, and create a framework for reviewing both.

Where there is a clear scope for a new body or bodies is with technical concerns. A dedicated regulator that navigates contentious geopolitics (as much as possible), avoids overreach, and performs a pragmatic monitoring function on broadly objective criteria is urgently needed. Think of something like the International Atomic Energy Agency or even a trade body like the International Air Transport Association. Rather than having an organization that itself directly regulates, builds, or controls technology, I would start with something like an AI Audit Authority—the AAA. Focused on fact-finding and auditing model scale and when capability thresholds are crossed, the AAA would increase global transparency at the frontier, asking questions like: Does the system show signs of being able to self-improve capabilities? Can it specify its own goals? Can it acquire more resources without human oversight? Is it deliberately trained in deception or manipulation? Similar audit commissions could operate in almost every area of the wave, and would, again, offer a foundation for government licensing efforts while also helping the push for a nonproliferation treaty.

Hard realism has a much better chance of success than vague and unlikely proposals. We don't need to totally reinvent the institutional wheel, creating more opportunities for rivalry and grandstanding. We should just find every possible means of improving it—and fast.

8. CULTURE: RESPECTFULLY EMBRACING FAILURE

The common thread here is governance: of software systems, of microchips, of businesses and research institutes, of countries, and of the international community. At each level is a thicket of incentives, sunk costs, institutional inertia, conflicting fiefdoms and worldviews that must be cut through. Make no mistake. Ethics, safety, containment—these will be products of good governance above all. But good governance doesn't just come from well-defined rules and effective institutional frameworks.

In the early days of jet engines, the 1950s, crashes—and fatalities—were worryingly common. By the early 2010s they were at just one death per 7.4 million passenger boardings. Years now go by with no fatal accidents whatsoever involving American commercial aircraft. Flying is just about the safest mode of transport there is: sitting thirty-five thousand feet in the sky is safer than sitting at home on your couch.

Airlines' impressive safety record comes down to numerous incremental technical and operational improvements over the years. But

behind them is something just as important: culture. The aviation industry takes a vigorous approach to learning from mistakes at every
level. Crashes are not just tragic accidents to mourn; they're foundational learning experiences in determining how systems fail, opportunities for diagnosing problems, fixing them, and sharing that knowledge
across the entire industry. Best practices are hence not corporate secrets, an edge over rival airlines: they're enthusiastically implemented
by competitors in the common interests of collective industry trust
and safety.

That's what's needed for the coming wave: real, gut-level buy-in
from everyone involved in frontier technologies. It's all very well devising and promoting initiatives and policies for ethics and safety, but
you need the people delivering to actually believe in them.

While the tech industry talks a big game when it comes to "embracing failure," it rarely does so when it comes to privacy or safety or
technical breaches. Launching a product that doesn't catch on is one
thing, but owning a language model that causes a misinformation
apocalypse or a drug that causes adverse reactions is far more uncomfortable. Criticism of tech is, not without good reason, unrelentingly
fierce. Competition likewise. One consequence is that as soon as a new
technology or product goes awry, a culture of secrecy takes over. The
openness and mutual trust that characterize portions of the development process get lost. Opportunities for learning, and then broadcasting that learning, disappear. Even admitting to mistakes, opening the
floodgates, is seen as a risk, a corporate no-no.

Fear of failure and public opprobrium is leading to stasis. Immediate self-reporting of problems should be a baseline for individuals and
organizations alike. But rather than being commended for experimentation, companies and teams are hung out to dry. Doing the right thing
only triggers a backlash of cynicism, Twitter flaming, and vicious public point scoring. Why would anyone actually admit their mistakes in
this context? This has got to stop if we want to produce better, more
responsible, more containable technologies.

Embracing failure must be real, not a sound bite. For a start, being
utterly open about failures even on uncomfortable topics should be

met with praise, not insults. The first thing a technology company should do when encountering any kind of risk, downside, or failure mode is to safely communicate to the wider world. When a lab leaks, the first thing it should do is advertise the fact, not cover it up. The first things other actors in the space—other companies, research groups, governments—need to then do are listen, reflect, offer support, and most crucially learn and actively implement that learning. This attitude saved many thousands of lives in the sky. It could save millions more in years to come.

Containment can't just be about this or that policy, checklist, or initiative, but needs to ensure that there is a self-critical culture that actively wants to implement them, that welcomes having regulators in the room, in the lab, a culture where regulators want to learn from technologists and vice versa. It needs everyone to want in, own it, love it. Otherwise safety remains an afterthought. Among many, and not only in AI, there's a sense we are "just" researchers, "just" exploring and experimenting. That's not been the case for years, and is a prime example of where we need a culture shift. Researchers must be encouraged to step back from the constant rush toward publication. Knowledge is a public good, but it should no longer be the default. Those actively conducting frontier research need to be the first to recognize this, as their peers in areas of nuclear physics and virology already have. In AI, capabilities like recursive self-improvement and autonomy are, I think, boundaries we should not cross. This will have technical and legal components, but also needs moral, emotional, cultural buy-in from the people and organizations closest to it.

In 1973, one of the inventors of genetic engineering, Paul Berg, gathered a group of scientists on the Monterey Peninsula in California. He'd begun to worry about what his invention might unleash and wanted to set some ground rules and moral foundations for going forward. At the Asilomar conference center, they asked the difficult questions thrown up by this new discipline: Should we start genetically engineering humans? If so, what traits might be permissible? Two years later they returned in even larger numbers for the Asilomar Conference on Recombinant DNA. The stakes in that sea-lapped hotel were high. It was a turning point in the biosciences, establishing durable principles for governing genetic research and technology that set guidelines and moral limits on what experiments could take place.

I attended a conference in Puerto Rico in 2015 that aimed to do something similar for AI. With a mixed group, it wanted to raise the profile of AI safety, start building a culture of caution, and sketch real answers. We met again in 2017, at the symbolic venue of Asilomar, to draft a set of AI principles that I along with many others in the field signed on to. They were about building an explicitly responsible culture of AI research and inspired a raft of further initiatives. As the wave keeps building, we will need to self-consciously return again and again to the spirit—and letter—of Asilomar.

For millennia, the Hippocratic oath has been a moral lodestar for the medical profession. In Latin, *Primum non nocere*. First, do no harm. The Nobel Peace Prize winner and British-Polish scientist Joseph Rotblat, a man who left Los Alamos on the grounds of conscience, argued that scientists need something similar. Social and moral responsibility was, he believed, not something any scientist could ever set aside. I agree, and we should consider a contemporary version for technologists: ask not just what doing no harm means in an age of globe-spanning algorithms and edited genomes but how that can be enacted daily in what are often morally ambiguous circumstances.

Precautionary principles like this are a good first step. Pause before building, pause before publishing, review everything, sit down and hammer out the second-, third-, *n*th-order impacts. Find all the evidence and look at it coldly. Relentlessly course correct. Be willing to stop. Do all this not just because it says so in some form, but because it's what's right, it's what technologists do.

Actions like this can't just operate as laws or corporate mantras. Laws are only national, corporate mantras transitory, too often cosmetic. They must instead operate at a deeper level whereby the culture of technology is not that just-go-for-it "engineering mindset" but something more wary, more curious about what might happen. A healthy culture is one happy to leave fruit on the tree, say no, delay benefits for however long it takes to be safe, one where technologists remember that technology is just a means to an end, not the end itself.

9. MOVEMENTS: PEOPLE POWER

Throughout this book the word "we" has featured. It might have referred to "we" the author and co-author, "we" AI researchers and entrepreneurs, "we" the scientific and technology community more widely, "we" in the global West, or "we" the sum total of humanity. (Facing fully global- and species-altering technology is one of the few places where talking about a human "we" actually is warranted.)

When people talk about technology—myself included—they often make an argument like the following. Because *we* build technology, *we* can fix the problems it creates. This is true in the broadest sense. But, the problem is, there is no functional "we" here. There is no consensus and no agreed mechanism for forming a consensus. There actually is no "we," and there is certainly no lever any "we" can pull. This should be obvious, but it bears repeating. Even the president of the United States has remarkably limited powers to alter the course of, say, the internet.

Instead, countless distributed actors work sometimes together and sometimes at cross-purposes. Companies and nations, as we have seen, have divergent priorities, fractured, conflicting incentives. For the most part concerns over technology like those outlined in this book are elite pursuits, nice talking points for the business-class lounge, op-eds for *bien-pensant* publications, or topics for the presentation halls at Davos or TED. Most of humanity doesn't yet worry about these things in any kind of systematic way. Off Twitter, out of the bubble, most people have very different concerns, other problems demanding attention in a fragile world. Communication around AI hasn't always helped, tending to fall into simplistic narratives.

So, if the invocation of the grand "we" is at present meaningless, it prompts an obvious follow-up: let's build one. Throughout history change came about because people self-consciously worked for it. Popular pressure created new norms. The abolition of slavery, women's suffrage, civil rights—these are huge moral achievements that happened because people fought hard, building broad-based coalitions that took a big claim seriously and then effected change based on it. Climate wasn't just put on the map because people noticed the weather getting more extreme. They noticed because grassroots activists and scientists and then later (some) writers, celebrities, CEOs, and politicians agitated for meaningful change. And they acted on it out of a desire to do the right thing.

Research shows that when introduced to the topic of emerging technologies and their risks, people really do care and want to find solutions. Although many of the harms are still a way off, I believe people are perfectly capable of reading the runes here. I've yet to find anyone who's watched a Boston Dynamics video of a robot dog or considered the prospect of another pandemic without a shudder of dread.

Here is a huge role for popular movements. Over the last five or so years, a burgeoning civil society movement has begun to highlight these problems. The media, trade unions, philanthropic organizations, grassroots campaigns—all are getting involved, proactively looking at ways to create contained technology. I hope that my generation of founders and builders energizes these movements rather than stands in the way. Meanwhile, citizen assemblies offer a mechanism for bringing a wider group into the conversation. One proposal is to host a lottery to choose a representative sample of the population to intensively debate and come up with proposals for how to manage these technologies. Given access to tools and advice, this would be one way of making containment a more collective, attentive, grounded process.

Change happens when people demand it. The "we" that builds technology is scattered, subject to a mass of competing and different national, commercial, and research incentives. The more the "we" that is subject to it speaks clearly in one voice, a critical public mass agitating for change, demanding an alignment of approaches, the better chance of good outcomes. Anyone anywhere can make a difference. Fundamentally, neither technologists nor governments will solve this problem alone. But together "we" all might.

10. THE NARROW PATH: THE ONLY WAY IS THROUGH

Just a few days after the release of GPT-4, thousands of AI scientists signed an open letter calling for a six-month moratorium on researching the most powerful AI models. Referencing the Asilomar principles, they cited reasons familiar to those reading this book: "Recent months have seen AI labs locked in an out-of-control race to develop and deploy ever more powerful digital minds that no one—not even their creators—can understand, predict, or reliably control." Shortly after, Italy banned ChatGPT. A complaint against LLMs was filed with the Federal Trade Commission aiming for much tighter regulatory control. Questions about AI risk were asked at the White House press briefing. Millions of people discussed the impacts of technology—at work, at the dinner table.

Something is building. Containment it is not, but for the first time the questions of the coming wave are being treated with the urgency they deserve.

Each of the ideas outlined so far represents the beginning of a seawall, a tentative tidal barrier starting with the specifics of the technology itself and expanding outward to the imperative of forming a massive global movement for positive change. None of them works alone. Knit measures like this together, however, and an outline of containment comes into view.

One good example comes from the MIT biotechnologist Kevin Esvelt. Few people have considered biosecurity threats in more detail. Those bespoke pathogens designed to cause maximum fatalities? Kevin is determined to use every tool to stop them from happening. His program is one of the most holistic containment strategies around. It's built around three pillars: delay, detect, and defend.

To delay, he echoes the language of nuclear technology, proposing a "pandemic test-ban treaty," an international agreement to stop experimentation on the most pathogenic materials. Any experiments that would seriously raise the risk of a pandemic event, including gain-of-function research, would be banned. He also advocates an entirely new regime of insurance and liability for anyone working with viruses or other potentially harmful biomaterials. It would amp up the costs of responsibility in an immediately tangible way by literally factoring low-probability but catastrophic consequences—currently negative externalities borne by everyone else—into the price of the research. Not only would institutions conducting potentially dangerous research have to take out additional insurance, but a trigger law would mean anyone shown to be responsible for a major biohazard or catastrophic event would become liable.

DNA screening on all synthesizers is an absolute must, and moreover the whole system should be cloud based so that it could update in real time according to newly understood and emerging threats. Swiftly detecting an outbreak is just as important in this schema, especially for subtle pathogens with long incubation periods. Think of a disease dormant for years. If you aren't aware of what's happening, you can't contain it.

Then, if the worst happens, defend. Resilient and prepared countries are vital: the most extreme pandemics would make even maintaining food, power, water supplies, law and order, and health care difficult. Having stockpiles of state-of-the-art pandemic-proof PPE equipment ready for all essential workers would make a massive difference. So would strong supply lines of medical equipment capable of withstanding a serious shock. Those low-wavelength lightbulbs that can destroy viruses? They need to be *everywhere*, before the pandemic starts, or at the very least ready to get rolled out.

Put all the elements here together and there is an outline of what will meet and match the coming wave.

1. Technical safety	Concrete technical measures to alleviate possible harms and maintain control.
2. Audits	A means of ensuring the transparency and accountability of technology.
3. Choke points	Levers to slow development and buy time for regulators and defensive technologies.
4. Makers	Ensuring responsible developers build appropriate controls into technology from the start.

5. Businesses	Aligning the incentives of the organizations behind technology with its containment.
6. Government	Supporting governments, allowing them to build technology, regulate technology, and implement mitigation measures.
7. Alliances	Creating a system of international cooperation to harmonize laws and programs.
8. Culture	A culture of sharing learning and failures to quickly disseminate means of addressing them.
9. Movements	All of this needs public input at every level, including to put pressure on each component and make it accountable.

Step 10 is about *coherence*, ensuring that each element works in harmony with the others, that containment is a virtuous circle of mutually reinforcing measures and not a gap-filled cacophony of competing programs. In this sense, containment isn't about this or that specific suggestion but is an emergent phenomenon of their collective interplay, a by-product of societies that learn to manage and mitigate the risks thrown up by *Homo technologicus*. One move alone isn't going to work, whether with pathogens or quantum computers or AI, but a scheme like this gains force from the careful accretion of interlocking countermeasures, guardrail layered on guardrail from international treaties to supply chain reinforcement of protective new technologies. Proposals like "delay, detect, and defend" are, moreover, not end states, destinations. Safety in the context of the coming wave is not somewhere we arrive but something that must be continually enacted.

Containment is not a resting place. It's a narrow and never-ending path.

———

THE ECONOMIST DARON ACEMOGLU and the political scientist James
Robinson share the view that liberal democracies are much less secure
than they might look. They see the state as an inherently unstable
"shackled Leviathan": vast and powerful, but held in check by persistent civil societies and norms. Over time, countries like the United
States entered what they call a "narrow corridor" that kept them in this
precarious balance. On either side of this corridor lie traps. On the one
hand, the power of the state breaks that of wider society and completely dominates it, creating despotic Leviathans like China. On the
other, the state falls apart, producing absent Leviathans, zombies,
where the state has no real control over society, as in places like Soma-
lia or Lebanon. Both have terrible consequences for their populations.

Acemoglu and Robinson's point is that states constantly walk this
corridor. At any moment, they could fall. For every increase in state
capacity there needs to be a corresponding increase in social capacity
to counterbalance it. There's a constant pressure toward despotic Leviathans that needs constant weight to stop. There is no final destination, no happy, safe, and continual existence at the corridor's end;
rather, it's a dynamic, unstable space where elites and citizens contest
outcomes and at any time shackled Leviathans can either disappear or
grow despotic. Safety is a matter of inching forward and carefully
maintaining balance.

I think this metaphor holds for how we approach technology, and
not just because the argument here is that technology now makes that
balance so much more precarious. Safe, contained technology is, like
liberal democracy, not a final end state; rather, it is an ongoing process,
a delicate equilibrium that must be actively maintained, constantly
fought for and protected. There's no moment when we say, aha, we've
solved the problem of proliferating technology! Instead, it's about finding a way through, ensuring sufficient numbers of people are committed to keeping the unending balance between openness and closure.

Rather than a corridor, which implies a clear direction of travel, I
imagine containment as a narrow and treacherous path, wreathed in

fog, a plunging precipice on either side, catastrophe or dystopia just a small slip away; you can't see far ahead, and as you tread, the path twists and turns, throws up unexpected obstacles.

On the one hand, total openness to all experimentation and development is a straightforward recipe for catastrophe. If everyone in the world can play with nuclear bombs, at some stage you have a nuclear war. Open-source has been a boon to technological development and a major spur to progress more widely. But it's not an appropriate philosophy for powerful AI models or synthetic organisms; here it should be banned. They should not be shared, let alone deployed or developed, without rigorous due process.

Safety relies on things not failing, not getting into the wrong hands, forever. Some level of policing the internet, DNA synthesizers, AGI research programs, and so on is going to be essential. It's painful to write. As a young twentysomething, I started out from a privacy maximalist position, believing spaces of communication and work completely free from oversight were foundational rights and important parts of healthy democracy. Over the years, though, as the arguments became clearer and the technology more and more developed, I've updated that view. It's just not acceptable to create situations where the threat of catastrophic outcomes is ever present. Intelligence, life, raw power—these are not playthings, and should be treated with the respect, care, and control they deserve. Technologists and the general public alike will have to accept greater levels of oversight and regulation than have ever been the case before. Just as most of us wouldn't want to live in societies without laws and police, most of us wouldn't want to live in a world of unrestricted technology either.

Some measure of anti-proliferation is necessary. And yes, let's not shy away from the facts; that means real censorship, possibly well beyond national borders. There are times when this will be seen—perhaps rightly—as unbridled U.S. hegemony, Western arrogance, and selfishness. Quite honestly, I'm not always sure where the right balance is, but I now firmly believe that complete openness will push humanity off the narrow path. On the other side of the ledger, though, as should also be clear, complete surveillance and complete closure are inconceivable, wrong, and disastrous. Overreach on control is a fast track to dystopia. It too has to be resisted.

In this framework countries are always at risk. And yet some have managed to keep going for centuries, working hard to stay ahead, stay balanced, stay just shackled enough. Every single aspect of containment, all of what we've described, will have to tread this excruciating tightrope. Every measure discussed here or in the future needs to be seen on this spectrum—pushed far enough to offer meaningful protection and yet prevented from going too far.

IS CONTAINMENT OF THE coming wave possible?

Looking at the myriad paths forward, all the possible directions where technology will take human experience, the capabilities unleashed, the capacity to transform our world, it seems containment fails in many of them. The narrow path must be walked forever from here on out, and all it takes is one misstep to tumble into the abyss.

History suggests this pattern of diffusion and development is locked in. Immense incentives appear entrenched. Technologies surprise even their creators with the speed and power of their development. Every day seems to herald a new breakthrough, product, or company. The cutting edge diffuses in a matter of months. Nation-states charged with regulating this revolution are flailing because of it.

And yet, while there is compelling evidence that containment is not possible, temperamentally I remain an optimist. The ideas presented here help give us the tools and means to keep walking, step by step, down that path, the lamps and ropes and maps for wandering the tortuous route forward. The blunt challenge of containment is not a reason to turn away; it is a call to action, a generational mission we all need to face.

If we—*we* humanity—can change the context with a surge of committed new movements, businesses, and governments, with revised incentives, with boosted technical capacities, knowledge, and safeguards, then we can create conditions for setting off down that teetering path with a spark of hope. And while the sheer scale of the challenge is huge, each section here drills down into plenty of smaller areas where any individual can still make a difference. It will require an awe-

some effort to fundamentally change our societies, our human in-
stincts, and the patterns of history. It's far from certain. It looks
impossible. But meeting the great dilemma of the twenty-first century
must be possible.

We should all get comfortable with living with contradictions
in this era of exponential change and unfurling powers. Assume the
worst, plan for it, give it everything. Stick doggedly to the narrow path.
Get a world beyond the elites engaged and pushing. If enough people
start building that elusive "we," those glimmers of hope will become
raging fires of change.

LIFE AFTER
THE ANTHROPOCENE

I
T WAS QUIET. WINDOWS AND SHUTTERS WERE CLOSED, FIRES AND
candles put out, meals eaten. The bustle and hum of the busy day re-
ceded, and only the occasional bark of a dog, or scratching in the un-
dergrowth, or soft rustle of the wind in the trees broke the hush. The
world exhaled and slumbered.

They came under cover of this darkness, when they wouldn't be
recognized. Dozens of them, masked, disguised, armed, angry. In the
cool and still of the night there might be a chance for justice, if only
they could hold their nerve.

They crept wordlessly toward the large, hulking building on the edge
of town. A square, secure, forbidding presence in the gloom, the structure housed expensive and controversial new technologies—machines
they believed were the enemy. Get caught, and the intruders would lose
everything, even their lives. But they'd made an oath. This was it. There
was no going back. The machines, the bosses, they could not win.

Outside they paused and then charged. Battering at the locked door,
they eventually broke it down, streaming in. Using hammers and cud-
gels, they began smashing the machines. The clang of metal on metal
reverberated. As debris was strewn across the floor, alarms began to
sound. Shutters flew open, watchmen's lanterns were hurriedly lit.
The saboteurs—the Luddites—ran to the exit and melted into the soft
moonlight. The stillness would not be returning.

AROUND THE TURN OF the nineteenth century Britain was in the
throes of an earlier wave. Technologies premised on steam and me-

chanical automation were ripping up the rules of production, labor, value, wealth, capability, and power. What we've come to call the First Industrial Revolution was in full swing, mill by mill changing the country and the world. In 1785, the inventor Edmund Cartwright debuted the power loom, a new mechanized means of weaving. At first it didn't catch on. Soon, though, further iterations revolutionized textile manufacturing.

Not everyone was happy. The power loom could be operated by a single child, producing as much fabric as three and a half traditional weavers. Mechanization meant that weavers' wages were more than halved in the forty-five years after 1770 even as the price of basic foodstuffs leapt. Men lost out in the new world to women and children. Textile work, from weaving to dyeing, had always been backbreaking, but in the factories it was noisy, regimented, dangerous, and oppressive. Underperforming children would be strung up from the ceiling or forced to wear heavy weights. Deaths were common. Hours punishing. To those on the front lines, paying the human costs of industrialization, this wasn't a brave new techno-utopia; it was a world of satanic mills, servitude, and slights.

Traditional weavers and textile workers felt the new machines and the capital backing them were taking away their jobs, collapsing their wages, stealing their dignity, and unpicking a rich way of life. Labor-saving machinery was great for the owners of the factories, but for the high-skilled and well-paid workers who had traditionally dominated textiles, it was a disaster.

Inspired by a mythical figure called Ned Ludd, weavers across the English Midlands grew angry and organized. They refused to accept that picture, that proliferation would be the default and the wave of technology breaking around them was an economic inevitability. They decided to fight back.

In 1807, six thousand weavers demonstrated over pay cuts, a protest broken up by saber-wielding dragoons who killed a protester. From there a more violent campaign began to form. In 1811 the saboteurs got a name after a Nottingham mill owner received a series of letters from "General Ludd and the Army of Redressers." No reply was forthcoming, and on March 11 unemployed weavers raided local mills, destroying sixty-three machines and stepping up the campaign.

In the months of clandestine raids that followed, hundreds of frames were destroyed. "Ned Ludd's Army" hit back. All they wanted, they felt, was a fair wage and dignity. Their demands were often small—modest increases in pay, a phased approach to the introduction of new machinery, some kind of profit-sharing mechanism. It didn't seem too much to ask.

The Luddite protests began to peter out, stamped down by a draconian set of laws and counter-militias. Around this time, England had only a few thousand automatic looms. But by 1850 there were a quarter of a million. The battle had been lost, the technology diffused, the old life of weavers destroyed, the world changed. To those losing out, this is what an uncontained wave of technology looks like.

AND YET . . .

In the long term, the same industrial technologies that caused so much pain gave rise to a prodigious improvement in living standards. Decades, centuries later, the descendants of those weavers lived in conditions the Luddites could have scarcely imagined, habituated to that precarious world we take for granted. The vast majority of them came home to warm houses in winter, with refrigerators full of exotic food. When they got ill, they received miraculous health care. They lived much longer lives.

Just like us today, the Luddites were in a bind. Their pain and disruption were real, but so too were the improvements in living standards that benefited their children and grandchildren and that are enjoyed unthinkingly by you and me today. Back then, the Luddites failed to contain technology. But humanity adapted anyway. The challenge today is clear. We have to claim the benefits of the wave without being overwhelmed by its harms. The Luddites lost their campaign, and I think it's likely that those who would stop technology today will, once again, not be successful.

The only way, then, is to do this right, first time. To make sure that an adaptation to technology is not simply foisted on people, as it was in the Industrial Revolution. But to ensure that technology is, from the start, adapted to people, to their lives and hopes. Adapted technologies are contained technologies. The most urgent task is not to ride or vainly stop the wave but to sculpt it.

The coming wave is going to change the world. Ultimately, human beings may no longer be the primary planetary drivers, as we have become accustomed to being. We are going to live in an epoch when the majority of our daily interactions are not with other people but with AIs. This might sound intriguing or horrifying or absurd, but it is happening. I'm guessing you already spend a sizable portion of your waking hours in front of a screen. Indeed, you may spend more time looking at the collective screens in your life than at any given human, spouses and children included.

So it's no great leap to see that we will spend more and more time talking to and engaging with these new machines. The type and nature of the artificial and biological intelligences we encounter and interact with will be radically different from now. They will be the ones doing our work for us, finding information, assembling presentations, writing that program, ordering our shopping and this year's Christmas presents, advising on the best way to approach a problem, or maybe just chatting and playing.

They will be our personal intelligences, our companions and helpers, confidants and colleagues, chiefs of staff, assistants, and translators. They'll organize our lives and listen to our burning desires and darkest fears. They'll help run our businesses, treat our ailments, and fight our battles. Many different personality types, capabilities, and forms will crop up over the course of the average day. Our mental, conversational worlds will inextricably include this new and strange menagerie of intelligences. Culture, politics, the economy; friendship, play, love: all will evolve in tandem.

The world of tomorrow will be a place where factories grow their outputs locally, almost like farms in previous eras. Drones and robots will be ubiquitous. The human genome will be an elastic thing, and so, necessarily, will be the very idea of the human itself. Life spans will be much longer than our own. Many will disappear almost entirely into virtual worlds. What once seemed a settled social contract will contort and buckle. Learning to live and thrive in this world is going to be a part of everyone's life in the twenty-first century.

The Luddite reaction is natural, expected. But as always, it will be futile. Back then, though, technologists were not thinking of adapting their technology to human ends, just as Carl Benz and the first oil barons were not thinking about the earth's atmosphere. Instead, technology was created, capital funded it, and everyone else got on board, whatever the long-term consequences.

This time containment must rewrite that story. There might not yet be a global "we," but there is a group of people who are building this technology right now. We bear a huge weight of responsibility to ensure that the adaptation does not go one way. That, unlike power looms, unlike the climate, the coming wave is adapted to human needs, is built around human concerns. The coming wave should not be created to serve distant interests, following an agenda of blind techno-logic—or worse.

Too many visions of the future start with what technology can or might do and work from there. That's completely the wrong foundation. Technologists should focus not just on the engineering minutiae but on helping to imagine and realize a richer, social, human future in the broadest sense, a complex tapestry of which technology is just one strand. Technology is central to how the future will unfold—that's undoubtedly true—but technology is not the point of the future, or what's really at stake. We are.

Technology should amplify the best of us, open new pathways for creativity and cooperation, work with the human grain of our lives and most precious relationships. It should make us happier and healthier, the ultimate complement to human endeavor and life well lived—but always on our terms, democratically decided, publicly debated, with benefits widely distributed. Amid the turbulence, we must never lose sight of this: a vision even the most ardent of Luddites could embrace.

But before we get there, before we can fulfill the boundless potential of coming technologies, the wave and its central dilemma need containment, need an intensified, unprecedented, all-too-human grip on the entire technosphere. It will require epic determination over

decades across the spectrum of human endeavor. This is a monumental challenge whose outcome will, without hyperbole, determine the
quality and nature of day-to-day life in this century and beyond.

The risks of failure scarcely bear thinking about, but face them we
must. The prize, though, is awesome: nothing less than the secure,
long-term flourishing of our precious species.

That is worth fighting for.

ACKNOWLEDGMENTS

BOOKS TOO ARE ONE OF HISTORY'S MOST TRANSFORMATIVE TECHnologies. And like any instance of transformative technology, they are innately team enterprises. This one is no exception. It has, for a start, been an epic authorial collaboration spanning more than twenty years of friendship and constant discussion.

Crown has been an incredible supporter of this project from a very early stage. David Drake has been a wise and energizing presence guiding the book with a brilliant publishing vision. We've been incredibly lucky to have as our editor Paul Whitlatch, who has again and again made countless improvements to the book with remarkable patience and perspicacity. Thanks too go to Madison Jacobs, Katie Berry, and Chris Brand. Stuart Williams at Bodley Head in London has been another smart editorial voice and staunch supporter, and we've been privileged to have two fantastic agents in Tina Bennett and Sophie Lambert. From early in the project, Celia Pannetier worked as our invaluable researcher and was a vital part of marshaling the evidence, while Sean Lavery cast his fact-checking eye over the entire book.

A huge number of people have fed into this book over many years. They have met for detailed conversations, read chapters, pushed back on arguments, generated ideas, corrected mistakes. So many calls, seminars, interviews, edits, and suggestions have helped create this book. Each of the people here devoted time and attention to talking, sharing expertise, debating, and teaching us. Particular thanks go to the many people who read the entire draft and commented in detail;

their generosity and extraordinary level of insight were completely invaluable in getting to the final manuscript.

A huge thanks to Gregory Allen, Graham Allison (and the faculty and staff of Harvard's Belfer Center more widely), Sahar Amer, Anne Applebaum, Julian Baker, Samantha Barber, Gabriella Blum, Nick Bostrom, Ian Bremmer, Erik Brynjolfsson, Ben Buchanan, Sarah Carter, Rewon Child, George Church, Richard Danzig, Jennifer Doudna, Alexandra Eitel, Maria Eitel, Henry Elkus, Kevin Esvelt, Jeremy Fleming, Jack Goldsmith, Al Gore, Tristan Harris, Zaid Hassan, Jordan Hoffman, Joi Ito, Ayana Elizabeth Johnson, Danny Kahneman, Angela Kane, Melanie Katzman, Henry Kissinger, Kevin Klyman, Heinrich Küttler, Eric Lander, Sean Legassick, Aitor Lewkowycz, Leon Marshall, Jason Matheny, Andrew McAfee, Greg McKelvey, Dimitri Mehlhorn, David Miliband, Martha Minow, Geoff Mulgan, Aza Raskin, Tobias Rees, Stuart Russell, Jeffrey Sachs, Eric Schmidt, Bruce Schneier, Marilyn Thompson, Mayo Thompson, Thomas Viney, Maria Vogelauer, Mark Walport, Morwenna White, Scott Young, and Jonathan Zittrain.

My co-founders of Inflection, Reid Hoffman and Karén Simonyan, for being wonderful collaborators. And my DeepMind co-founders, Demis Hassabis and Shane Legg, for their partnership over an extraordinary decade. Michael would like to thank his co-founders at Canelo, Iain Millar and Nick Barreto, for their ongoing support, but most of all his incredible wife, Dani, and sons, Monty and Dougie.

NOTES

FOR A BIBLIOGRAPHY OF BOOKS CONSULTED, PLEASE VISIT THE WEBsite the-coming-wave.com/bibliography.

CHAPTER 1: CONTAINMENT IS NOT POSSIBLE

12 **Costing a few tens of thousands** For example, the Kilobaser DNA & RNA Synthesizer, sold starting at $25,000. See its website: kilobaser.com/dna-and-rna
-synthesizer.

CHAPTER 2: ENDLESS PROLIFERATION

24 **Twenty years after Benz's patent** TÜV Nord Group, "A Brief History of the Internal Combustion Engine," TÜV Nord Group, April 18, 2019, www.tuev-nord.de
/explore/en/remembers/a-brief-history-of-the-internal-combustion-engine.

24 **Ford kept ramping up production** Burton W. Folsom, "Henry Ford and the Triumph of the Auto Industry," Foundation for Economic Education, Jan. 1, 1998, fee.org
/articles/henry-ford-and-the-triumph-of-the-auto-industry.

24 **In 1915 only 10 percent of Americans** "Share of US Households Using Specific Technologies, 1915 to 2005," Our World in Data, ourworldindata.org/grapher
/technology-adoption-by-households-in-the-united-states?country=~Automobile.

25 **Around 1.4 billion** "How Many Cars Are There in the World in 2023?," Hedges & Company, June 2021, hedgescompany.com/blog/2021/06/how-many-cars-are
-there-in-the-world; "Internal Combustion Engine—the Road Ahead," Industr, Jan. 22, 2019, www.industr.com/en/internal-combustion-engine-the-road-ahead
-2357709#.

25 **It is the story of technology itself** There is a voluminous academic debate over the precise definition of technology. In this book we go with a commonsense, everyday definition: the application of scientific knowledge (in the broadest possible sense) to produce tools or practical outcomes. However, the full, multifaceted complexity of the term is also acknowledged. Technology extends back into cultures and practices. It is not just transistors, screens, and keyboards. It is the explicit and tacit knowledge of coders, the social lives and societies that support them.

25 **Technology has a clear** Scholars of technology make distinctions between diffusion and proliferation that are for the most part elided here. We mean them more in their colloquial rather than formal senses.

25 **As science produces new discoveries** This also works in the other direction: technology produces new tools and insights that spur science, as when the steam engine helped clarify the need for the science of thermodynamics or sophisticated glasswork created the telescopes that transformed our understanding of space.

26 **Put simply, a wave is a set** Robert Ayres, "Technological Transformations and Long Waves. Part I," *Technological Forecasting and Social Change* 37, no. 1 (March 1990), www.sciencedirect.com/science/article/abs/pii/004016259090573.

26   **By "general-purpose"** This term is surprisingly new for something that has become so central to the understanding of technology, dating back to an economics paper from the early 1990s. See Timothy F. Bresnahan and Manuel Trajtenberg, "General Purpose Technologies 'Engines of Growth'?," (working paper, NBER, Aug. 1992), www.nber.org/papers/w4148.

26   **It had a pronounced impact on evolution** Richard Wrangham, *Catching Fire: How Cooking Made Us Human* (London: Profile Books, 2010).

27   **General-purpose technologies ripple** Account taken from Richard Lipsey, Kenneth Carlaw, and Clifford Bekar, *Economic Transformations: General Purpose Technologies and Long-Term Economic Growth* (Oxford: Oxford University Press, 2005).

27   **Language, agriculture, writing** Technically, language might again be regarded as a proto or foundational general-purpose technology.

27   **One major study pegged** Lipsey, Carlaw, and Bekar, *Economic Transformations*.

27   **Throughout history, population size** For a powerful account of how this process worked, see Oded Galor, *The Journey of Humanity: The Origins of Wealth and Inequality* (London: Bodley Head, 2022).

27   **Bigger and more connected populations** Michael Muthukrishna and Joseph Henrich, "Innovation in the Collective Brain," *Philosophical Transactions of the Royal Society B* 371, no. 1690 (2016), royalsocietypublishing.org/doi/10.1098/rstb.2015.0192.

28   **At the dawn** Galor, *The Journey of Humanity*, 46.

28   **As the Harvard anthropologist** Muthukrishna and Henrich, "Innovation in the Collective Brain."

29   **The ten thousand years** Lipsey, Carlaw, and Bekar, *Economic Transformations*.

29   **And in the last hundred** The remainder coming between 1000 BCE and 1700 CE.

29   **For the futurist Alvin Toffler** Alvin Toffler, *The Third Wave* (New York: Bantam, 1984). See also the work of Nikolai Kondratiev on long-cycle waves.

29   **The great philosopher of technology** Lewis Mumford, *Technics and Civilization* (Chicago: University of Chicago Press, 1934).

29   **More recently the economist** Carlota Perez, *Technological Revolutions and Financial Capital: The Dynamics of Bubbles and Golden Ages* (Cheltenham, U.K.: Edward Elgar, 2002).

30   **Once diffusion starts, however** Indeed, an early sign of accelerating proliferation might be that, compared with the millennia-long spread of water mills, within a few years of first being invented, the windmill was seen everywhere from the north of England to Syria. See Lynn White Jr., *Medieval Technology and Social Change* (Oxford: Oxford University Press, 1962), 87.

30   **But just fifty years later** Elizabeth L. Eisenstein, *The Printing Press as an Agent of Change: Communications and Cultural Transformations in Early-Modern Europe* (Cambridge, U.K.: Cambridge University Press, 1979).

30   **In the seventeenth century** Eltjo Buringh and Jan Luiten Van Zanden, "Charting the 'Rise of the West': Manuscripts and Printed Books in Europe, a Long-Term Perspective from the Sixth Through Eighteenth Centuries," *Journal of Economic History*, June 1, 2009, www.cambridge.org/core/journals/journal-of-economic-history/article/abs/charting-the-rise-of-the-west-manuscripts-and-printed-books-in-europe-a-longterm-perspective-from-the-sixth-through-eighteenth-centuries/0740F5F9030A706BB7E9FACCD5D975D4.

30   **One analysis estimates** Max Roser and Hannah Ritchie, "Price of Books: Productivity in Book Production," Our World in Data, ourworldindata.org/books.

30   **The first electricity power stations** Polish Member Committee of the World Energy Council, "Energy Sector of the World and Poland: Beginnings, Development, Present State," World Energy Council, Dec. 2014, www.worldenergy.org/assets/images/imported/2014/12/Energy_Sector_of_the_world_and_Poland_EN.pdf.

30   **In 1900 global electricity generation** Vaclav Smil, "Energy in the Twentieth Century: Resources, Conversions, Costs, Uses, and Consequences," *Annual Review of Energy and the Environment* 25 (2000), www.annualreviews.org/doi/pdf/10.1146/annurev.energy.25.1.21.

31   **As a result, the average person** William D. Nordhaus, "Do Real Output and Real

Wage Measures Capture Reality? The History of Lighting Suggests Not," Cowles Foundation for Research in Economics at Yale University, Jan. 1996, cowles.yale .edu/sites/default/files/files/pub/d10/d1078.pdf.

31 **Ten years later there were 5.8 million** Galor, *The Journey of Humanity,* 46.
31 **Today America has many** If you include both landlines and mobile phones.
31 **Increasing quality joins decreasing** "Televisions Inflation Calculator," Official Data Foundation, www.in2013dollars.com/Televisions/price-inflation.
31 **Mimicry spurs competition** Anuraag Singh et al., "Technological Improvement Rate Predictions for All Technologies: Use of Patent Data and an Extended Domain Description," *Research Policy* 50, no. 9 (Nov. 2021), www.sciencedirect.com/science /article/pii/S0048733321000950#. There are considerable variations between different sets of technology, however.
32 **Like the internal combustion engine** Of course, the proposals date back further, at least to Babbage and Lovelace in the nineteenth century.
32 **By 1945, an important precursor** George Dyson, *Turing's Cathedral: The Origins of the Digital Universe* (London: Allen Lane, 2012).
32 **Early in that decade IBM's president** Nick Carr, "How Many Computers Does the World Need? Fewer Than You Think," *Guardian,* Feb. 21, 2008, www.theguardian .com/technology/2008/feb/21/computing.supercomputers.
32 *Popular Mechanics* **magazine made** James Meigs, "Inside the Future: How PopMech Predicted the Next 110 Years," *Popular Mechanics,* Dec. 21, 2012, www.popular mechanics.com/technology/a8562/inside-the-future-how-popmech-predicted-the -next-110-years-14831802/#.
33 **Their power has increased by ten** See, for example, Darrin Qualman, "Unimaginable Output: Global Production of Transistors," *Darrin Qualman Blog,* April 24, 2017, www.darrinqualman.com/global-production-transistors/; Azeem Azhar, *Exponential: How Accelerating Technology Is Leaving Us Behind and What to Do About It* (London: Random House Business, 2021), 21; and Vaclav Smil, *How the World Really Works: A Scientist's Guide to Our Past, Present and Future* (London: Viking, 2022), 128.
33 **In the early 1970s** John B. Smith, "Internet Chronology," UNC Computer Science, www.cs.unc.edu/~jbs/resources/Internet/internet_chron.html.
33 **Now the number of computers** Mohammad Hasan, "State of IoT 2022: Number of Connected IoT Devices Growing 18% to 14.4 Billion Globally," IoT Analytics, May 18, 2022, iot-analytics.com/number-connected-iot-devices/; Steffen Schenkluhn, "Market Size and Connected Devices: Where's the Future of IoT?," *Bosch Connected World Blog,* blog.bosch-si.com/internetofthings/market-size-and-connected -devices-wheres-the-future-of-iot. However, the Ericsson Mobility Report estimates up to twenty-nine billion: "Ericsson Mobility Report, November 2022," Ericsson, Nov. 2022, www.ericsson.com/4ae28d/assets/local/reports-papers/mobility-report /documents/2022/ericsson-mobility-report-november-2022.pdf.
33 **It created a yet more** Azhar, *Exponential,* 219.
33 **Now humans produce hundreds** Ibid., 228.

CHAPTER 3: THE CONTAINMENT PROBLEM

36 **Understanding technology is, in part** Robert K. Merton, *On Social Structure and Science* (Chicago: University of Chicago Press, 1996), gives the classic study, but see also Ulrich Beck, *Risk Society: Toward a New Modernity* (London: SAGE, 1992), for how society has become dominated by the management of risks it has itself created. See also Edward Tenner, *Why Things Bite Back: Technology and the Revenge of Unintended Consequences* (New York: Vintage, 1997), and Charles Perrow, *Normal Accidents: Living with High-Risk Technologies* (Princeton, N.J.: Princeton University Press, 1984).
37 **For many, the word "containment"** George F. Kennan, "The Sources of Soviet Conduct," *Foreign Affairs,* July 1947, www.cvce.eu/content/publication/1999/1/1/aofo 3730-dde8-4f06-a6ed-d740770dc423/publishable_en.pdf.
38 **As the printing press roared** This account is taken from Anton Howes, "Age of In-

vention: Did the Ottomans Ban Print?," *Age of Invention,* May 19, 2021, antonhowes.substack.com/p/age-of-invention-did-the-ottomans

39   **John Kay, the inventor** Examples taken from Joel Mokyr, *The Lever of Riches: Technological Creativity and Economic Progress* (Oxford: Oxford University Press, 1990).

39   **Similarly, China dismissed** Harold Marcuse, "Ch'ien Lung (Qianlong) Letter to George III (1792)," UC Santa Barbara History Department, marcuse.faculty.history.ucsb.edu/classes/2c/texts/1792QianlongLetterGeorgeIII.htm.

40   **Few societies have ever** See, for example, Joseph A. Tainter, *The Collapse of Complex Societies* (Cambridge, U.K.: Cambridge University Press, 1988), and Jared Diamond, *Collapse: How Societies Choose to Fail or Survive* (London: Penguin, 2005), for more on this process.

41   **On September 11, 1933** Waldemar Kaempffert, "Rutherford Cools Atomic Energy Hope," *New York Times,* Sept. 12, 1933, timesmachine.nytimes.com/timesmachine/1933/09/12/99846601.html.

41   **Weeks later a Boeing B-29** Alex Wellerstein, "Counting the Dead at Hiroshima and Nagasaki," *Bulletin of the Atomic Scientists,* Aug. 4, 2020, thebulletin.org/2020/08/counting-the-dead-at-hiroshima-and-nagasaki.

42   **In 1946 the Acheson-Lilienthal Report** See David Lilienthal et al., "A Report on the International Control of Atomic Energy," March 16, 1946, fissilematerials.org/library/ach46.pdf.

42   **Although countries like China** "Partial Test Ban Treaty," Nuclear Threat Initiative, Feb. 2008, www.nti.org/education-center/treaties-and-regimes/treaty-banning-nuclear-test-atmosphere-outer-space-and-under-water-partial-test-ban-treaty-ptbt/.

43   **A turning point came in 1968** "Timeline of the Nuclear Nonproliferation Treaty (NPT)," Arms Control Association, Aug. 2022, www.armscontrol.org/factsheets/Timeline-of-the-Treaty-on-the-Non-Proliferation-of-Nuclear-Weapons-NPT.

44   **After all, it was only in 2019** Liam Stack, "Update Complete: U.S. Nuclear Weapons No Longer Need Floppy Disks," *New York Times,* Oct. 24, 2019, www.nytimes.com/2019/10/24/us/nuclear-weapons-floppy-disks.html.

44   **Accidents are legion** The accounts here are largely drawn from Eric Schlosser, *Command and Control* (London: Penguin, 2014), and John Hughes-Wilson, *Eve of Destruction: The Inside Story of Our Dangerous Nuclear World* (London: John Blake, 2021).

44   **Tiny hardware malfunctions** William Burr, "False Warnings of Soviet Missile Attacks Put U.S. Forces on Alert in 1979–1980," National Security Archive, March 16, 2020, nsarchive.gwu.edu/briefing-book/nuclear-vault/2020-03-16/false-warnings-soviet-missile-attacks-during-1979-80-led-alert-actions-us-strategic-forces.

44   **North Korea went to extraordinary** Paul K. Kerr, "Iran–North Korea–Syria Ballistic Missile and Nuclear Cooperation," Congressional Research Service, Feb. 26, 2016, sgp.fas.org/crs/nuke/R43480.pdf.

44   **China, India, and Pakistan are** Graham Allison, "Nuclear Terrorism: Did We Beat the Odds or Change Them?," *PRISM,* May 15, 2018, cco.ndu.edu/News/Article/1507316/nuclear-terrorism-did-we-beat-the-odds-or-change-them.

44   **Brazil and Argentina even** José Goldemberg, "Looking Back: Lessons from the Denuclearization of Brazil and Argentina," Arms Control Association, April 2006, www.armscontrol.org/act/2006-04/looking-back-lessons-denuclearization-brazil-argentina.

45   **Plenty of nuclear material** Richard Stone, "Dirty Bomb Ingredients Go Missing from Chornobyl Monitoring Lab," *Science,* March 25, 2022, www.science.org/content/article/dirty-bomb-ingredients-go-missing-chornobyl-monitoring-lab.

45   **In 2018, plutonium** Patrick Malone and R. Jeffrey Smith, "Plutonium Is Missing, but the Government Says Nothing," Center for Public Integrity, July 16, 2018, publicintegrity.org/national-security/plutonium-is-missing-but-the-government-says-nothing.

45   **It may sound fanciful** Zaria Gorvett, "The Lost Nuclear Bombs That No One Can Find," *BBC Future,* Aug. 4, 2022, www.bbc.com/future/article/20220804-the-lost-nuclear-bombs-that-no-one-can-find.

46 **Chemical weapons were recently** "Timeline of Syrian Chemical Weapons Activity, 2012–2022," Arms Control Association, May 2021, www.armscontrol.org/factsheets /Timeline-of-Syrian-Chemical-Weapons-Activity.

46 **Without them, modeling suggests** Paul J. Young, "The Montreal Protocol Protects the Terrestrial Carbon Sink," *Nature*, Aug. 18, 2021, www.nature.com/articles /s41586-021-03737-3.epdf.

CHAPTER 4: THE TECHNOLOGY OF INTELLIGENCE

53 **After just three pairs** Natalie Wolchover, "How Many Different Ways Can a Chess Game Unfold?," *Popular Science*, Dec. 15, 2010, www.popsci.com/science/article /2010-12/fyi-how-many-different-ways-can-chess-game-unfold.

53 **In total, the board has** "AlphaGo," DeepMind, www.deepmind.com/research /highlighted-research/alphago. Some, however, report an even higher number; for example, *Scientific American* cites 10^{360} configurations. See Christof Koch, "How the Computer Beat the Go Master," *Scientific American*, March 19, 2016, www .scientificamerican.com/article/how-the-computer-beat-the-go-master.

56 **The more technologies there are** W. Brian Arthur, *The Nature of Technology: What It Is and How It Evolves* (London: Allen Lane, 2009), 31.

56 **The technology scholar Everett Rogers** Everett M. Rogers, *Diffusion of Innovations* (New York: Free Press, 1962), or see the writings on industrial revolutions from scholars like Joel Mokyr.

57 **The engineer and futurist Ray Kurzweil** Ray Kurzweil, *How to Create a Mind: The Secret of Human Thought Revealed* (New York: Viking Penguin, 2012).

57 **We see this now on** See, for example, Azalia Mirhoseini et al., "A Graph Placement Methodology for Fast Chip Design," *Nature*, June 9, 2021, www.nature.com /articles/s41586-021-03544-w; and Lewis Grozinger et al., "Pathways to Cellular Supremacy in Biocomputing," *Nature Communications*, Nov. 20, 2019, www.nature .com/articles/s41467-019-13232-z.

58 **The breakthrough moment took** Alex Krizhevsky et al., "ImageNet Classification with Deep Convolutional Neural Networks," Neural Information Processing Systems, Sept. 30, 2012, proceedings.neurips.cc/paper/2012/file/c399862d3b9d6b76c 8436e924a68c45b-Paper.pdf.

59 **In 2012, AlexNet beat** Jerry Wei, "AlexNet: The Architecture That Challenged CNNs," *Towards Data Science*, July 2, 2019, towardsdatascience.com/alexnet-the -architecture-that-challenged-cnns-e406d5297951.

60 **Thanks to deep learning** Chanan Bos, "Tesla's New HW3 Self-Driving Computer— It's a Beast," CleanTechnica, June 15, 2019, cleantechnica.com/2019/06/15/teslas -new-hw3-self-driving-computer-its-a-beast-cleantechnica-deep-dive.

60 **It helps fly drones** Jeffrey De Fauw et al., "Clinically Applicable Deep Learning for Diagnosis and Referral in Retinal Disease," *Nature Medicine*, Aug. 13, 2018, www .nature.com/articles/s41591-018-0107-6.

60 **By the 2020s there were almost two thousand** "Advances in Neural Information Processing Systems," NeurIPS, papers.nips.cc.

60 **In the last six years** "Research & Development," in *Artificial Intelligence Index Report 2021*, Stanford University Human-Centered Artificial Intelligence, March 2021, aiindex .stanford.edu/wp-content/uploads/2021/03/2021-AI-Index-Report-_Chapter-1 .pdf.

61 **Everywhere you look, software** To paraphrase Marc Andreessen.

61 **At DeepMind we developed systems** "DeepMind AI Reduces Google Data Centre Cooling Bill by 40%," DeepMind, July 20, 2016, www.deepmind.com/blog/deep mind-ai-reduces-google-data-centre-cooling-bill-by-40.

64 **With 1.5 billion parameters** "Better Language Models and Their Implications," OpenAI, Feb. 14, 2019, openai.com/blog/better-language-models.

65 **Over the next few years** See Martin Ford, *Rule of the Robots: How Artificial Intelligence Will Transform Everything* (London: Basic Books, 2021), for a developed comparison.

65 **More realistically, the average American** Amy Watson, "Average Reading Time in the

U.S. from 2018 to 2021, by Age Group," *Statista*, Aug. 3, 2022, www.statista.com /statistics/412454/average-daily-time-reading-us-by-age.

66   **First hundreds of millions** Microsoft and NVIDIA built a transformer model with 530 billion parameters, the Megatron-Turing Natural Language Generation model (MT-NLG), thirty-one times larger than their own most powerful transformer models of just a year before. Then came Wu Dao, from the Beijing Academy of Artificial Intelligence, with an alleged 1.75 trillion parameters—ten times GPT-3. See, for example, Tanushree Shenwai, "Microsoft and NVIDIA AI Introduces MT-NLG: The Largest and Most Powerful Monolithic Transformer Language NLP Model," *MarkTech Post*, Oct. 13, 2021, www.marktechpost.com/2021/10/13/microsoft-and -nvidia-ai-introduces-mt-nlg-the-largest-and-most-powerful-monolithic-transformer -language-nlp-model.

66   **The Chinese company Alibaba** "Alibaba DAMO Academy Creates World's Largest AI Pre-training Model, with Parameters Far Exceeding Google and Microsoft," *Pandaily*, Nov. 8, 2021, pandaily.com/alibaba-damo-academy-creates-worlds-largest-ai -pre-training-model-with-parameters-far-exceeding-google-and-microsoft.

66   **Google's PaLM uses** A fantastic image from Alyssa Vance, assuming each "drop" constitutes 0.5 milliliters: mobile.twitter.com/alyssamvance/status/1542682154483589127.

68   **But it uses an efficient training** William Fedus et al., "Switch Transformers: Scaling to Trillion Parameter Models with Simple and Efficient Sparsity," *Journal of Machine Learning Research*, June 16, 2022, arxiv.org/abs/2101.03961.

68   **Or look at DeepMind's Chinchilla** Alberto Romero, "A New AI Trend: Chinchilla (70B) Greatly Outperforms GPT-3 (175B) and Gopher (280B)," *Towards Data Science*, April 11, 2022, towardsdatascience.com/a-new-ai-trend-chinchilla-70b-greatly -outperforms-gpt-3-175b-and-gopher-280b-408b9b4510.

68   **At the other end of the spectrum** See github.com/karpathy/nanoGPT for more details.

69   **Meta has open-sourced** Susan Zhang et al., "Democratizing Access to Large-Scale Language Models with OPT-175B," Meta AI, May 3, 2022, ai.facebook.com/blog /democratizing-access-to-large-scale-language-models-with-opt-175b.

69   **Within days someone had found** See, for example, twitter.com/miolini/status /1634982361757790209.

69   **One analysis suggests it makes engineers** Eirini Kalliamvakou, "Research: Quantifying GitHub Copilot's Impact on Developer Productivity and Happiness," GitHub, Sept. 7, 2022, github.blog/2022-09-07-research-quantifying-github-copilots-impact -on-developer-productivity-and-happiness.

69   **In the words of an eminent** Matt Welsh, "The End of Programming," *Communications of the ACM*, Jan. 2023, cacm.acm.org/magazines/2023/1/267976-the-end-of -programming/fulltext.

70   **Yet when given the same prompt** Emily Sheng et al., "The Woman Worked as a Babysitter: On Biases in Language Generation," arXiv, Oct. 23, 2019, arxiv.org/pdf /1909.01326.pdf.

72   **Over many hours, Lemoine** Nitasha Tiku, "The Google Engineer Who Thinks the Company's AI Has Come to Life," *Washington Post*, June 11, 2022, www .washingtonpost.com/technology/2022/06/11/google-ai-lamda-blake-lemoine.

72   **He told an incredulous** *Wired* **interviewer** Steven Levy, "Blake Lemoine Says Google's LaMDA AI Faces 'Bigotry,'" *Wired*, June 17, 2022, www.wired.com/story/blake -lemoine-google-lamda-ai-bigotry.

73   **"As soon as it works"** Quoted in Moshe Y. Vardi, "Artificial Intelligence: Past and Future," *Communications of the ACM*, Jan. 2012, cacm.acm.org/magazines/2012/1 /144824-artificial-intelligence-past-and-future/fulltext.

73   **They argue that AI may be slowing** Joel Klinger et al., "A Narrowing of AI Research?," *Computers and Society*, Jan. 11, 2022, arxiv.org/abs/2009.10385.

73   **Critics like NYU professor Gary Marcus** Gary Marcus, "Deep Learning Is Hitting a Wall," *Nautilus*, March 10, 2022, nautil.us/deep-learning-is-hitting-a-wall-14467.

73   **eminent professor of complexity Melanie Mitchell** See Melanie Mitchell, *Artificial Intelligence: A Guide for Thinking Humans* (London: Pelican Books, 2020), and Steven

Strogatz, "Melanie Mitchell Takes AI Research Back to Its Roots," *Quanta Magazine,* April 19, 2021, www.quantamagazine.org/melanie-mitchell-takes-ai-research-back-to-its-roots-20210419.

76   **I think it will be done** The Alignment Research Center has already tested GPT-4 for precisely this kind of capability. GPT-4 was, at this stage, "ineffective" at acting autonomously, the research found. "GPT-4 System Card," OpenAI, March 14, 2023, cdn.openai.com/papers/gpt-4-system-card.pdf. Within days of launch people were getting surprisingly close; see, for example, mobile.twitter.com/jacksonfall/status/1636107218859745286. The version of the test here, though, requires far more autonomy than displayed there.

CHAPTER 5: THE TECHNOLOGY OF LIFE

79   **Just as everything from the steam engine** Susan Hockfield, *The Age of Living Machines: How Biology Will Build the Next Technology Revolution* (New York: W. W. Norton, 2019).

80   **Then, working on bacteria in 1973** Stanley N. Cohen et al., "Construction of Biologically Functional Bacterial Plasmids In Vitro," *PNAS,* Nov. 1, 1973, www.pnas.org/doi/abs/10.1073/pnas.70.11.3240.

80   **This was a thirteen-year** "Human Genome Project," National Human Genome Research Institute, Aug. 24, 2022, www.genome.gov/about-genomics/educational-resources/fact-sheets/human-genome-project.

81   **While Moore's law justifiably** "Life 2.0," *Economist,* Aug. 31, 2006, www.economist.com/special-report/2006/08/31/life-20.

81   **Thanks to ever-improving techniques** See "The Cost of Sequencing a Human Genome," National Human Genome Research Institute, Nov. 1, 2021, www.genome.gov/about-genomics/fact-sheets/Sequencing-Human-Genome-cost; and Elizabeth Pennisi, "A $100 Genome? New DNA Sequencers Could Be a 'Game Changer' for Biology, Medicine," *Science,* June 15, 2022, www.science.org/content/article/100-genome-new-dna-sequencers-could-be-game-changer-biology-medicine.

81   **That is, the price dropped** Azhar, *Exponential,* 41.

82   **After the initial CRISPR paper** Jian-Feng Li et al., "Multiplex and Homologous Recombination-Mediated Genome Editing in *Arabidopsis* and *Nicotiana benthamiana* Using Guide RNA and Cas9," *Nature Biotechnology,* Aug. 31, 2013, www.nature.com/articles/nbt.2654.

82   **Fields like RNA editing** Sara Reardon, "Step Aside CRISPR, RNA Editing Is Taking Off," *Nature,* Feb. 4, 2020, www.nature.com/articles/d41586-020-00272-5.

82   **New techniques like Craspase** Chunyi Hu et al., "Craspase Is a CRISPR RNA-Guided, RNA-Activated Protease," *Science,* Aug. 25, 2022, www.science.org/doi/10.1126/science.add5064.

82   **CRISPR use cases are multiplying** Michael Le Page, "Three People with Inherited Diseases Successfully Treated with CRISPR," *New Scientist,* June 12, 2020, www.newscientist.com/article/2246020-three-people-with-inherited-diseases-successfully-treated-with-crispr; Jie Li et al., "Biofortified Tomatoes Provide a New Route to Vitamin D Sufficiency," *Nature Plants,* May 23, 2022, www.nature.com/articles/s41477-022-01154-6.

82   **In the future, it could offer** Mohamed Fareh, "Reprogrammed CRISPR-Cas13b Suppresses SARS-CoV-2 Replication and Circumvents Its Mutational Escape Through Mismatch Tolerance," *Nature,* July 13, 2021, www.nature.com/articles/s41467-021-24577-9; "How CRISPR Is Changing Cancer Research and Treatment," National Cancer Institute, July 27, 2020, www.cancer.gov/news-events/cancer-currents-blog/2020/crispr-cancer-research-treatment; Zhihao Zhang et al., "Updates on CRISPR-Based Gene Editing in HIV-1/AIDS Therapy," *Virologica Sinica,* Feb. 2022, www.sciencedirect.com/science/article/pii/S1995820X22000177; Giulia Maule et al., "Gene Therapy for Cystic Fibrosis: Progress and Challenges of Genome Editing," *International Journal of Molecular Sciences,* June 2020, www.ncbi.nlm.nih.gov/pmc/articles/PMC7313467.

82   **These will create crops** Raj Kumar Joshi, "Engineering Drought Tolerance in Plants Through CRISPR/Cas Genome Editing," *3 Biotech*, Sept. 2020, www.ncbi.nlm.nih .gov/pmc/articles/PMC7438458; Muhammad Rizwan Javed et al., "Current Situation of Biofuel Production and Its Enhancement by CRISPR/Cas9-Mediated Genome Engineering of Microbial Cells," *Microbiological Research*, Feb. 2019, www .sciencedirect.com/science/article/pii/S0944501318308346.

82   **Today technologies like CRISPR** Nessa Carey, *Hacking the Code of Life: How Gene Editing Will Rewrite Our Futures* (London: Icon Books, 2019), 136.

82   **You can now buy a benchtop** See, for example, kilobaser.com/shop.

83   **Now they can print millions** Yiren Lu, "The Gene Synthesis Revolution," *New York Times*, Nov. 24, 2021, www.nytimes.com/2021/11/24/magazine/gene-synthesis .html.

83   **The London DNA Foundry** "Robotic Labs for High-Speed Genetic Research Are on the Rise," *Economist*, March 1, 2018, www.economist.com/science-and -technology/2018/03/01/robotic-labs-for-high-speed-genetic-research-are-on-the -rise.

83   **Companies such as DNA Script** Bruce Rogers, "DNA Script Set to Bring World's First DNA Printer to Market," *Forbes*, May 17, 2021, www.forbes.com/sites/bruce rogers/2021/05/17/dna-script-set-to-bring-worlds-first-dna-printer-to-market.

83   **Furthermore, new techniques** Michael Eisenstein, "Enzymatic DNA Synthesis Enters New Phase," *Nature Biology*, Oct. 5, 2020, www.nature.com/articles/s41587 -020-0695-9.

84   **Put it all together** Synbio uses not just DNA synthesis but the growing understanding of how genes can be switched on and off, coupled with the discipline of metabolic engineering whereby cells can be encouraged to produce desired substances.

84   **In the words of the Stanford bioengineer** Drew Endy, "Endy:Research," OpenWet Ware, Aug. 4, 2017, openwetware.org/wiki/Endy:Research.

84   **In 2010 a team led by Craig Venter** "First Self-Replicating Synthetic Bacterial Cell," JCVI, www.jcvi.org/research/first-self-replicating-synthetic-bacterial-cell.

84   **Just three years later** Jonathan E. Venetz et al., "Chemical Synthesis Rewriting of a Bacterial Genome to Achieve Design Flexibility and Biological Functionality," *PNAS*, April 1, 2019, www.pnas.org/doi/full/10.1073/pnas.1818259116.

84   **While Venter's experiments** ETH Zurich, "First Bacterial Genome Created Entirely with a Computer," *Science Daily*, April 1, 2019, www.sciencedaily.com/releases /2019/04/190401171343.htm. That year a team from Cambridge also produced a fully synthetic *E. coli* genome. Julius Fredens, "Total Synthesis of *Escherichia coli* with a Recoded Genome," *Nature*, May 15, 2019, www.nature.com/articles/s41586 -019-1192-5.

84   **Now the global GP-write Consortium** See GP-write Consortium, Center of Excellence for Engineering Biology, engineeringbiologycenter.org/gp-write-consortium.

85   **Using a gene for light-detecting proteins** José-Alain Sahel et al., "Partial Recovery of Visual Function in a Blind Patient After Optogenetic Therapy," *Nature Medicine*, May 24, 2021, www.nature.com/articles/s41591-021-01351-4.

85   **CAR T-Cell therapies engineer bespoke** "CureHeart—a Cure for Inherited Heart Muscle Diseases," British Heart Foundation, www.bhf.org.uk/what-we-do/our -research/cure-heart; National Cancer Institute, "CAR T-Cell Therapy," National Institutes of Health, www.cancer.gov/publications/dictionaries/cancer-terms/def /car-t-cell-therapy.

85   **The field of systems biology** See, for example, Astrid M. Vicente et al., "How Personalised Medicine Will Transform Healthcare by 2030: The ICPerMed Vision," *Journal of Translational Medicine*, April 28, 2020, translational-medicine.biomedcentral .com/articles/10.1186/s12967-020-02316-w.

85   **Its chief scientist, Richard Klausner** Antonio Regalado, "How Scientists Want to Make You Young Again," *MIT Technology Review*, Oct. 25, 2022, www .technologyreview.com/2022/10/25/1061644/how-to-be-young-again.

85   **This experimental approach aims** Jae-Hyun Yang et al., "Loss of Epigenetic Informa-

tion as a Cause of Mammalian Aging," *Cell,* Jan. 12, 2023, www.cell.com/cell/fulltext/S0092-8674(22)01570-7.

86 **A world where life spans** See, for example, David A. Sinclair and Matthew D. LaPlante, *Lifespan: Why We Age—and Why We Don't Have To* (New York: Atria Books, 2019).

86 **Initial work suggests memory** See, for example, Harvard research on memory: "Researchers Identify a Neural Circuit and Genetic 'Switch' That Maintain Memory Precision," Harvard Stem Cell Institute, March 12, 2018, hsci.harvard.edu/news/researchers-identify-neural-circuit-and-genetic-switch-maintain-memory-precision.

86 **Calls for a moratorium** John Cohen, "New Call to Ban Gene-Edited Babies Divides Biologists," *Science,* March 13, 2019, www.science.org/content/article/new-call-ban-gene-edited-babies-divides-biologists.

87 **Arnold's method is fifteen times** S. B. Jennifer Kan et al., "Directed Evolution of Cytochrome C for Carbon-Silicon Bond Formation: Bringing Silicon to Life," *Science,* Nov. 25, 2016, www.science.org/doi/10.1126/science.aah6219.

87 **This kind of synthetic biology is helping** James Urquhart, "Reprogrammed Bacterium Turns Carbon Dioxide into Chemicals on Industrial Scale," *Chemistry World,* March 2, 2022, www.chemistryworld.com/news/reprogrammed-bacterium-turns-carbon-dioxide-into-chemicals-on-industrial-scale/4015307.article.

87 **"What if we could grow"** Elliot Hershberg, "Atoms Are Local," *Century of Bio,* Nov. 7, 2022, centuryofbio.substack.com/p/atoms-are-local.

87 **Theoretically, the entirety of the world's** "The Future of DNA Data Storage," Potomac Institute for Policy Studies, Sept. 2018, potomacinstitute.org/images/studies/Future_of_DNA_Data_Storage.pdf.

88 **McKinsey estimates that up** McKinsey Global Institute, "The Bio Revolution: Innovations Transforming Economies, Societies, and Our Lives," McKinsey & Company, May 13, 2020, www.mckinsey.com/industries/life-sciences/our-insights/the-bio-revolution-innovations-transforming-economies-societies-and-our-lives.

88 **If you used traditional brute-force computation** DeepMind, "AlphaFold: A Solution to a 50-Year-Old Grand Challenge in Biology," DeepMind Research, Nov. 20, 2020, www.deepmind.com/blog/alphafold-a-solution-to-a-50-year-old-grand-challenge-in-biology.

89 **Mohammed AlQuraishi, a well-known researcher** Mohammed AlQuraishi, "Alpha-Fold @ CASP13: 'What Just Happened?,'" *Some Thoughts on a Mysterious Universe,* Dec. 9, 2018, moalquraishi.wordpress.com/2018/12/09/alphafold-casp13-what-just-happened.

89 **One headline said it all** Tanya Lewis, "One of the Biggest Problems in Biology Has Finally Been Solved," *Scientific American,* Oct. 31, 2022, www.scientific american.com/article/one-of-the-biggest-problems-in-biology-has-finally-been-solved.

90 **The result has been an explosion** Ewen Callaway, "What's Next for AlphaFold and the AI Protein-Folding Revolution," *Nature,* April 13, 2022, www.nature.com/articles/d41586-022-00997-5.

90 **DeepMind uploaded some 200 million** Madhumita Murgia, "DeepMind Research Cracks Structure of Almost Every Known Protein," *Financial Times,* July 28, 2022, www.ft.com/content/6a088953-66d7-48db-b61c-79005a0a351a; DeepMind, "Alpha-Fold Reveals the Structure of the Protein Universe," DeepMind Research, July 28, 2022, www.deepmind.com/blog/alphafold-reveals-the-structure-of-the-protein-universe.

91 **In 2019, electrodes surgically implanted** Kelly Servick, "In a First, Brain Implant Lets Man with Complete Paralysis Spell Out 'I Love My Cool Son,'" *Science,* March 22, 2022, www.science.org/content/article/first-brain-implant-lets-man-complete-paralysis-spell-out-thoughts-i-love-my-cool-son.

91 **Scientists at a start-up called Cortical Labs** Brett J. Kagan et al., "*In Vitro* Neurons Learn and Exhibit Sentience When Embodied in a Simulated Game-World," *Neuron,* Oct. 12, 2022, www.cell.com/neuron/fulltext/S0896-6273(22)00806-6.

CHAPTER 6: THE WIDER WAVE

94   **Amazon's "first fully autonomous mobile robot"** Mitchell Clark, "Amazon Announces Its First Fully Autonomous Mobile Warehouse Robot," *Verge,* June 21, 2022, www .theverge.com/2022/6/21/23177756/amazon-warehouse-robots-proteus-autonomous -cart-delivery.

95   **Amazon's Sparrow is the first** Dave Lee, "Amazon Debuts New Warehouse Robot That Can Do Human Jobs," *Financial Times,* Nov. 10, 2022, www.ft.com/content /c8933d73-74a4-43ff-8060-7ff9402eccf1.

95   **Robots are already performing intricate surgery** James Gaines, "The Past, Present, and Future of Robotic Surgery," *Smithsonian Magazine,* Sept. 15, 2022, www.smith sonianmag.com/innovation/the-past-present-and-future-of-robotic-surgery -180980763.

95   **They built a fleet** "Helper Robots for a Better Everyday," Everyday Robots, every dayrobots.com.

95   **With honeybee populations** Chelsea Gohd, "Walmart Has Patented Autonomous Robot Bees," World Economic Forum, March 19, 2018, www.weforum.org/agenda /2018/03/autonomous-robot-bees-are-being-patented-by-walmart.

96   **As costs fall** *Artificial Intelligence Index Report 2021,* aiindex.stanford.edu/report.

96   **The police department had a bomb disposal** Sara Sidner and Mallory Simon, "How Robot, Explosives Took Out Dallas Sniper in Unprecedented Way," CNN, July 12, 2016, cnn.com/2016/07/12/us/dallas-police-robot-c4-explosives/index.html.

97   **In 2019, Google announced** Elizabeth Gibney, "Hello Quantum World! Google Publishes Landmark Quantum Supremacy Claim," *Nature,* Oct. 23, 2019, www.nature .com/articles/d41586-019-03213-z; Frank Arute et al., "Quantum Supremacy Using a Programmable Superconducting Processor," *Nature,* Oct. 23, 2019, www.nature .com/articles/s41586-019-1666-5.

97   **Chilled to a temperature colder** Neil Savage, "Hands-On with Google's Quantum Computer," *Scientific American,* Oct. 24, 2019, www.scientificamerican.com/article /hands-on-with-googles-quantum-computer.

98   **To store equivalent information** Gideon Lichfield, "Inside the Race to Build the Best Quantum Computer on Earth," *MIT Technology Review,* Feb. 26, 2022, www .technologyreview.com/2020/02/26/916744/quantum-computer-race-ibm-google.

98   **Its key attraction is that each** Matthew Sparkes, "IBM Creates Largest Ever Superconducting Quantum Computer," *New Scientist,* Nov. 15, 2021, www.newscientist .com/article/2297583-ibm-creates-largest-ever-superconducting-quantum -computer.

98   **Indeed, a relatively small number** For certain tasks, at any rate. Charles Choi, "Quantum Leaps in Quantum Computing?," *Scientific American,* Oct. 25, 2017, www .scientificamerican.com/article/quantum-leaps-in-quantum-computing.

98   **Researchers at Microsoft and Ford** Ken Washington, "Mass Navigation: How Ford Is Exploring the Quantum World with Microsoft to Help Reduce Congestion," Ford Medium, Dec. 10, 2019, medium.com/@ford/mass-navigation-how-ford-is -exploring-the-quantum-world-with-microsoft-to-help-reduce-congestion-a9de6db 32338.

100 **Renewable energy will become** Camilla Hodgson, "Solar Power Expected to Surpass Coal in 5 Years, IEA Says," *Financial Times,* Dec. 10, 2022, www.ft.com/content /98cec49f-6682-4495-b7be-793bf2589c6d.

100 **In 2000, solar energy cost** "Solar PV Module Prices," Our World in Data, ourworld indata.org/grapher/solar-pv-prices.

100 **With meaningful private capital** Tom Wilson, "Nuclear Fusion: From Science Fiction to 'When, Not If,' " *Financial Times,* Dec. 17, 2022, www.ft.com/content/65e8f125 -5985-4aa8-a027-0c9769e764ad.

101 **Scaled up, it could power a Tesla** Eli Dourado, "Nanotechnology's Spring," *Works in Progress,* Oct. 12, 2022, www.worksinprogress.co/issue/nanotechnologys -spring.

CHAPTER 7: FOUR FEATURES OF THE COMING WAVE

103 **Instead, a unit of about thirty** Julian Borger, "The Drone Operators Who Halted Russian Convoy Headed for Kyiv," *Guardian*, March 28, 2022, www.theguardian .com/world/2022/mar/28/the-drone-operators-who-halted-the-russian -armoured-vehicles-heading-for-kyiv.

104 **A thousand-strong group of nonmilitary** Marcin Wyrwał, "Wojna w Ukrainie. Jak sztuczna inteligencja zabija Rosjan," *Onet*, July 13, 2022, www.onet.pl/informacje /onetwiadomosci/rozwiazali-problem-armii-ukrainy-ich-pomysl-okazal-sie-dla -rosjan-zabojczy/pkzrkoz,79cfc278.

104 **A precision missile in a conventional** Patrick Tucker, "AI Is Already Learning from Russia's War in Ukraine, DOD Says," *Defense One*, April 21, 2022, www.defenseone .com/technology/2022/04/ai-already-learning-russias-war-ukraine-dod-says/365978.

104 **American, British, and European forces** "Ukraine Support Tracker," Kiel Institute for the World Economy, Dec. 2022, www.ifw-kiel.de/index.php?id=17142.

106 **In the words of the security expert** Audrey Kurth Cronin, *Power to the People: How Open Technological Innovation Is Arming Tomorrow's Terrorists* (New York: Oxford University Press, 2020), 2.

106 **The Shenzhen-based company DJI** Scott Gilbertson, "Review: DJI Phantom 4," *Wired*, April 22, 2016, www.wired.com/2016/04/review-dji-phantom-4.

106 **Combating attacks is difficult** Cronin, *Power to the People*, 320; Derek Hawkins, "A U.S. 'Ally' Fired a $3 Million Patriot Missile at a $200 Drone. Spoiler: The Missile Won," *Washington Post*, March 17, 2017, www.washingtonpost.com/news/morning-mix /wp/2017/03/17/a-u-s-ally-fired-a-3-million-patriot-missile-at-a-200-drone-spoiler -the-missile-won.

108 **Should it hold, in ten years** Azhar, *Exponential*, 249.

108 **Outside the weightless world of code** See, for example, Michael Bhaskar, *Human Frontiers: The Future of Big Ideas in an Age of Small Thinking* (Cambridge, Mass.: MIT Press, 2021); Tyler Cowen, *The Great Stagnation: How America Ate All the Low-Hanging Fruit of Modern History, Got Sick, and Will (Eventually) Feel Better* (New York: Dutton, 2011); and Robert Gordon, *The Rise and Fall of American Growth: The U.S. Standard of Living Since the Civil War* (Princeton, N.J.: Princeton University Press, 2017), among many others.

108 **César Hidalgo argues** César Hidalgo, *Why Information Grows: The Evolution of Order, from Atoms to Economies* (London: Allen Lane, 2015).

109 **AI already helps find new** Neil Savage, "Machines Learn to Unearth New Materials," *Nature*, June 30, 2021, www.nature.com/articles/d41586-021-01793-3.

109 **For example, scientists have used** Andrij Vasylenko et al., "Element Selection for Crystalline Inorganic Solid Discovery Guided by Unsupervised Machine Learning of Experimentally Explored Chemistry," *Nature Communications*, Sept. 21, 2021, www.nature.com/articles/s41467-021-25343-7.

109 **AI has helped design and build** Matthew Greenwood, "Hypercar Created Using 3D Printing, AI, and Robotics," Engineering.com, June 23, 2021, www.engineering .com/story/hypercar-created-using-3d-printing-ai-and-robotics.

109 **Now simulations speed up** Elie Dolgin, "Could Computer Models Be the Key to Better COVID Vaccines?," *Nature*, April 5, 2022, www.nature.com/articles/d41586 -022-00924-8.

109 **Computational tools help automate** Anna Nowogrodzki, "The Automatic-Design Tools That Are Changing Synthetic Biology," *Nature*, Dec. 10, 2018, www.nature .com/articles/d41586-018-07662-w.

109 **Quantum technologies, many millions** Vidar, "Google's Quantum Computer Is About 158 Million Times Faster Than the World's Fastest Supercomputer," Medium, Feb. 28, 2021, medium.com/predict/googles-quantum-computer-is-about -158-million-times-faster-than-the-world-s-fastest-supercomputer-36df56747f7f.

110 **Discovering new drugs** Jack W. Scannell et al., "Diagnosing the Decline in Pharmaceutical R&D Efficiency," *Nature Reviews Drug Discovery*, March 1, 2012, www .nature.com/articles/nrd3681.

110   **Life expectancy leveled off** Patrick Heuveline, "Global and National Declines in Life Expectancy: An End-of-2021 Assessment," *Population and Development Review* 48, no. 1 (March 2022), onlinelibrary.wiley.com/doi/10.1111/padr.12477. These declines are, however, on the back of significant long-term improvements.

110   **Progress on conditions like Alzheimer's** "Failed Drug Trials," Alzheimer's Research UK, www.alzheimersresearchuk.org/blog-tag/drug-trials/failed-drug-trials.

110   **AI techniques can search through** Michael S. Ringel et al., "Breaking Eroom's Law," *Nature Reviews Drug Discovery*, April 16, 2020, www.nature.com/articles/d41573 -020-00059-3.

110   **In 2020 an AI system** Jonathan M. Stokes, "A Deep Learning Approach to Antibiotic Discovery," *Cell*, Feb. 20, 2020, www.cell.com/cell/fulltext/S0092-8674(20)30102-1.

110   **Start-ups like Exscientia** "Exscientia and Sanofi Establish Strategic Research Collaboration to Develop AI-Driven Pipeline of Precision-Engineered Medicines," Sanofi, Jan. 7, 2022, www.sanofi.com/en/media-room/press-releases/2022/2022 -01-07-06-00-00-2362917.

110   **To date eighteen clinical assets** Nathan Benaich and Ian Hogarth, *State of AI Report 2022*, Oct. 11, 2022, www.stateof.ai.

110   **In six hours it identified** Fabio Urbina et al., "Dual Use of Artificial-Intelligence-Powered Drug Discovery," *Nature Machine Intelligence*, March 7, 2022, www.nature .com/articles/s42256-022-00465-9.

110   **At launch, the PlayStation 2** K. Thor Jensen, "20 Years Later: How Concerns About Weaponized Consoles Almost Sunk the PS2," *PCMag*, May 9, 2020, www.pcmag .com/news/20-years-later-how-concerns-about-weaponized-consoles-almost -sunk-the-ps2; Associated Press, "Sony's High-Tech Playstation2 Will Require Military Export License," *Los Angeles Times*, April 17, 2000, www.latimes.com/archives /la-xpm-2000-apr-17-fi-20482-story.html.

111   **A more appropriate term** For more on the term "multi-use," see, for example, Cronin, *Power to the People*.

111   **Now single systems like DeepMind's** Scott Reed et al., "A Generalist Agent," DeepMind, Nov. 10, 2022, www.deepmind.com/publications/a-generalist-agent.

114   **Internal research on GPT-4** @GPT-4 Technical Report, OpenAI, March 14, 2023, cdn .openai.com/papers/gpt-4.pdf. See mobile.twitter.com/michalkosinski/status /1636683810631974912 for one of the early experiments.

114   **Early research even claimed** Sébastien Bubeck et al., "Sparks of Artificial General Intelligence: Early Experiments with GPT-4," arXiv, March 27, 2023, arxiv.org /abs/2303.12712.

115   **AIs are already finding ways** Alhussein Fawzi et al., "Discovering Novel Algorithms with AlphaTensor," DeepMind, Oct. 5, 2022, www.deepmind.com/blog/discovering -novel-algorithms-with-alphatensor.

115   **The AI researcher Stuart Russell** Stuart Russell, *Human Compatible: AI and the Problem of Control* (London: Allen Lane, 2019).

115   **Indeed, there is a strong case** Manuel Alfonseca et al., "Superintelligence Cannot Be Contained: Lessons from Computability Theory," *Journal of Artificial Intelligence Research*, Jan. 5, 2021, jair.org/index.php/jair/article/view/12202; Jaime Sevilla and John Burden, "Response to Superintelligence Cannot Be Contained: Lessons from Computability Theory," Centre for the Study of Existential Risk, Feb. 25, 2021, www.cser.ac.uk/news/response-superintelligence-contained.

CHAPTER 8: UNSTOPPABLE INCENTIVES

117   **Even days before its first public competition** See, for example, Cade Metz, *Genius Makers: The Mavericks Who Brought AI to Google, Facebook and the World* (London: Random House Business, 2021), 170.

118   **More than 280 million people** Google, "The Future of Go Summit: 23 May–27 May, Wuzhen, China," Google Events, events.google.com/alphago2017.

120   **This was a crisis for America** Paul Dickson, "Sputnik's Impact on America," *Nova*, PBS, Nov. 6, 2007, www.pbs.org/wgbh/nova/article/sputnik-impact-on-america.

120 **In the words of Xi Jinping** Lo De Wei, "Full Text of Xi Jinping's Speech at China's Party Congress," Bloomberg, Oct. 18, 2022, www.bloomberg.com/news/articles /2022-10-18/full-text-of-xi-jinping-s-speech-at-china-20th-party-congress-2022.

121 **China's top-down model** See, for example, Nigel Inkster, *The Great Decoupling: China, America and the Struggle for Technological Supremacy* (London: Hurst, 2020).

121 **"By 2030, China's AI theories"** Graham Webster et al., "Full Translation: China's 'New Generation Artificial Intelligence Development Plan,'" DigiChina, Stanford University, Aug. 1, 2017, digichina.stanford.edu/work/full-translation-chinas-new -generation-artificial-intelligence-development-plan-2017.

121 **Indeed, Tsinghua publishes more** Benaich and Hogarth, *State of AI*; Neil Savage, "The Race to the Top Among the World's Leaders in Artificial Intelligence," *Nature Index*, Dec. 9, 2020, www.nature.com/articles/d41586-020-03409-8; "Tsinghua University May Soon Top the World League in Science Research," *Economist*, Nov. 17, 2018, www.economist.com/china/2018/11/17/tsinghua-university-may-soon-top -the-world-league-in-science-research.

121 **China has a growing and impressive** Sarah O'Meara, "Will China Lead the World in AI by 2030?," *Nature*, Aug. 21, 2019, www.nature.com/articles/d41586-019-02360-7; Akira Oikawa and Yuta Shimono, "China Overtakes US in AI Research," *Nikkei Asia*, Aug. 10, 2021, asia.nikkei.com/Spotlight/Datawatch/China-overtakes-US-in -AI-research.

121 **In terms of volume of AI research** Daniel Chou, "Counting AI Research: Exploring AI Research Output in English- and Chinese-Language Sources," Center for Security and Emerging Technology, July 2022, cset.georgetown.edu/publication /counting-ai-research.

121 **China overtook the United States** Remco Zwetsloot, "China Is Fast Outpacing U.S. STEM PhD Growth," Center for Security and Emerging Technology, Aug. 2021, cset.georgetown.edu/publication/china-is-fast-outpacing-u-s-stem-phd-growth.

121 **In the early years of the twenty-first century** Graham Allison et al., "The Great Tech Rivalry: China vs the U.S.," Harvard Kennedy School Belfer Center, Dec. 2021, www.belfercenter.org/sites/default/files/GreatTechRivalry_ChinavsUS_211207 .pdf.

122 **On current trends it will** Xinhua, "China Authorizes Around 700,000 Invention Patents in 2021: Report," XinhuaNet, Jan. 8, 2021, english.news.cn/20220108/de d0496b77c24a3a8712fb26bba390c3/c.html; "U.S. Patent Statistics Chart, Calendar Years 1963–2020," U.S. Patent and Trademark Office, May 2021, www.uspto.gov /web/offices/ac/ido/oeip/taf/us_stat.htm. Figures for the United States are, however, from 2020. It's also important to say that high-value patents are also growing quickly: State Council of the People's Republic of China, "China Sees Growing Number of Invention Patents," Xinhua, Jan. 2022, english.www.gov .cn/statecouncil/ministries/202201/12/content_WS61deb7c8c6d09c94e48a3883 .html.

122 **It has more of the world's** Joseph Hincks, "China Now Has More Supercomputers Than Any Other Country," *Time*, Nov. 14, 2017, time.com/5022859/china-most -supercomputers-world.

122 **Xi Jinping has explicitly called** Jason Douglas, "China's Factories Accelerate Robotics Push as Workforce Shrinks," *Wall Street Journal*, Sept. 18, 2022, www.wsj.com/articles /chinas-factories-accelerate-robotics-push-as-workforce-shrinks-11663493405.

122 **In 2014, China filed the same number** Allison et al., "Great Tech Rivalry."

122 **A year later the Chinese built** Zhang Zhihao, "Beijing-Shanghai Quantum Link a 'New Era,'" *China Daily USA*, Sept. 30, 2017, usa.chinadaily.com.cn/china/2017-09 /30/content_32669867.htm.

122 **They're investing more than $10 billion** Amit Katwala, "Why China's Perfectly Placed to Be Quantum Computing's Superpower," *Wired*, Nov. 14, 2018, www.wired.co .uk/article/quantum-computing-china-us.

122 **Hefei scientists even claimed to have built** Han-Sen Zhong et al., "Quantum Computational Advantage Using Photons," *Science*, Dec. 3, 2020, www.science.org/doi /10.1126/science.abe8770.

122   **Micius's lead researcher** Quoted in Amit Katwala, *Quantum Computing* (London: Random House Business, 2021), 88.

123   **China is already ahead** Allison et al., "Great Tech Rivalry."

123   **"We have no competing fighting chance"** Katrina Manson, "US Has Already Lost AI Fight to China, Says Ex-Pentagon Software Chief," *Financial Times*, Oct. 10, 2021, www.ft.com/content/f939db9a-40af-4bd1-b67d-10492535f8e0.

123   **"Advanced technology is the sharp weapon"** Quoted in Inkster, *The Great Decoupling*, 193.

125   **Almost every country now** For a detailed breakdown, see "National AI Policies & Strategies," OECD.AI, oecd.ai/en/dashboards.

125   **Vladimir Putin believes the leader** "Putin: Leader in Artificial Intelligence Will Rule World," CNBC, Sept. 4, 2017, www.cnbc.com/2017/09/04/putin-leader-in -artificial-intelligence-will-rule-world.html.

125   **The French president Emmanuel Macron** Thomas Macaulay, "Macron's Dream of a European Metaverse Is Far from a Reality," *Next Web*, Sept. 14, 2022, thenextweb .com/news/prospects-for-europes-emerging-metaverse-sector-macron-vestager -meta.

125   **Security, wealth, prestige** "France 2030," Agence Nationale de la Recherche, Feb. 27, 2023, anr.fr/en/france-2030/france-2030.

125   **By 2030 its economy** "India to Be a $30 Trillion Economy by 2050: Gautam Adani," *Economic Times*, April 22, 2022, economictimes.indiatimes.com/news/economy /indicators/india-to-be-a-30-trillion-economy-by-2050-gautam-adani/article show/90985771.cms.

126   **Under it, India established** Trisha Ray and Akhil Deo, "Priorities for a Technology Foreign Policy for India," Washington International Trade Association, Sept. 25, 2020, www.wita.org/atp-research/tech-foreign-policy-india.

127   **We live in an age** Cronin, *Power to the People*.

128   **For example, GitHub has** Neeraj Kashyap, "GitHub's Path to 128M Public Repositories," *Towards Data Science*, March 4, 2020, towardsdatascience.com/githubs-path -to-128m-public-repositories-f6f656ab56b1.

129   **The original such service** arXiv, "About ArXiv," arxiv.org/about.

129   **The great stock of the world's** "The General Index," Internet Archive, Oct. 7, 2021, archive.org/details/GeneralIndex.

129   **Worldwide R&D spending** "Research and Development: U.S. Trends and International Comparisons," National Center for Science and Engineering Statistics, April 28, 2022, ncses.nsf.gov/pubs/nsb20225.

129   **Amazon's R&D budget alone** Prableen Bajpai, "Which Companies Spend the Most in Research and Development (R&D)?," Nasdaq, June 21, 2021, www.nasdaq.com /articles/which-companies-spend-the-most-in-research-and-development-rd-2021 -06-21.

129   **Alphabet, Apple, Huawei, Meta** "Huawei Pumps $22 Billion into R&D to Beat U.S. Sanctions," Bloomberg News, April 25, 2022, www.bloomberg.com/news/articles /2022-04-25/huawei-rivals-apple-meta-with-r-d-spending-to-beat-sanctions; Jennifer Saba, "Apple Has the Most Growth Fuel in Hand," Reuters, Oct. 28, 2021, www .reuters.com/breakingviews/apple-has-most-growth-fuel-hand-2021-10-28.

130   **And yet it was also LeCun** Metz, *Genius Makers*, 58.

130   **NVIDIA wasn't complaining** Mitchell, *Artificial Intelligence*, 103.

131   **Two hundred and fifty passengers** "First in the World: The Making of the Liverpool and Manchester Railway," Science+Industry Museum, Dec. 20, 2018, www .scienceandindustrymuseum.org.uk/objects-and-stories/making-the-liverpool -and-manchester-railway.

131   **Five years in, it was delivering** This and the wider account are drawn from William Quinn and John D. Turner, *Boom and Bust: A Global History of Financial Bubbles* (Cambridge, U.K.: Cambridge University Press, 2022).

131   **At their peak, railway stocks** Ibid.

132   **The railway boom of the 1840s** "The Beauty of Bubbles," *Economist*, Dec. 18, 2008, www.economist.com/christmas-specials/2008/12/18/the-beauty-of-bubbles.

132 **Carlota Perez sees an equivalent** Perez, *Technological Revolutions and Financial Capital.*

132 **Science has to be converted** An extensive economics literature examines the micro-economics of innovation, showing how sensitive and wrapped in economic incentives this process is. See, for example, Lipsey, Carlaw, and Bekar, *Economic Transformations,* for an overview.

133 **Per capita GDP has risen** See Angus Maddison, *The World Economy: A Millenarian Perspective* (Paris: OECD Publications, 2001), or the more up-to-date "GDP Per Capita, 1820 to 2018," Our World in Data, ourworldindata.org/grapher/gdp-per-capita-maddison-2020?yScale=log.

133 **Now, globally, this sits** Nishant Yonzan et al., "Projecting Global Extreme Poverty up to 2030: How Close Are We to World Bank's 3% Goal?," *World Bank Data Blog,* Oct. 9, 2020, blogs.worldbank.org/opendata/projecting-global-extreme-poverty-2030-how-close-are-we-world-banks-3-goal.

133 **In the nineteenth century, inventions** Alan Greenspan and Adrian Wooldridge, *Capitalism in America: A History* (London: Allen Lane, 2018), 15.

133 **Isaac Singer's sewing machine** Ibid., 47.

133 **In Germany, for example** Charlie Giattino and Esteban Ortiz-Ospina, "Are We Working More Than Ever?," Our World in Data, ourworldindata.org/working-more-than-ever.

134 **Tech is by far the biggest** "S&P 500 Data," S&P Dow Jones Indices, July 2022, www.spglobal.com/spdji/en/indices/equity/sp-500/#data.

134 **Hundreds of billions of dollars** In 2021 alone more than $600 billion of venture capital was invested globally, mainly in tech and biotech businesses, ten times the amount a decade earlier. See Gené Teare, "Funding and Unicorn Creation in 2021 Shattered All Records," *Crunchbase News,* Jan. 5, 2022, news.crunchbase.com/business/global-vc-funding-unicorns-2021-monthly-recap. Meanwhile, private equity investments in technology also spiked to more than $400 billion in 2021, by far the largest single category. See Laura Cooper and Preeti Singh, "Private Equity Backs Record Volume of Tech Deals," *Wall Street Journal,* Jan. 3, 2022, www.wsj.com/articles/private-equity-backs-record-volume-of-tech-deals-11641207603.

134 **Investment in AI technologies** See, for example, *Artificial Intelligence Index Report 2021,* although the numbers have certainly grown in the generative AI boom since then.

134 **PwC forecasts AI will add** "Sizing the Prize—PwC's Global Artificial Intelligence Study: Exploiting the AI Revolution," PwC, 2017, www.pwc.com/gx/en/issues/data-and-analytics/publications/artificial-intelligence-study.html.

134 **McKinsey forecasts a $4 trillion boost** Jacques Bughin et al., "Notes from the AI Frontier: Modeling the Impact of AI on the World Economy," McKinsey, Sept. 4, 2018, www.mckinsey.com/featured-insights/artificial-intelligence/notes-from-the-ai-frontier-modeling-the-impact-of-ai-on-the-world-economy; Michael Ciu, "The Bio Revolution: Innovations Transforming Economies, Societies, and Our Lives," McKinsey Global Institute, May 13, 2020, www.mckinsey.com/industries/pharmaceuticals-and-medical-products/our-insights/the-bio-revolution-innovations-transforming-economies-societies-and-our-lives.

134 **Boosting world robot installations** "How Robots Change the World," Oxford Economics, June 26, 2019, resources.oxfordeconomics.com/hubfs/How%20Robots%20Change%20the%20World%20(PDF).pdf.

135 **Consider that the world economy** The World Economy in the Second Half of the Twentieth Century," OECD, Sept. 22, 2006, read.oecd-ilibrary.org/development/the-world-economy/the-world-economy-in-the-second-half-of-the-twentieth-century_9789264022621-5-en#page1.

136 **With generalist AI** Philip Trammell et al., "Economic Growth Under Transformative AI," Global Priorities Institute, Oct. 2020, globalprioritiesinstitute.org/wp-content/uploads/Philip-Trammell-and-Anton-Korinek_economic-growth-under-transformative-ai.pdf. This leads to the extraordinary and impossible scenario of an increase "rapid enough to produce infinite output in a finite period of time."

136 **Assuming favorable weather conditions** Hannah Ritchie et al., "Crop Yields," Our World in Data, ourworldindata.org/crop-yields.

137 **In the twenty-first century, yields** "Farming Statistics—Final Crop Areas, Yields, Livestock Populations and Agricultural Workforce at 1 June 2020 United Kingdom," U.K. Government Department for Environment, Food & Rural Affairs, Dec. 22, 2020, assets.publishing.service.gov.uk/government/uploads/system /uploads/attachment_data/file/946161/structure-jun2020final-uk-22dec20.pdf.

137 **Corn yields per hectare** Ritchie et al., "Crop Yields."

137 **The labor required** Smil, *How the World Really Works*, 66.

137 **In 1945, around 50 percent** Max Roser and Hannah Ritchie, "Hunger and Undernourishment," Our World in Data, ourworldindata.org/hunger-and-undernourishment.

138 **While clean electricity generation** Smil, *How the World Really Works*, 36.

138 **Since the start of the twenty-first century** Ibid., 42.

138 **Imagine the average tomato** Ibid., 61.

138 **What's more, to meet global demand** Daniel Quiggin et al., "Climate Change Risk Assessment 2021," Chatham House, Sept. 14, 2021, www.chathamhouse.org/2021 /09/climate-change-risk-assessment-2021?7J7ZL,68TH2Q,UNIN9.

139 **And yet it's largely not been invented** Elizabeth Kolbert, *Under a White Sky: The Nature of the Future* (New York: Crown, 2022), 155.

139 **AI has helped design an enzyme** Hongyuan Lu et al., "Machine Learning–Aided Engineering of Hydrolases for PET Depolymerization," *Nature*, April 27, 2022, www .nature.com/articles/s41586-022-04599-z.

140 **"When you see something"** "J. Robert Oppenheimer 1904–67," in *Oxford Essential Quotations*, ed. Susan Ratcliffe (Oxford: Oxford University Press, 2016), www .oxfordreference.com/view/10.1093/acref/9780191826719.001.0001/q-oro-ed4 -00007996.

141 **"What we are creating now"** Quoted in Dyson, *Turing's Cathedral*.

CHAPTER 9: THE GRAND BARGAIN

147 **At its heart, the nation-state** There is clearly a lot of complexity with and a large literature on the use of the terms "nation-state" and "state." However, here we use them in a fairly basic way: nation-states are the countries of the world, their people, and their governments (with all the great diversity and complexity that implies); states are the governments and systems of rule and social service within those nation-states. Ireland, Israel, India, and Indonesia are all very different kinds of nations and states, yet we can still think about them as a coherent set of bodies despite their many distinctions. Nation-states have always been "something of a fiction," in the words of Wendy Brown (*Walled States, Waning Sovereignty* [New York: Zone Books, 2010], 69)—how can the people be sovereign if power is exercised over them? Nonetheless, the nation-state is an incredibly useful and powerful fiction.

152 **Literacy rates, life expectancy** Max Roser and Esteban Ortiz-Ospina, "Literacy," Our World in Data, ourworldindata.org/literacy.

152 **Western societies in particular** In the words of William Davies, *Nervous States: How Feeling Took Over the World* (London: Jonathan Cape, 2018).

153 **Trust in government** One-third (35 percent) of the U.K. population reported that they trust their national government, lower than the average across the OECD countries (41 percent). Half (49 percent) of the U.K. population said they did not trust the national government. "Building Trust to Reinforce Democracy: Key Findings from the 2021 OECD Survey on Drivers of Trust in Public Institutions," OECD, www.oecd.org/governance/trust-in-government.

153 **For recent presidents such as Obama** "Public Trust in Government: 1958–2022," Pew Research Center, June 6, 2022, www.pewresearch.org/politics/2022/06/06/public -trust-in-government-1958-2022.

153 **Quite remarkably, a 2018 study** Lee Drutman et al., "Follow the Leader: Exploring American Support for Democracy and Authoritarianism," Democracy Fund

Voter Study Group, March 2018, fsi-live.s3.us-west-1.amazonaws.com/s3fs-public
/followtheleader_2018mar13.pdf.

153   **No less than 85 percent of Americans** "Bipartisan Dissatisfaction with the Direction
of the Country and the Economy," AP NORC, June 29, 2022, apnorc.org/projects
/bipartisan-dissatisfaction-with-the-direction-of-the-country-and-the-economy.

153   **Distrust extends to nongovernment** See, for example, Daniel Drezner, *The Ideas Industry: How Pessimists, Partisans, and Plutocrats Are Transforming the Marketplace of
Ideas* (New York: Oxford University Press, 2017), and the Edelman Trust Barometer: "2022 Edelman Trust Barometer," Edelman, www.edelman.com/trust/2022
-trust-barometer.

153   **A Democracy Perception Index poll** Richard Wike et al., "Many Across the Globe Are
Dissatisfied with How Democracy Is Working," Pew Research Center, April 29,
2019, www.pewresearch.org/global/2019/04/29/many-across-the-globe-are
-dissatisfied-with-how-democracy-is-working/; Dalia Research et al., "Democracy
Perception Index 2018," Alliance of Democracies, June 2018, www.allianceof
democracies.org/wp-content/uploads/2018/06/Democracy-Perception-Index
-2018-1.pdf.

153   **Since 2010, more countries** "New Report: The Global Decline in Democracy Has
Accelerated," Freedom House, March 3, 2021, freedomhouse.org/article/new
-report-global-decline-democracy-has-accelerated.

153   **A key catalyst of instability** See, for example, Thomas Piketty, *Capital in the Twenty-
first Century* (Cambridge, Mass.: Harvard University Press, 2014), and Anthony B.
Atkinson, *Inequality: What Can Be Done?* (Cambridge, Mass.: Harvard University
Press, 2015), for wider surveys.

153   **Between 1980 and 2021** "Top 1% National Income Share," World Inequality Database, wid.world/world/#sptinc_p99p100_z/US;FR;DE;CN;ZA;GB;WO/last/eu
/k/p/yearly/s/false/5.6579999999999995/30/curve/false/country.

153   **Wealth is ever more** Richard Mille, "Forbes World's Billionaires List: The Richest in
2023," *Forbes,* www.forbes.com/billionaires/. While it's true GDP is a flow, not a
stock like wealth, the comparison is still arresting.

153   **Government policy, a shrinking** Alistair Dieppe, "The Broad-Based Productivity
Slowdown, in Seven Charts," *World Bank Blogs: Let's Talk Development,* July 14, 2020,
blogs.worldbank.org/developmenttalk/broad-based-productivity-slowdown
-seven-charts.

154   **Forty million people in the United States** Jessica L. Semega et al., "Income and Poverty
in the United States: 2016," U.S. Census Bureau, www.census.gov/content/dam
/Census/library/publications/2017/demo/P60-259.pdf, reported in digitallibrary
.un.org/record/1629536?ln=en.

154   **These are especially worrying trends** See, for example, Christian Houle et al., "Social
Mobility and Political Instability," *Journal of Conflict Resolution,* Aug. 8, 2017,
journals.sagepub.com/doi/full/10.1177/0022002717723434; and Carles Boix, "Economic Roots of Civil Wars and Revolutions in the Contemporary World," *World
Politics* 60, no. 3 (April 2008): 390–437.

154   **It would take a brave** The demise of the nation-state is hardly a novel idea; see, for
example, Rana Dasgupta, "The Demise of the Nation State," *Guardian,* April 5,
2018, www.theguardian.com/news/2018/apr/05/demise-of-the-nation-state-rana
-dasgupta.

155   **A meta-analysis published** Philipp Lorenz-Spreen et al., "A Systematic Review of
Worldwide Causal and Correlational Evidence on Digital Media and Democracy,"
Nature Human Behaviour, Nov. 7, 2022, www.nature.com/articles/s41562-022-01460-1.

156   **As the historian of technology** Langdon Winner, *Autonomous Technology: Technics-
Out-of-Control as a Theme in Political Thought* (Cambridge, Mass.: MIT Press, 1977), 6.

156   **While technology doesn't simplistically** See, for example, Jenny L. Davis, *How Artifacts Afford: The Power and Politics of Everyday Things* (Cambridge, Mass.: MIT
Press, 2020). Technologies are, in the words of Ursula M. Franklin (*The Real World
of Technology* [Toronto: House of Anansi, 1999]), *prescriptive;* that is, their creation

or use prompts or requires certain behaviors, divisions of labor, or outcomes. Farmers in possession of a tractor will go about their work and structure their needs in a different way from farmers with two oxen and a plow. The division of labor prompted by a factory system produces different kinds of social organizations from a society of hunter-gatherers—a culture of compliance and administration. "Patterns laid down in the practice of technology become part of a society's life" (55).

157 **The clock produced set times** See Mumford, *Technics and Civilization,* for a brilliant analysis on the impacts of mechanical clocks.

157 **The printing press helped** Benedict Anderson, *Imagined Communities: Reflections on the Origin and Spread of Nationalism* (London: Verso, 1983).

158 **On one trajectory, some liberal** The Cambridge political scientist David Runciman talks about "zombie democracies," which means something similar: "The basic idea is that the people are simply watching a performance in which their role is to give or withhold applause at the appropriate moments. Democratic politics has become an elaborate show." David Runciman, *How Democracy Ends* (London: Profile Books, 2019), 47.

CHAPTER 10: FRAGILITY AMPLIFIERS

160 **The NHS had been hit** See, for example, S. Ghafur et al., "A Retrospective Impact Analysis of the WannaCry Cyberattack on the NHS," *NPJ Digital Medicine,* Oct. 2, 2019, www.nature.com/articles/s41746-019-0161-6, for more.

160 **WannaCry tricked some users** Mike Azzara, "What Is WannaCry Ransomware and How Does It Work?," Mimecast, May 5, 2021, www.mimecast.com/blog/all-you -need-to-know-about-wannacry-ransomware.

161 **The ensuing damage cost** Andy Greenberg, "The Untold Story of NotPetya, the Most Devastating Cyberattack in History," *Wired,* Aug. 22, 2018, www.wired.com /story/notpetya-cyberattack-ukraine-russia-code-crashed-the-world.

161 **In the words of one NSA staffer** James Bamford, "Commentary: Evidence Points to Another Snowden at the NSA," Reuters, Aug. 22, 2016, www.reuters.com/article /us-intelligence-nsa-commentary-idUSKCN10X01P.

161 **"An equivalent scenario"** Brad Smith, "The Need for Urgent Collective Action to Keep People Safe Online: Lessons from Last Week's Cyberattack," *Microsoft Blogs: On the Issues,* May 14, 2017, blogs.microsoft.com/on-the-issues/2017/05/14/need -urgent-collective-action-keep-people-safe-online-lessons-last-weeks-cyberattack.

163 **Power is "the ability or capacity"** Definitions taken from Oxford Languages, languages.oup.com.

165 **In the words of a** *New York Times* Ronen Bergman et al., "The Scientist and the A.I.-Assisted, Remote-Control Killing Machine," *New York Times,* Sept. 18, 2021, www.nytimes.com/2021/09/18/world/middleeast/iran-nuclear-fakhrizadeh -assassination-israel.html.

166 **The cost of military-grade drones** Azhar, *Exponential,* 192.

166 **By 2028, $26 billion a year** Fortune Business Insights, "Military Drone Market to Hit USD 26.12 Billion by 2028; Rising Military Spending Worldwide to Augment Growth," Global News Wire, July 22, 2021, www.globenewswire.com/en/news -release/2021/07/22/2267009/0/en/Military-Drone-Market-to-Hit-USD-26-12 -Billion-by-2028-Rising-Military-Spending-Worldwide-to-Augment-Growth-Fortune -Business-Insights.html.

166 **In May 2021, for example** David Hambling, "Israel Used World's First AI-Guided Combat Drone Swarm in Gaza Attacks," *New Scientist,* June 30, 2021, www .newscientist.com/article/2282656-israel-used-worlds-first-ai-guided-combat -drone-swarm-in-gaza-attacks.

166 **Start-ups like Anduril** Dan Primack, "Exclusive: Rebellion Defense Raises $150 Million at $1 Billion Valuation," *Axios,* Sept. 15, 2021, www.axios.com/2021/09/15 /rebellion-defense-raises-150-million-billion-valuation; Ingrid Lunden, "Anduril Is Raising Up to $1.2B, Sources Say at a $7B Pre-money Valuation, for Its Defense

Tech," TechCrunch, May 24, 2022, techcrunch.com/2022/05/24/filing-anduril-is
-raising-up-to-1-2b-sources-say-at-a-7b-pre-money-valuation-for-its-defense-tech.

167 **As the cybersecurity expert** Bruce Schneier, "The Coming AI Hackers," Harvard Kennedy School Belfer Center, April 2021, www.belfercenter.org/publication/coming
-ai-hackers.

167 **Researchers at Meta created** Anton Bakhtin et al., "Human-Level Play in the Game
of *Diplomacy* by Combining Language Models with Strategic Reasoning," *Science*,
Nov. 22, 2022, www.science.org/doi/10.1126/science.ade9097.

168 **When non-state** See Benjamin Wittes and Gabriella Blum, *The Future of Violence:
Robots and Germans, Hackers and Drones—Confronting A New Age of Threat* (New
York: Basic Books, 2015), for a more developed version of this argument.

169 **Both looked and sounded** First reported in Nilesh Cristopher, "We've Just Seen the
First Use of Deepfakes in an Indian Election Campaign," *Vice*, Feb. 18, 2020, www
.vice.com/en/article/jgedjb/the-first-use-of-deepfakes-in-indian-election-by-bjp.

170 **In another widely publicized incident** Melissa Goldin, "Video of Biden Singing 'Baby
Shark' Is a Deepfake," Associated Press, Oct. 19, 2022, apnews.com/article/fact
-check-biden-baby-shark-deepfake-412016518873; "Doctored Nancy Pelosi Video
Highlights Threat of 'Deepfake' Tech," CBS News, May 25, 2019, www.cbsnews
.com/news/doctored-nancy-pelosi-video-highlights-threat-of-deepfake-tech-2019
-05-25.

170 **If you want to watch** TikTok @deeptomcruise, www.tiktok.com/@deeptom
cruise?lang=en.

170 **A bank in Hong Kong** Thomas Brewster, "Fraudsters Cloned Company Director's
Voice in \$35 Million Bank Heist, Police Find," *Forbes*, Oct. 14, 2021, www.forbes
.com/sites/thomasbrewster/2021/10/14/huge-bank-fraud-uses-deep-fake-voice
-tech-to-steal-millions.

170 **All the documents seemed** Catherine Stupp, "Fraudsters Used AI to Mimic CEO's
Voice in Unusual Cybercrime Case," *Wall Street Journal*, Aug. 30, 2019, www.wsj
.com/articles/fraudsters-use-ai-to-mimic-ceos-voice-in-unusual-cybercrime
-case-11567157402.

170 **It's not the president charging** Which is a real deepfake. See Kelly Jones, "Viral Video
of Biden Saying He's Reinstating the Draft Is a Deepfake," *Verify*, March 1, 2023,
www.verifythis.com/article/news/verify/national-verify/viral-video-of-biden
-saying-hes-reinstating-the-draft-is-a-deepfake/536-d721f8cb-d26a-4873-b2a8-91dd91
288365.

171 **His radicalizing messages were** Josh Meyer, "Anwar al-Awlaki: The Radical Cleric
Inspiring Terror from Beyond the Grave," NBC News, Sept. 21, 2016, www
.nbcnews.com/news/us-news/anwar-al-awlaki-radical-cleric-inspiring-terror
-beyond-grave-n651296; Alex Hern, "'YouTube Islamist' Anwar al-Awlaki Videos
Removed in Extremism Clampdown," *Guardian*, Nov. 13, 2017, www.theguardian
.com/technology/2017/nov/13/youtube-islamist-anwar-al-awlaki-videos-removed
-google-extremism-clampdown.

171 **Soon these videos will be fully** Eric Horvitz, "On the Horizon: Interactive and Com-
positional Deepfakes," ICMI '22: Proceedings of the 2022 International Conference
on Multimodal Interaction, arxiv.org/abs/2209.01714.

172 **According to Facebook** U.S. Senate, Report of the Select Committee on Intelligence:
Russian Active Measures Campaigns and Interference in the 2016 U.S. Election,
vol. 5, Counterintelligence Threats and Vulnerabilities, 116th Congress, 1st sess.,
www.intelligence.senate.gov/sites/default/files/documents/report_volume5
.pdf; Nicholas Fandos et al., "House Intelligence Committee Releases Incendiary
Russian Social Media Ads," *New York Times*, Nov. 1, 2017, www.nytimes.com/2017
/11/01/us/politics/russia-technology-facebook.html.

172 **Unfortunately, it's far from just Russia** It is, however, often Russia. In 2021, 58 percent
of cyberattacks came from Russia alone. See Tom Burt, "Russian Cyberattacks
Pose Greater Risk to Governments and Other Insights from Our Annual Report,"
Microsoft Blogs: On the Issues, Oct. 7, 2021, blogs.microsoft.com/on-the-issues
/2021/10/07/digital-defense-report-2021.

172 **More than seventy countries** Samantha Bradshaw et al., "Industrialized Disinformation: 2020 Global Inventory of Organized Social Media Manipulation," Oxford University Programme on Democracy & Technology, Jan. 13, 2021, demtech.oii.ox
.ac.uk/research/posts/industrialized-disinformation.

172 **The CIA, too, is no stranger** See, for example, Krassi Twigg and Kerry Allen, "The
Disinformation Tactics Used by China," BBC News, March 12, 2021, www.bbc
.co.uk/news/56364952; Kenddrick Chan and Mariah Thornton, "China's Changing
Disinformation and Propaganda Targeting Taiwan," *Diplomat*, Sept. 19, 2022,
thediplomat.com/2022/09/chinas-changing-disinformation-and-propaganda
-targeting-taiwan/; and Emerson T. Brooking and Suzanne Kianpour, "Iranian
Digital Influence Efforts: Guerrilla Broadcasting for the Twenty-first Century," Atlantic Council, Feb. 11, 2020, www.atlanticcouncil.org/in-depth-research-reports
/report/iranian-digital-influence-efforts-guerrilla-broadcasting-for-the-twenty
-first-century.

172 **Eighty-two percent of influential users** Virginia Alvino Young, "Nearly Half of
the Twitter Accounts Discussing 'Reopening America' May Be Bots," Carnegie
Mellon University, May 27, 2020, www.cmu.edu/news/stories/archives/2020/may
/twitter-bot-campaign.html.

172 **Cue an "Infocalypse"** See Nina Schick, *Deep Fakes and the Infocalypse: What You
Urgently Need to Know* (London: Monoray, 2020); and Ben Buchanan et al., "Truth,
Lies, and Automation," Center for Security and Emerging Technology, May 2021,
cset.georgetown.edu/publication/truth-lies-and-automation.

173 **In the words of a Brookings Institution** William A. Galston, "Is Seeing Still Believing?
The Deepfake Challenge to Truth in Politics," Brookings, Jan. 8, 2020, www
.brookings.edu/research/is-seeing-still-believing-the-deepfake-challenge-to-truth
-in-politics.

173 **First discovered in China** Figure taken from William MacAskill, *What We Owe the
Future: A Million-Year View* (London: Oneworld, 2022), 112, who cites a variety of
sources, although acknowledges none are certain about this number. See also H. C.
Kung et al., "Influenza in China in 1977: Recurrence of Influenza Virus A Subtype
H1N1," *Bulletin of the World Health Organization* 56, no. 6 (1978), www.ncbi.nlm.nih
.gov/pmc/articles/PMC2395678/pdf/bullwho00443-0095.pdf.

173 **What was unusual about the H1N1 flu** Joel O. Wertheim, "The Re-emergence of
H1N1 Influenza Virus in 1977: A Cautionary Tale for Estimating Divergence Times
Using Biologically Unrealistic Sampling Dates," *PLOS ONE*, June 17, 2010, journals
.plos.org/plosone/article?id=10.1371/journal.pone.0011184.

174 **A version of the earlier virus** See, for example, Edwin D. Kilbourne, "Influenza
Pandemics of the 20th Century," *Emerging Infectious Diseases* 12, no. 1 (Jan. 2006),
www.ncbi.nlm.nih.gov/pmc/articles/PMC3291411; and Michelle Rozo and Gigi
Kwik Gronvall, "The Reemergent 1977 H1N1 Strain and the Gain-of-Function
Debate," *mBio*, Aug. 18, 2015, www.ncbi.nlm.nih.gov/pmc/articles/PMC4542197.

174 **And yet accidents and leaks** See, for example, good accounts in Alina Chan and Matt
Ridley, *Viral: The Search for the Origin of Covid-19* (London: Fourth Estate, 2022), and
MacAskill, *What We Owe the Future*.

174 **Just two years later anthrax spores** Kai Kupferschmidt, "Anthrax Genome Reveals
Secrets About a Soviet Bioweapons Accident," *Science*, Aug. 16, 2016, www.science
.org/content/article/anthrax-genome-reveals-secrets-about-soviet-bioweapons
-accident.

174 **In 2007 a leaking pipe** T. J. D. Knight-Jones and J. Rushton, "The Economic Impacts
of Foot and Mouth Disease—What Are They, How Big Are They, and Where Do
They Occur?," *Preventive Veterinary Medicine*, Nov. 2013, www.ncbi.nlm.nih.gov
/pmc/articles/PMC3989032/#bib0005. It should be noted the damage was much
less than the 2001 outbreak, which was from natural causes.

174 **In 2021, a pharmaceutical company** Maureen Breslin, "Lab Worker Finds Vials
Labeled 'Smallpox' at Merck Facility," *The Hill*, Nov. 17, 2021, thehill.com/policy
/healthcare/581915-lab-worker-finds-vials-labeled-smallpox-at-merck-facility-near
-philadelphia.

174   **Before it was eradicated** Sophie Ochmann and Max Roser, "Smallpox," Our World in Data, ourworldindata.org/smallpox; Kelsey Piper, "Smallpox Used to Kill Millions of People Every Year. Here's How Humans Beat It," *Vox*, May 8, 2022, www .vox.com/future-perfect/21493812/smallpox-eradication-vaccines-infectious -disease-covid-19.

174   **Quite incredibly, it escaped** See, for example, Kathryn Senio, "Recent Singapore SARS Case a Laboratory Accident," *Lancet Infectious Diseases*, Nov. 2003, www .thelancet.com/journals/laninf/article/PIIS1473-3099(03)00815-6/fulltext; Jane Parry, "Breaches of Safety Regulations Are Probable Cause of Recent SARS Outbreak, WHO Says," *BMJ*, May 20, 2004, www.bmj.com/content/328/7450/1222.3; and Martin Furmanski, "Laboratory Escapes and 'Self-Fulfilling Prophecy' Epidemics," Arms Control Center, Feb. 17, 2014, armscontrolcenter.org/wp-content /uploads/2016/02/Escaped-Viruses-final-2-17-14-copy.pdf.

175   **Even as the number of BSL-4 labs** Alexandra Peters, "The Global Proliferation of High-Containment Biological Laboratories: Understanding the Phenomenon and Its Implications," *Revue Scientifique et Technique*, Dec. 2018, pubmed.ncbi.nlm.nih .gov/30964462. The number of labs has gone from fifty-nine to sixty-nine in the last two years, most are in urbanized contexts, and the number of labs handling deadly pathogens is above a hundred. A new generation of "BSL-3+" labs have also boomed. See Filippa Lentzos et al., "Global BioLabs Report 2023," King's College London, May 16, 2023, www.kcl.ac.uk/warstudies/assets/global-biolabs-report-2023.pdf.

175   **Between 1975 and 2016** David Manheim and Gregory Lewis, "High-Risk Human-Caused Pathogen Exposure Events from 1975–2016," F1000Research, July 8, 2022, f1000research.com/articles/10-752.

175   **A survey of biosafety officers** David B. Manheim, "Results of a 2020 Survey on Reporting Requirements and Practices for Biocontainment Laboratory Accidents," *Health Security* 19, no. 6 (2021), www.liebertpub.com/doi/10.1089/hs.2021.0083.

175   **A U.S. risk assessment from 2014** Lynn C. Klotz and Edward J. Sylvester, "The Consequences of a Lab Escape of a Potential Pandemic Pathogen," *Frontiers in Public Health*, Aug. 11, 2014, www.frontiersin.org/articles/10.3389/fpubh.2014.00116/full.

175   **Few areas of biology are as controversial** Thanks in particular to Jason Matheny and Kevin Esvelt for their discussion on this topic.

176   **Work with an avian flu** Martin Enserink and John Cohen, "One of Two Hotly Debated H5N1 Papers Finally Published," *Science*, May 2, 2012, www.science.org /content/article/one-two-hotly-debated-h5n1-papers-finally-published.

176   **For a time U.S. funding agencies** Amber Dance, "The Shifting Sands of 'Gain-of-Function' Research," *Nature*, Oct. 27, 2021, www.nature.com/articles/d41586-021 -02903-x.

176   **There is at least some indication** Chan and Ridley, *Viral;* "Controversial New Research Suggests SARS-CoV-2 Bears Signs of Genetic Engineering," *Economist*, Oct. 27, 2022, www.economist.com/science-and-technology/2022/10/22/a-new -paper-claims-sars-cov-2-bears-signs-of-genetic-engineering.

176   **Both the FBI and the U.S. Department of Energy** See, for example, Max Matza and Nicholas Yong, "FBI Chief Christopher Wray Says China Lab Leak Most Likely," BBC, March 1, 2023, www.bbc.co.uk/news/world-us-canada-64806903.

176   **In late 2022, an NIH study** Da-Yuan Chen et al., "Role of Spike in the Pathogenic and Antigenic Behavior of SARS-CoV-2 BA.1 Omicron," bioRxiv, Oct. 14, 2022, www .biorxiv.org/content/10.1101/2022.10.13.512134v1.

176   **Many felt the research shouldn't** Kiran Stacey, "US Health Officials Probe Boston University's Covid Virus Research," *Financial Times*, Oct. 20, 2022, www.ft.com /content/f2e88a9c-104a-4515-8de1-65d72a5903d0.

178   **Early analysis of ChatGPT** Shakked Noy and Whitney Zhang, "Experimental Evidence on the Productivity Effects of Generative Artificial Intelligence," MIT Economics, March 10, 2023, economics.mit.edu/sites/default/files/inline-files/Noy _Zhang_1_0.pdf.

179   **That in turn could affect hiring** The likely total is less, however, but still considerable. See James Manyika et al., "Jobs Lost, Jobs Gained: What the Future of Work Will

Mean for Jobs, Skills, and Wages," McKinsey Global Institute, Nov. 28, 2017, www
.mckinsey.com/featured-insights/future-of-work/jobs-lost-jobs-gained-what-the
-future-of-work-will-mean-for-jobs-skills-and-wages. Exact wording: "We estimate
that about half of all the activities people are paid to do in the world's workforce
could potentially be automated by adapting currently demonstrated technologies." Second statistic from Mark Muro et al., "Automation and Artificial Intelligence: How Machines Are Affecting People and Places," Metropolitan Policy
Program, Brookings, Jan. 2019, www.brookings.edu/wp-content/uploads/2019
/01/2019.01_BrookingsMetro_Automation-AI_Report_Muro-Maxim-Whiton
-FINAL-version.pdf.

179 **The economists Daron Acemoglu** Daron Acemoglu and Pascual Restrepo, "Robots
and Jobs: Evidence from US Labor Markets," *Journal of Political Economy* 128, no. 6
(June 2020), www.journals.uchicago.edu/doi/abs/10.1086/705716.

179 **Today algorithms perform the vast** Ibid.; Edward Luce, *The Retreat of Western Liberal-
ism* (London: Little, Brown, 2017), 54. See also Justin Baer and Daniel Huang, "Wall
Street Staffing Falls Again," *Wall Street Journal*, Feb. 19, 2015, www.wsj.com/articles
/wall-street-staffing-falls-for-fourth-consecutive-year-1424366858; Ljubica Nedel-
koska and Glenda Quintini, "Automation, Skills Use, and Training," OECD, March 8,
2018, www.oecd-ilibrary.org/employment/automation-skills-use-and-training_2e2f4
eea-en.

179 **Economists like David Autor** David H. Autor, "Why Are There Still So Many Jobs?
The History and Future of Workplace Automation," *Journal of Economic Perspectives*
29, no. 3 (Summer 2015), www.aeaweb.org/articles?id=10.1257/jep.29.3.3.

179 **Buying into that fear** This is the view of Azeem Azhar: "Overall, though, the lasting
impact of automation will not be the loss of jobs" (Azhar, *Exponential*, 141).

180 **Labor markets also have immense friction** See Daniel Susskind, *A World Without Work:
Technology, Automation and How We Should Respond* (London: Allen Lane, 2021), for
a developed account of these frictions.

180 **The Private Sector Job Quality Index** "U.S. Private Sector Job Quality Index (JQI),"
University at Buffalo School of Management, Feb. 2023, ubwp.buffalo.edu/job
-quality-index-jqi. See also Ford, *Rule of the Robots*.

181 **Even those who don't foresee** Autor, "Why Are There Still So Many Jobs?"

CHAPTER 11: THE FUTURE OF NATIONS

183 **At first blush, stirrups** White, *Medieval Technology and Social Change*. The account is
not universally accepted, however. For a more skeptical reading of Lynn White's
famous thesis, see, for example, "The Great Stirrup Controversy," The Medieval
Technology Pages, web.archive.org/web/20141009082354/http://scholar.chem.nyu
.edu/tekpages/texts/strpcont.html.

185 **This ungovernable "post-sovereign" world** Brown, *Walled States, Waning Sovereignty*.

186 **Its customs, duties, and dividends** William Dalrymple, *The Anarchy: The Relentless
Rise of the East India Company* (London: Bloomsbury, 2020), 233.

186 **Organizations too are a kind of intelligence** Richard Danzig first proposed this idea
to me over dinner and then published an excellent paper: "Machines, Bureaucracies, and Markets as Artificial Intelligences," Center for Security and Emerging Technology, Jan. 2022, cset.georgetown.edu/wp-content/uploads/Machines
-Bureaucracies-and-Markets-as-Artificial-Intelligences.pdf.

187 **To get a sense of these concentrations** "Global 500," *Fortune*, fortune.com/global500/.
As of October 2022. World Bank numbers suggest somewhat lower: World Bank,
"GDP (Current USs)," World Bank Data, data.worldbank.org/indicator/NY.GDP
.MKTP.CD.

187 **Companies already control the largest clusters** Benaich and Hogarth, *State of AI Report 2022*.

188 **There is already a pronounced** James Manyika et al., "Superstars: The Dynamics of
Firms, Sectors, and Cities Leading the Global Economy," McKinsey Global Institute,

Oct. 24, 2018, www.mckinsey.com/featured-insights/innovation-and-growth/superstars-the-dynamics-of-firms-sectors-and-cities-leading-the-global-economy.

189 **Ninety percent of these disputes** Colin Rule, "Separating the People from the Problem," *The Practice,* July 2020, thepractice.law.harvard.edu/article/separating-the-people-from-the-problem.

190 **Zero marginal cost production** See, for example, Jeremy Rifkin, *The Zero Marginal Cost Society: The Internet of Things, the Collaborative Commons, and the Eclipse of Capitalism* (New York: Palgrave, 2014).

190 **What's more, owners of the best systems** Erik Brynjolfsson calls a situation where AI takes over more and more of the economy, locking large numbers of people in an equilibrium where they have no work, no wealth, and no meaningful power, the "Turing Trap." Erik Brynjolfsson, "The Turing Trap: The Promise & Peril of Human-Like Artificial Intelligence," Stanford Digital Economy Lab, Jan. 11, 2022, arxiv.org/pdf/2201.04200.pdf.

191 **Little wonder there is talk** See, for example, Joel Kotkin, *The Coming of Neo-feudalism: A Warning to the Global Middle Class* (New York: Encounter Books, 2020).

192 **Despite the best efforts of revolutionaries** James C. Scott, *Seeing Like a State: How Certain Schemes to Improve the Human Condition Have Failed* (New Haven, Conn.: Yale University Press, 1998).

193 **On the way, and throughout the day** "How Many CCTV Cameras Are There in London?," CCTV.co.uk, Nov. 18, 2020, www.cctv.co.uk/how-many-cctv-cameras-are-there-in-london.

193 **Compared with the West** Benaich and Hogarth, *State of AI Report 2022.*

194 **By 2015 this was the inspiration** Dave Gershgorn, "China's 'Sharp Eyes' Program Aims to Surveil 100% of Public Space," *OneZero,* March 2, 2021, onezero.medium.com/chinas-sharp-eyes-program-aims-to-surveil-100-of-public-space-ddc22d63e015.

194 **A team of leading researchers** Shu-Ching Jean Chen, "SenseTime: The Faces Behind China's Artificial Intelligence Unicorn," *Forbes,* March 7, 2018, www.forbes.com/sites/shuchingjeanchen/2018/03/07/the-faces-behind-chinas-omniscient-video-surveillance-technology.

194 **Chinese police even have sunglasses** Sofia Gallarate, "Chinese Police Officers Are Wearing Facial Recognition Sunglasses," Fair Planet, July 9, 2019, www.fairplanet.org/story/chinese-police-officers-are-wearing-facial-recogni%C2%ADtion-sunglasses.

194 **Around half the world's billion CCTV** This and below stats taken from a *New York Times* investigation: Isabelle Qian et al., "Four Takeaways from a Times Investigation into China's Expanding Surveillance State," *New York Times,* June 21, 2022, www.nytimes.com/2022/06/21/world/asia/china-surveillance-investigation.html.

195 **This AI-enabled system could spot** Ross Andersen, "The Panopticon Is Already Here," *Atlantic,* Sept. 2020, www.theatlantic.com/magazine/archive/2020/09/china-ai-surveillance/614197.

195 **Authorities have built an iris-scan** Qian et al., "Four Takeaways from a Times Investigation into China's Expanding Surveillance State."

195 **In 2019, the U.S. government banned** "NDAA Section 889," GSA SmartPay, smartpay.gsa.gov/content/ndaa-section-889.

195 **Yet, just a year later, three federal agencies** Conor Healy, "US Military & Gov't Break Law, Buy Banned Dahua/Lorex, Congressional Committee Calls for Investigation," IPVM, Dec. 1, 2019, ipvm.com/reports/usg-lorex.

195 **More than one hundred U.S. towns** Zack Whittaker, "US Towns Are Buying Chinese Surveillance Tech Tied to Uighur Abuses," TechCrunch, May 24, 2021, techcrunch.com/2021/05/24/united-states-towns-hikvision-dahua-surveillance.

196 **In smart warehouses** Joshua Brustein, "Warehouses Are Tracking Workers' Every Muscle Movement," Bloomberg, Nov. 5, 2019, www.bloomberg.com/news/articles/2019-11-05/am-i-being-tracked-at-work-plenty-of-warehouse-workers-are.

196 **Companies like Vigilant Solutions** Kate Crawford, *Atlas of AI: Power, Politics, and the Planetary Costs of Artificial Intelligence* (New Haven, Conn.: Yale University Press, 2021).

196 **Even your take-out pizza** Joanna Fantozzi, "Domino's Using AI Cameras to Ensure Pizzas Are Cooked Correctly," *Nation's Restaurants News,* May 29, 2019, www.nrn .com/quick-service/domino-s-using-ai-cameras-ensure-pizzas-are-cooked -correctly.

196 **Before the coming wave** Consider that an up-to-date novel about surveillance dystopias like Dave Eggers's *The Every* hasn't really moved in terms of what exactly is surveilled and is presented not as far-out science fiction but as a satire on contemporary technology companies.

197 **It may be the best-armed** The analyst was Brigadier General (Ret.) Assaf Orion of Israel's Institute for National Security Studies. "The Future of U.S.-Israel Relations Symposium," Council on Foreign Relations, Dec. 2, 2019, www.cfr.org/event /future-us-israel-relations-symposium, quoted in Kali Robinson, "What Is Hezbollah?," Council on Foreign Relations, May 25, 2022, www.cfr.org/backgrounder /what-hezbollah.

197 **It also conducts various commercial** See, for example, "Explained: How Hezbollah Built a Drug Empire via Its 'Narcoterrorist Strategy,'" *Arab News,* May 3, 2021, www.arabnews.com/node/1852636/middle-east.

197 **It is instead a strange** Lina Khatib, "How Hezbollah Holds Sway over the Lebanese State," Chatham House, June 30, 2021, www.chathamhouse.org/sites/default /files/2021-06/2021-06-30-how-hezbollah-holds-sway-over-the-lebanese-state -khatib.pdf.

197 **The coming wave, however** This would simply be to vastly expand certain existing trends whereby, as in centralization, private actors take on more roles traditionally thought to be the preserve of the state. See, for example, Rodney Bruce Hall and Thomas J. Biersteker, *The Emergence of Private Authority in Global Governance* (Cambridge, U.K.: Cambridge University Press, 2002).

198 **Recall that over just the last decade** "Renewable Power Generation Costs in 2019," IRENA, June 2020, www.irena.org/publications/2020/Jun/Renewable-Power-Costs -in-2019.

201 **Hyper-libertarian technologists** James Dale Davidson and William Rees-Mogg, *The Sovereign Individual: Mastering the Transition to the Information Age* (New York: Touchstone, 1997).

201 **A bonfire of public services** Peter Thiel, "The Education of a Libertarian," *Cato Unbound,* April 13, 2009, www.cato-unbound.org/2009/04/13/peter-thiel/education -libertarian. See Balaji Srinivasan, *The Network State* (1729 publishing, 2022), for a more thoughtful take on how technological constructs might supersede the nation-state.

CHAPTER 12: THE DILEMMA

205 **England's population** Niall Ferguson, *Doom: The Politics of Catastrophe* (London: Allen Lane, 2021), 131.

205 **World War I killed** Numbers are from ibid.

209 **A novel human transmissible virus** Numbers taken from a confidential briefing, but we understand this is considered plausible by biosecurity experts.

211 **It's not hard to see** It is remarkable that a third of scientists working on AI believe it could lead to a catastrophe. Jeremy Hsu, "A Third of Scientists Working on AI Say It Could Cause Global Disaster," *New Scientist,* Sept. 22, 2022, www.newscientist .com/article/2338644-a-third-of-scientists-working-on-ai-say-it-could-cause-global -disaster.

212 **Founded in the 1980s, Aum Shinrikyo** See Richard Danzig and Zachary Hosford, "Aum Shinrikyo—Second Edition—English," CNAS, Dec. 20, 2012, www.cnas.org /publications/reports/aum-shinrikyo-second-edition-english; and Philipp C. Bleak, "Revisiting Aum Shinrikyo: New Insights into the Most Extensive Non-state Biological Weapons Program to Date," James Martin Center for Nonproliferation Studies, Dec. 10, 2011, www.nti.org/analysis/articles/revisiting-aum-shinrikyo-new -insights-most-extensive-non-state-biological-weapons-program-date-1.

212 **At Aum Shinrikyo's peak popularity** Federation of American Scientists, "The Operation of the Aum," in Global Proliferation of Weapons of Mass Destruction: A Case Study of the Aum Shinrikyo, Senate Government Affairs Permanent Subcommittee on Investigations, Oct. 31, 1995, irp.fas.org/congress/1995_rpt/aum/part04.htm.

214 **As a report on the implications** Danzig and Hosford, "Aum Shinrikyo."

215 **Some will inevitably say** See, for example, Nick Bostrom, "The Vulnerable World Hypothesis," Sept. 6, 2019, nickbostrom.com/papers/vulnerable.pdf, for perhaps the most developed version of this thesis. In a thought experiment responding to the prospect of "easy nukes," he envisages a "high-tech panopticon" where everyone has a "freedom tag," "worn around the neck and bedecked with multidirectional cameras and microphones. Encrypted video and audio is continuously uploaded from the device to the cloud and machine-interpreted in real time. AI algorithms classify the activities of the wearer, his hand movements, nearby objects, and other situational cues. If suspicious activity is detected, the feed is relayed to one of several patriot monitoring stations."

215 **The wave provides both motive** Martin Bereaja et al., "AI-tocracy," *Quarterly Journal of Economics,* March 13, 2023, academic.oup.com/qje/advance-article-abstract/doi/10.1093/qje/qjad012/7076890.

217 **And on the continuum** Balaji Srinivasan foresees something very like this outcome, with America the zombie, China the demon: "As America descends into anarchy, the CCP points to their functional-but-highly-unfree system as the only alternative, and exports a turnkey version of their surveillance state to other countries as the next version of Belt and Road, as a piece of 'infrastructure' that comes complete with a SaaS subscription to China's all-seeing AI eye." Srinivasan, *The Network State,* 162.

217 **The philosopher of technology** Isis Hazewindus, "The Threat of the Megamachine," *IfThenElse,* Nov. 21, 2021, www.ifthenelse.eu/blog/the-threat-of-the-megamachine.

218 **A survey of sixty civilizations** Michael Shermer, "Why ET Hasn't Called," *Scientific American,* Aug. 2002, michaelshermer.com/sciam-columns/why-et-hasnt-called.

218 **Without new technologies** Ian Morris, *Why the West Rules—for Now: The Patterns of History and What They Reveal About the Future* (London: Profile Books, 2010); Tainter, *The Collapse of Complex Societies;* Diamond, *Collapse.*

219 **Over the next century** Stein Emil Vollset et al., "Fertility, Mortality, Migration, and Population Scenarios for 195 Countries and Territories from 2017 to 2100: A Forecasting Analysis for the Global Burden of Disease Study," *Lancet,* July 14, 2020, www.thelancet.com/article/S0140-6736(20)30677-2/fulltext.

219 **Countries including Japan, Germany** Peter Zeihan, *The End of the World Is Just the Beginning: Mapping the Collapse of Globalization* (New York: Harper Business, 2022).

219 **China is a major part** Xiujian Peng, "Could China's Population Start Falling?" BBC Future, June 6, 2022, www.bbc.com/future/article/20220531-why-chinas-population-is-shrinking.

220 **All of this means** Zeihan, *The End of the World Is Just the Beginning,* 203.

220 **Demand for lithium, cobalt** "Climate-Smart Mining: Minerals for Climate Action," World Bank, www.worldbank.org/en/topic/extractiveindustries/brief/climate-smart-mining-minerals-for-climate-action.

220 **Given the population and resource constraints** Galor, *The Journey of Humanity,* 130.

221 **In 1955, toward the end of his life** John von Neumann, "Can We Survive Technology?," in *The Neumann Compendium* (River Edge, N.J.: World Scientific, 1995), geosci.uchicago.edu/~kite/doc/von_Neumann_1955.pdf.

CHAPTER 13: CONTAINMENT MUST BE POSSIBLE

226 **How do they account for an age** David Cahn et al., "AI 2022: The Explosion," Coatue Venture, coatue-external.notion.site/AI-2022-The-Explosion-e76afd140f824f2eb6b049c5b85a7877.

228 **As we've seen, even wealthy nations** "2021 GHS Index Country Profile for United States," Global Health Security Index, www.ghsindex.org/country/united-states.

228 **Yet a catalog of disastrous decisions** Edouard Mathieu et al., "Coronavirus (COVID-19) Deaths," Our World in Data, ourworldindata.org/covid-deaths.

228 **National budgets for such things** For example, compared with during the 1957 Asian flu, the U.S. federal budget is vastly bigger, in absolute terms of course, but also as a percentage of GDP (16.2 percent versus 20.8 percent). In 1957 there was no dedicated Department of Health, and the forerunner of the CDC was still a relatively fledgling organization at eleven years old. Ferguson, *Doom*, 234.

229 **The most ambitious legislation** "The Artificial Intelligence Act," Future of Life Institute, artificialintelligenceact.eu.

229 **Some argue it's too focused** See, for example, "FLI Position Paper on the EU AI Act," Future of Life Institute, Aug. 4, 2021, futureoflife.org/wp-content/uploads /2021/08/FLI-Position-Paper-on-the-EU-AI-Act.pdf?x72900; and David Matthews, "EU Artificial Intelligence Act Not 'Futureproof,' Experts Warn MEPs," Science Business, March 22, 2022, sciencebusiness.net/news/eu-artificial-intelligence-act -not-futureproof-experts-warn-meps.

229 **Some believe it lets big tech** Khari Johnson, "The Fight to Define When AI Is High Risk," *Wired*, Sept. 1, 2021, www.wired.com/story/fight-to-define-when-ai-is -high-risk.

230 **And yet 1.35 million people** "Global Road Safety Statistics," Brake, www.brake.org .uk/get-involved/take-action/mybrake/knowledge-centre/global-road-safety#.

231 **The government has issued** Jennifer Conrad, "China Is About to Regulate AI—and the World Is Watching," *Wired*, Feb. 22, 2022, www.wired.com/story/china -regulate-ai-world-watching.

231 **It proactively banned various** Christian Smith, "China's Gaming Laws Are Cracking Down Even Further," SVG, March 15, 2022, www.svg.com/799717/chinas-gaming -laws-are-cracking-down-even-further.

231 **Draft regulation of recommendation** "The National Internet Information Office's Regulations on the Administration of Internet Information Service Algorithm Recommendations (Draft for Comment) Notice of Public Consultation," Cyberspace Administration of China, Aug. 27, 2021, www.cac.gov.cn/2021-08/27/c_1631652502 874117.htm.

231 **It doesn't describe how countries** See, for example, Alex Engler, "The Limited Global Impact of the EU AI Act," Brookings, June 14, 2022, www.brookings.edu /blog/techtank/2022/06/14/the-limited-global-impact-of-the-eu-ai-act. A study of 250,000 international treaties suggests they tend not to achieve their ends. See Steven J. Hoffman et al., "International Treaties Have Mostly Failed to Produce Their Intended Effects," *PNAS*, Aug. 1, 2022, www.pnas.org/doi/10.1073/pnas.2122854119.

236 **Our prehistoric brains** See George Marshall, *Don't Even Think About It: Why Our Brains Are Wired to Ignore Climate Change* (New York: Bloomsbury, 2014), for a detailed elaboration of this point.

236 **As recently as the 1970s** Rebecca Lindsey, "Climate Change: Atmospheric Carbon Dioxide," Climate.gov, June 23, 2022, www.climate.gov/news-features/understanding -climate/climate-change-atmospheric-carbon-dioxide.

CHAPTER 14: TEN STEPS TOWARD CONTAINMENT

241 **The International Atomic Energy Agency** "IAEA Safety Standards," International Atomic Energy Agency, www.iaea.org/resources/safety-standards/search?facility =All&term_node_tid_depth_2=All&field_publication_series_info_value= &combine=&items_per_page=100.

241 **The main monitor of bioweapons** Toby Ord, *The Precipice: Existential Risk and the Future of Humanity* (London: Bloomsbury, 2020), 57.

242 **The number of AI safety researchers** Benaich and Hogarth, *State of AI Report 2022*.

242 **Given there are around** For an estimate the number of AI researchers, see "What Is Effective Altruism?," www.effectivealtruism.org/articles/introduction-to-effective -altruism#fn-15.

242 **The original Apollo missions** NASA, "Benefits from Apollo: Giant Leaps in Technol-

ogy," NASA Facts, July 2004, www.nasa.gov/sites/default/files/80660main
_ApolloFS.pdf.

242 **Giving off light** Kevin M. Esvelt, "Delay, Detect, Defend: Preparing for a Future in
Which Thousands Can Release New Pandemics," Geneva Centre for Security
Policy, Nov. 14, 2022, dam.gcsp.ch/files/doc/gcsp-geneva-paper-29-22.

243 **There's also great work being done** Jan Leike, "Alignment Optimism," *Aligned,*
Dec. 5, 2022, aligned.substack.com/p/alignment-optimism.

244 **The computer scientist Stuart Russell** Russell, *Human Compatible.*

246 **This means attacking your systems** Deep Ganguli et al., "Red Teaming Language
Models to Reduce Harms: Methods, Scaling Behaviors, and Lessons Learned,"
arXiv, Nov. 22, 2022, arxiv.org/pdf/2209.07858.pdf.

247 **On the technical side** Sam R. Bowman et al., "Measuring Progress on Scalable Oversight for Large Language Models," arXiv, Nov. 11, 2022, arxiv.org/abs/2211.03540.

247 **At present only a fraction** Security DNA Project, "Securing Global Biotechnology,"
SecureDNA, www.securedna.org.

249 **Xi Jinping was worried** Ben Murphy, "Chokepoints: China's Self-Identified Strategic
Technology Import Dependencies," Center for Security and Emerging Technology,
May 2022, cset.georgetown.edu/publication/chokepoints.

249 **Indeed, China spends more** Chris Miller, *Chip War: The Fight for the World's Most Critical Technology* (New York: Scribner, 2022).

250 **One technology executive** Demetri Sevastopulo and Kathrin Hille, "US Hits China
with Sweeping Tech Export Controls," *Financial Times,* Oct. 7, 2022, www.ft.com
/content/6825bee4-52a7-4c86-b1aa-31c100708c3e.

250 **In the short to medium term** Gregory C. Allen, "Choking Off China's Access to the
Future of AI," Center for Strategic & International Studies, Oct. 11, 2022, www.csis
.org/analysis/choking-chinas-access-future-ai.

250 **If it takes hundreds of billions** Julie Zhu, "China Readying $143 Billion Package for
Its Chip Firms in Face of U.S. Curbs," Reuters, Dec. 14, 2022, www.reuters.com
/technology/china-plans-over-143-bln-push-boost-domestic-chips-compete-with
-us-sources-2022-12-13.

250 **NVIDIA, the American manufacturer** Stephen Nellis and Jane Lee, "Nvidia Tweaks
Flagship H100 Chip for Export to China as H800," Reuters, March 22, 2023,
www.reuters.com/technology/nvidia-tweaks-flagship-h100-chip-export-china
-h800-2023-03-21.

251 **ASML's machines** Moreover, not just the machines but many component parts
have only one manufacturer, like high-end lasers from Cymer or mirrors from
Zeiss so pure that, were they the size of Germany, an irregularity would be only a
few millimeters wide.

251 **These three companies have** See, for example, Michael Filler on Twitter, May 25,
2022, twitter.com/michaelfiller/status/1529633698961833984.

251 **A crunch on the rare earth** "Where Is the Greatest Risk to Our Mineral Resource
Supplies?," USGS, Feb. 21, 2020, www.usgs.gov/news/national-news-release/new
-methodology-identifies-mineral-commodities-whose-supply-disruption?qt-news
_science_products=1#qt-news_science_products.

251 **Some 80 percent of the high-quality quartz** Zeihan, *The End of the World Is Just the
Beginning,* 314.

253 **Indeed, at times shrill criticism** Lee Vinsel, "You're Doing It Wrong: Notes on Criticism and Technology Hype," Medium, Feb. 1, 2021, sts-news.medium.com/youre
-doing-it-wrong-notes-on-criticism-and-technology-hype-18b08b4307e5.

254 **Promisingly, research on ethical AI** Stanford University Human-Centered Artificial
Intelligence, Artificial Intelligence Index Report 2021.

254 **Major shortfalls** For example, Shannon Vallor, "Mobilising the Intellectual Resources of the Arts and Humanities," Ada Lovelace Institute, June 25, 2021, www
.adalovelaceinstitute.org/blog/mobilising-intellectual-resources-arts-humanities.

257 **Forming a coalition** Kay C. James on Twitter, March 20, 2019, twitter.com/Kay
ColesJames/status/1108365238779498497.

258 **There's a good chance of positive** "B Corps 'Go Beyond' Business as Usual," B Lab,

March 1, 2023, www.bcorporation.net/en-us/news/press/b-corps-go-beyond
-business-as-usual-for-b-corp-month-2023.

259 **Although today companies have** "U.S. Research and Development Funding and Performance: Fact Sheet," Congressional Research Service, Sept. 13, 2022, sgp.fas.org
/crs/misc/R44307.pdf.

259 **Investing in science and technology** See, for example, Mariana Mazzucato, *The Entrepreneurial State: Debunking Public vs. Private Sector Myths* (London: Anthem Press,
2013).

259 **Instead, private sector salaries** The head of cybersecurity at the U.K. Treasury is
on a tenth the salary of private sector equivalents: See @Jontafkasi on Twitter,
March 29, 2023, mobile.twitter.com/Jontafkasi/status/1641193954778697728.

259 **Their first task should be** These points are well made in Jess Whittlestone and Jack
Clark, "Why and How Governments Should Monitor AI Development," arXiv,
Aug. 31, 2021, arxiv.org/pdf/2108.12427.pdf.

260 **In 2015 there was virtually** "Legislation Related to Artificial Intelligence," National
Conference of State Legislatures, Aug. 26, 2022, www.ncsl.org/research/tele
communications-and-information-technology/2020-legislation-related-to
-artificial-intelligence.aspx.

260 **The OECD AI Policy Observatory** OECD, "National AI Policies & Strategies,"
OECD AI Policy Observatory, oecd.ai/en/dashboards/overview.

260 **In 2022 the White House released** "Fact Sheet: Biden-Harris Administration Announces Key Actions to Advance Tech Accountability and Protect the Rights of
the American Public," White House, Oct. 4, 2022, www.whitehouse.gov/ostp
/news-updates/2022/10/04/fact-sheet-biden-harris-administration-announces
-key-actions-to-advance-tech-accountability-and-protect-the-rights-of-the-american
-public.

261 **Today U.S. labor is taxed** Daron Acemoglu et al., "Taxes, Automation, and the Future
of Labor," MIT Work of the Future, mitsloan.mit.edu/shared/ods/documents
?PublicationDocumentID=7929.

262 **This is sometimes called** Arnaud Costinot and Ivan Werning, "Robots, Trade, and
Luddism: A Sufficient Statistic Approach to Optimal Technology Regulation,"
Review of Economic Studies, Nov. 4, 2022, academic.oup.com/restud/advance-article
/doi/10.1093/restud/rdac076/6798670.

262 **MIT economists have argued** Daron Acemoglu et al., "Does the US Tax Code Favor
Automation?," *Brookings Papers on Economic Activity* (Spring 2020), www.brookings
.edu/wp-content/uploads/2020/12/Acemoglu-FINAL-WEB.pdf.

262 **In an era of hyper-scaling** Sam Altman, "Moore's Law for Everything," Sam Altman,
March 16, 2021, moores.samaltman.com.

263 **Use of blinding laser weapons** "The Convention on Certain Conventional Weapons,"
United Nations, www.un.org/disarmament/the-convention-on-certain-conventional
-weapons.

265 **A study of 106 countries** Françoise Baylis et al., "Human Germline and Heritable
Genome Editing: The Global Policy Landscape," *CRISPR Journal,* Oct. 20, 2020,
www.liebertpub.com/doi/10.1089/crispr.2020.0082.

265 **In the aftermath of the first** Eric S. Lander et al., "Adopt a Moratorium on Heritable
Genome Editing," *Nature,* March 13, 2019, www.nature.com/articles/d41586-019
-00726-5.

267 **By the early 2010s** Peter Dizikes, "Study: Commercial Air Travel Is Safer Than Ever,"
MIT News, Jan. 23, 2020, news.mit.edu/2020/study-commercial-flights-safer-ever
-0124.

270 **We met again in 2017** "AI Principles," Future of Life Institute, Aug. 11, 2017, future
oflife.org/open-letter/ai-principles.

270 **Social and moral responsibility** Joseph Rotblat, "A Hippocratic Oath for Scientists,"
Science, Nov. 19, 1999, www.science.org/doi/10.1126/science.286.5444.1475.

271 **Because *we* build technology** See, for example, proposals from Rich Sutton, "Creating Human-Level AI: How and When?," University of Alberta, Canada, futureoflife
.org/data/PDF/rich_sutton.pdf?x72900; Azeem Azhar, "We are the ones who de-

cide what we want from the tools we build" (Azhar, *Exponential*, 253); or Kai-Fu Lee, "We will not be passive spectators in the story of AI—we are the authors of it" (Kai-Fu Lee and Qiufan Cheng, *AI 2041: Ten Visions for Our Future* [London: W. H. Allen, 2021, 437]).

271 **Communication around AI** Patrick O'Shea et al., "Communicating About the Social Implications of AI: A FrameWorks Strategic Brief," FrameWorks Institute, Oct. 19, 2021, www.frameworksinstitute.org/publication/communicating-about -the-social-implications-of-ai-a-frameworks-strategic-brief.

272 **Research shows that when** Stefan Schubert et al., "The Psychology of Existential Risk: Moral Judgments About Human Extinction," *Nature Scientific Reports*, Oct. 21, 2019, www.nature.com/articles/s41598-019-50145-9.

272 **Meanwhile, citizen assemblies offer** Aviv Ovadya, "Towards Platform Democracy," Harvard Kennedy School Belfer Center, Oct. 18, 2021, www.belfercenter.org /publication/towards-platform-democracy-policymaking-beyond-corporate-ceos -and-partisan-pressure.

272 **Referencing the Asilomar principles** "Pause Giant AI Experiments: An Open Letter," Future of Life Institute, March 29, 2023, futureoflife.org/open-letter/pause-giant -ai-experiments.

273 **A complaint against LLMs** Adi Robertson, "FTC Should Stop OpenAI from Launching New GPT Models, Says AI Policy Group," *The Verge*, March 30, 2023, www.theverge.com/2023/3/30/23662101/ftc-openai-investigation-request-caidp -gpt-text-generation-bias.

273 **One good example comes** Esvelt, "Delay, Detect, Defend." For another example of a holistic approach to containment strategy, see Allison Duettmann, "Defend Against Physical Threats: Multipolar Active Shields," Foresight Institute, Feb. 14, 2022, foresightinstitute.substack.com/p/defend-physical.

276 **The economist Daron Acemoglu** Daron Acemoglu and James Robinson, *The Narrow Corridor: How Nations Struggle for Liberty* (London: Viking, 2019).

LIFE AFTER THE ANTHROPOCENE

285 **Technology should amplify** See, for example, arguments like that of Divya Siddarth et al., "How AI Fails Us," Edmond and Lily Safra Center for Ethics, Dec. 1, 2021, ethics.harvard.edu/how-ai-fails-us.

INDEX

ABOUT THE AUTHORS

MUSTAFA SULEYMAN is the co-founder and CEO of Inflection AI. Previously he co-founded DeepMind, one of the world's leading AI companies. After a decade at DeepMind, Suleyman became vice president of AI product management and AI policy at Google. When he was an undergraduate at Oxford, Suleyman dropped out to help start a nonprofit telephone counseling service. He lives in Palo Alto, California.

MICHAEL BHASKAR is a writer and publisher based in the UK. He is the author of *The Content Machine, Curation,* and *Human Frontiers.*

ABOUT THE TYPE

This book was set in Dante, a typeface designed by Giovanni Mardersteig (1892–1977). Conceived as a private type for the Officina Bodoni in Verona, Italy, Dante was originally cut only for hand composition by Charles Malin, the famous Parisian punch cutter, between 1946 and 1952. Its first use was in an edition of Boccaccio's *Trattatello in laude di Dante* that appeared in 1954. The Monotype Corporation's version of Dante followed in 1957. Though modeled on the Aldine type used for Pietro Cardinal Bembo's treatise *De Aetna* in 1495, Dante is a thoroughly modern interpretation of that venerable face.